Quantitative data analysis for social scientists

Most introductions to the techniques of statistical analysis concentrate on the often complex statistical formulae involved. Many students find these formulae extremely daunting, yet in practice computers are increasingly used to perform the same calculations in seconds.

Quantitative Data Analysis for Social Scientists is designed as a non-technical guide, ignoring the traditional formulaic methods and introducing students to the most widely used computer package for analysing quantitative data. This is the Statistical Package for the Social Sciences (SPSS), whose most recently released versions (for both mainframe computers and IBM-compatible personal computers) are here employed. The authors have assumed no previous familiarity with either statistics or computing, and take the reader step-by-step through each of the techniques for which SPSS can be used. Specific techniques covered include:

* correlation
* simple and multiple regression
* multivariate analysis of variance and covariance
* factor analysis

Each technique is illustrated by sets of data through which the reader can work, and tested again at the end of each chapter. Answers to the exercises are provided at the end of the book.

Designed specifically for social scientists, the book will be essential reading for psychology and sociology students following courses in statistics, data analysis, or research methods.

Quantitative data analysis for social scientists

Alan Bryman and Duncan Cramer

Department of Social Sciences,
Loughborough University of Technology

London and New York

For Sue, Sarah, and Stella

First published 1990
by Routledge
11 New Fetter Lane, London EC4P 4EE

Simultaneously published in the USA and Canada
by Routledge
a division of Routledge, Chapman and Hall, Inc.
29 West 35th Street, New York, NY 10001

Typeset by Leaper & Gard Ltd, Bristol, England
Printed and bound in Great Britain by Mackays of Chatham PLC, Chatham, Kent

British Library Cataloguing in Publication Data

Bryman, Alan, *1947–*
    Quantitative data analysis for social scientists.
    1. Statistical mathematics
    I. Title   II. Cramer, Duncan, *1948–*
    519.5

Library of Congress Cataloging in Publication Data

Bryman, Alan.
    Quantitative data analysis for social scientists/by Alan Bryman
    and Duncan Cramer.
    p.   cm.
    Includes bibliographical references.
    1. Social sciences—Data processing.   2. SPSS (Computer program)
    3. Analysis of variance.   I. Cramer, Duncan, 1948–   . II. Title.
    HA32.B79   1990
    300'.01'519535—dc20   89-27683
                                                           CIP

ISBN 0–415–02664–4
    0–415–02665–2 (pbk)

ontents

	List of tables	vi
	List of figures	xi
	Preface	xiii
1	Data analysis and the research process	1
2	Analysing data with computers: first steps with SPSS-X and SPSS/PC+	16
3	Analysing data with computers: further steps with SPSS-X and SPSS/PC+	43
4	Concepts and their measurement	61
5	Summarizing data	75
6	Sampling and statistical significance	98
7	Bivariate analysis: exploring differences between scores on two variables	114
8	Bivariate analysis: exploring relationships	150
9	Multivariate analysis: exploring differences among three or more variables	189
10	Multivariate analysis: exploring relationships among three or more variables	216
11	Aggregating variables: exploratory factor analysis	253
	Appendix	267
	Answers to exercises	271
	Bibliography	283
	Index	286

Tables

1.1	Data on television violence and aggression	8
2.1	The Job-Survey data	20–1
2.2	The SPSS names and location of the Job-Survey variables	24
2.3	Segment of SPSS **data list** table	29
2.4	First error message when column number on **data list** command is incorrect	34
3.1	**Frequencies** SPSS/PC+ output with and without **variable** and **value labels** (Job Survey)	59
4.1	Types of variable	66
5.1	The faculty membership of fifty-six students (imaginary data)	76
5.2	Frequency table for data on faculty membership	77
5.3	Frequency table for income data (Job-Survey data)	79
5.4	Frequency table and histogram for income data (SPSS-X output)	81
5.5	Numbers of undergraduates in universities in the UK, 1980–1	84
5.6	Results of a test of mathematical ability for the students of two teachers (imaginary data)	85
5.7	Probable mathematics marks (from data in Table 5.6)	95
6.1	Devising a stratified random sample: non-manual employees in a firm	101
6.2	The four possible outcomes of tossing a coin twice	105
6.3	Theoretical outcomes of tossing a coin sixty-four times and the probabilities of similar outcomes	107
6.4	Type I and Type II errors	112
7.1	Tests of differences for two variables	117
7.2	Binomial test comparing proportion of men and women (Job-Survey SPSS/PC+ output)	119
7.3	Binomial test comparing proportion of whites and non-whites (Job-Survey SPSS/PC+ output)	120
7.4	One-sample chi-square test comparing number of people	

	in ethnic groups (Job-Survey SPSS/PC+ output)	121
7.5	Chi-square test with insufficient cases (Job-Survey SPSS/PC+ output)	122
7.6	Chi-square test produced by **crosstabs** comparing numbers of white and non-white men and women (Job-Survey SPSS/PC+ output)	124
7.7	The Panel-Study data	125
7.8	McNemar test comparing attendance across two months (Panel-Study SPSS/PC+ output)	126
7.9	Cochran Q test comparing attendance across three months (Panel-Study SPSS/PC+ output)	127
7.10	One-sample Kolmogorov–Smirnov test comparing distribution of quality (Job-Survey SPSS/PC+ output)	128
7.11	Two-sample Kolmogorov–Smirnov test comparing distribution of quality in men and women (Job-Survey SPSS/PC+ output)	128
7.12	Median test comparing quality in men and women (Job-Survey SPSS/PC+ output)	129
7.13	Mann–Whitney test comparing quality in men and women (Job-Survey SPSS/PC+ output)	130
7.14	Kruskal–Wallis test comparing quality between ethnic groups (Job-Survey SPSS/PC+ output)	131
7.15	Sign test comparing quality across two months (Panel-Study SPSS/PC+ output)	132
7.16	Wilcoxon matched-pairs signed-ranks test comparing quality across two months (Panel-Study SPSS/PC+ output)	133
7.17	Friedman test comparing quality across three months (Panel-Study SPSS/PC+ output)	133
7.18	Unrelated t test comparing job satisfaction in men and women (Job-Survey SPSS/PC+ output)	136
7.19	Mann–Whitney test comparing job satisfaction in men and women (Job-Survey SPSS/PC+ output)	138
7.20	A oneway analysis-of-variance table (Job-Survey SPSS/PC+ output)	139
7.21	Descriptive group statistics with oneway analysis of variance comparing job satisfaction across ethnic groups (Job-Survey SPSS/PC+ output)	140
7.22	Statistic provided by a oneway contrast comparing job satisfaction in groups 1 and 2 (Job-Survey SPSS/PC+ output)	141
7.23	Statistics provided by a oneway Scheffé test comparing satisfaction across ethnic groups (Job-Survey SPSS/PC+ output)	142

7.24 Homogeneity of variance tests given by **oneway** (Job-Survey SPSS/PC+ output)   143
7.25 Related *t* test comparing satisfaction across months (Panel-Study SPSS/PC2 output)   145
7.26 Repeated-measures means and standard deviations for job satisfaction (Panel-Study SPSS/PC+ output)   146
7.27 Repeated-measures multivariate tests (Panel-Study SPSS/PC+ output)   146
7.28 Repeated-measures univariate tests of significance for transformed variables (Panel-Study SPSS/PC+ output)   147
7.29 Repeated-measures averaged test of significance (Panel-Study SPSS/PC+ output)   147
8.1   Data for thirty individuals on job satisfaction and absenteeism   152
8.2   Four possible combinations   153
8.3   The relationship between job satisfaction and absenteeism   153
8.4   Two types of relationship   154
8.5   Contingency table for rated skill by gender (SPSS-X output from Job-Survey data)   156
8.6   Rated skill by gender (Job-Survey data)   160
8.7   Data on age, income, and political liberalism   163
8.8   Matrix on Pearson product-moment correlation coefficients (SPSS-X output from Job-Survey data)   172
8.9   Matrix from Spearman's rho and Kendall's tau correlation coefficients (SPSS-X output from Job-Survey data)   174
8.10 Sample means SPSS-X output (Job-Survey data)   178
8.11 The impact of outliers: the relationship between size of firm and number of specialist functions (imaginary data) 185
9.1   The Depression-Project data   198
9.2   Means and standard deviations of post-test depression in the three treatments for men and women (Depression-Project SPSS/PC+ output)   200
9.3   Tests of significance for main and interaction effects of a factorial design (Depression-Project SPSS/PC+ output) 201
9.4   Tests of significance for specified contrasts (Depression-Project SPSS/PC+ output)   202
9.5   Tests of significance for effects on pre-test depression (Depression-Project SPSS/PC+ output)   203
9.6   Test of homogeneity of slope of regression line within cells (Depression-Project SPSS/PC+ output)   204
9.7   Significance of the relationship between the covariate and post-test depression (Depression-Project SPSS/PC+ output) 205
9.8   Analysis-of-covariance table (Depression-Project SPSS/PC+ output)   205

9.9	Observed and adjusted means of post-test depression in the three treatments (Depression-Project SPSS/PC+ output)	206
9.10	Box's M test (Depression-Project SPSS/PC+ output)	207
9.11	Bartlett's test of sphericity (Depression-Project SPSS/PC+ output)	207
9.12	Multivariate tests of significance for the treatment effect (Depression-Project SPSS/PC+ output)	207
9.13	Univariate tests of significance for the two dependent measures (Depression-Project SPSS/PC+ output)	208
9.14	The second renamed transformed variable (Depression-Project SPSS/PC+ output)	208
9.15	Test of significance for treatment (Depression-Project SPSS/PC+ output)	209
9.16	Tests of significance for the within-subject 'time' effect (Depression-Project SPSS/PC+ output)	209
9.17	Means and standard deviations of pre-test and post-test depression for the three treatments (Depression-Project SPSS/PC+ output)	210
9.18	Relationship between the covariate age and the two transformed variables (Depression-Project SPSS/PC+ output)	211
9.19	The renamed and transformed within-subject effect for time (Depression-Project SPSS/PC+ output)	211
9.20	Multivariate tests for the interaction between treatment, gender, and time (Depression-Project SPSS(PC+ output)	212
9.21	Univariate tests for the interaction effect between treatment, gender, and time (Depression-Project SPSS/PC+ output)	212
9.22	Group means of job satisfaction (Job-Survey SPSS/PC+ output)	213
9.23	Analysis-of-covariance table (Job-Survey SPSS/PC+ output)	214
10.1	Relationship between work variety and job satisfaction (imaginary data)	218
10.2	A spurious relationship: the relationship between work variety and job satisfaction, controlling for size of firm (imaginary data)	220
10.3	A non-spurious relationship: the relationship between work variety and job satisfaction, controlling for size of firm (imaginary data)	221
10.4	An intervening variable: the relationship between work variety and job satisfaction, controlling for interest in work (imaginary data)	224
10.5	A moderated relationship: the relationship between work	

	variety and job satisfaction, controlling for gender (imaginary data)	226
10.6	Two independent variables: the relationship between work variety and job satisfaction, controlling for participation at work (imaginary data)	228
10.7	Income, age, and support for the market economy (imaginary data)	232
10.8	Comparison of unstandardized and standardized regression coefficients with **satis** as the dependent variable	237
10.9	Creation of a dummy variable (**ethnicgp**)	241
10.10	Sample multiple-regression SPSS-X output (Job-Survey data)	242–3
10E.1	The relationship between approval of equal-pay legislation and gender	251
10E.2	The relationship between approval of equal-pay legislation and gender holding age constant	252
11.1	Correlation and significance-level matrices for items (Job-Survey SPSS/PC+ output)	257
11.2	Initial principal components and their variance (Job-Survey SPSS/PC+ output)	258
11.3	Initial principal axes and their variance (Job-Survey SPSS/PC+ output)	259
11.4	Item loadings on first two principal components (Job-Survey SPSS/PC+ output)	261
11.5	Item loadings on first two principal axes (Job-Survey SPSS/PC+ output)	261
11.6	Item loadings on orthogonally rotated factors (Job-Survey SPSS/PC+ output)	262
11.7	Item loadings on obliquely rotated factors (Job-Survey SPSS/PC+ output)	264
11.8	Correlations between oblique factors (Job-Survey SPSS/PC+ output)	264

Figures

1.1	The research process	3
1.2	A spurious relationship	9
1.3	An experiment	11
1.4	Three types of experimental design	13
1.5	A relationship between two variables	14
1.6	Is the relationship spurious?	14
1.7	Two possible causal interpretations of a relationship	15
4.1	Concepts, dimensions, and measurement	69
5.1	Bar chart of data on faculty membership	78
5.2	Histogram for income data (Job-Survey data)	79
5.3	The inter-quartile range	86
5.4	Stem and leaf diagram on undergraduates in the UK	89
5.5	Box and whisker plot	90
5.6	Box and whisker plot of undergraduates in the UK	91
5.7	Two normal distributions	92
5.8	The normal distribution and the mean	93
5.9	Properties of the normal distribution	94
5.10	Positively and negatively skewed distributions	96
6.1	The distribution of similar theoretical outcomes of tossing a coin twice	106
6.2	The distribution of similar theoretical outcomes of tossing a coin sixty-four times	108
6.3	The one-tailed and two-tailed 5 per cent levels of significance	111
7.1	A comparison of the distribution of the standard error of the differences in means for related and unrelated samples	144
8.1	Scatter diagram: political liberalism by income (SPSS/PC+ **plot**)	164
8.2	Scatter diagram: income by age (SPSS/PC+ **plot**)	165
8.3	A perfect relationship	166
8.4	No relationship (or virtually no relationship)	166
8.5	Three curvilinear relationships	167

8.6	Two positive relationships	168
8.7	Two negative relationships	169
8.8	The strength and direction of correlation coefficients	169
8.9	Types of relationship	170
8.10	A line of best fit	180
8.11	Regression: a negative relationship	181
8.12	Regression: a negative intercept	181
8.13	Regression: a perfect relationship	182
8.14	The accuracy of the line of best fit	183
8.15	Scatter diagrams for two identical levels of correlation	184
8.16	Heteroscedasticity	184
9.1	An example of an interaction between two variables	190
9.2	Examples of other interactions	191
9.3	Examples of no interactions	192
9.4	Schematic representation of a significant oneway effect	194
10.1	Is the relationship between work variety and job satisfaction spurious?	219
10.2	Is the relationship between work variety and job satisfaction affected by an intervening variable?	223
10.3	Is the relationship between work variety and job satisfaction moderated by gender?	225
10.4	Work variety and participation at work	227
10.5	The effects of controlling for a test variable	231
10.6	Path diagram for **satis**	247
10.7	Path diagram for **satis** with path coefficients	249
10.8	Path diagram for **absence**	250
11.1	Common and unique variance	256
11.2	Scree test of eigenvalues (Job-Survey SPSS/PC+ output)	260

Preface

In this book, we introduce readers to the main techniques of statistical analysis employed by psychologists and sociologists. However, we do not see the book as a standard introduction to statistics. We see the book as distinctively different because we are not concerned to introduce the often complex formulae that underlie the statistical methods covered. Students often find these formulae and the calculations that are associated with them extremely daunting, especially when their background in mathematics is weak. Moreover, in these days of powerful computers and packages of statistical programs, it seems gratuitous to put students through the anxiety of confronting complex calculations when machines can perform the bulk of the work. Indeed, most practitioners employ statistical packages that are run on computers to perform their calculations, so there seems little purpose in treating formulae and their application as a *rite de passage* for social scientists. Moreover, few students would come to understand fully the rationale for the formulae that they would need to learn. Indeed, we prefer the term 'quantitative data analysis' to 'statistics' because of the adverse image that the latter term has in the minds of many prospective readers.

In view of the widespread availability of statistical packages and computers, we feel that the two areas that students need to get to grips with are, first, how to decide which statistical procedures are suitable for which purpose, and second, how to interpret the ensuing results. We try to emphasize these two elements in this book.

In addition, the student needs to get to know how to operate the computer software needed to perform the statistical procedures described in this book. To this end, we introduce students to what is probably the most widely used suite of programs for statistical analysis in the social sciences – the Statistical Package for the Social Sciences (SPSS). This package was first developed in the 1960s and was the first major attempt to provide software for the social scientist. It has since undergone numerous revisions and refinements. Some years ago, SPSS^x was introduced as a major break with the preceding versions. This too has undergone a number of revisions and is now called SPSS-X. The latest version at the time of writing is Release 3.0, which was introduced in 1988. In this book, we will emphasize this latest version. SPSS was originally developed for mainframe computers and SPSS-X is still only usable with such machines. However, a version of SPSS for IBM PC-compatible machines appeared a few years ago. It has become increasingly popular and so we introduce this package, known as SPSS/PC+, as well. In order to distinguish methods of quantitative data analysis from SPSS commands, the latter are always in **bold**. We also present some data that students can work on and the names of the variables are also in **bold** (for example, **income**).

There are exercises at the end of each chapter and the answers are provided for all exercises at the end of the book. We hope that students and instructors alike find these useful; they can easily be adapted to provide further exercises.

The case for combining methods of quantitative data analysis used by both psychologists and sociologists in part derives from our belief that the requirements of students of the two subjects often overlap substantially. Nonetheless, instructors can omit particular techniques as they wish.

We wish to thank David Stonestreet of Routledge for his support of this project. We also wish to thank Louis Cohen, Max Hunt, and Tony Westaway for reading the manuscript and for making many useful suggestions for improvement. We accept that they cannot be held liable for any errors in this book: such errors are entirely of our own making, though we will undoubtedly blame each other for them.

Alan Bryman and Duncan Cramer,
Loughborough University

Chapter one

Data analysis and the research process

This book largely covers the field that is generally referred to as 'statistics', but as our Preface has sought to establish, we have departed in a number of respects from the way in which this subject is conventionally taught to under- and postgraduates. In particular, our preferences are for integrating data analysis with computer skills and for not burdening the student with formulae. These predilections constitute a departure from many, if not most, treatments of this subject. We prefer the term 'quantitative data analysis' because the emphasis is on the understanding and analysis of data rather than on the precise nature of the statistical techniques themselves.

Why should social-science students have to study quantitative data analysis, especially at a time when qualitative research is coming increasingly to the fore (Bryman 1988a)? After all, everyone has heard of the ways in which statistical materials can be distorted, as indicated by Disraeli's often-quoted dictum: 'There are lies, damn lies and statistics.' Why should serious researchers and students be prepared to get involved in such a potentially unworthy activity? If we take the first issue – why social-science students should study quantitative data analysis – it is necessary to remember that an extremely large proportion of the empirical research undertaken by social scientists is designed to generate or draws upon, quantitative data. In order to be able to appreciate the kinds of analyses that are conducted in relation to such data and possibly to analyse their own data (especially since many students are required to carry out projects), an acquaintance with the appropriate methods of analysis is highly desirable for social-science students. Further, although qualitative research has quite properly become a prominent strategy in sociology and some other areas of the social sciences, it is by no means as pervasive as quantitative research, and in any case many writers recognize that there is much to be gained from a fusion of the two research traditions (Bryman 1988a).

On the question of the ability of statisticians to distort the analyses that they carry out, the prospects for which are substantially enhanced in many people's eyes by books with such disconcerting titles as *How to Lie with*

Statistics (Huff 1973), it should be recognized that an understanding of the techniques to be covered in our book will greatly enhance the ability to see through the misrepresentations about which many people are concerned. Indeed, the inculcation of a sceptical appreciation of quantitative data analysis is beneficial in the light of the pervasive use of statistical data in everyday life. We are deluged with such data in the form of the results of opinion polls, market-research findings, attitude surveys, health and crime statistics, and so on. An awareness of quantitative data analysis greatly enhances the ability to recognize faulty conclusions or potentially biased manipulations of the information. There is even a fair chance that a substantial proportion of the readers of this book will get jobs in which at some point they will have to think about the question of how to analyse and present statistical material. Moreover, quantitative data analysis does not comprise a mechanical application of predetermined techniques by statisticians and others; it is a subject with its own controversies and debates, just like the social sciences themselves. Some of these areas of controversy will be brought to the reader's attention where appropriate.

Quantitative data analysis and the research process

In this section, the way in which quantitative data analysis fits into the research process – specifically the process of quantitative research – will be explored. As we will see, the area covered by this book does not solely address the question of how to deal with quantitative data, since it is also concerned with other aspects of the research process that impinge on data analysis.

Figure 1.1 provides an illustration of the chief steps in the process of quantitative research. Although there are grounds for doubting whether research always conforms to a neat linear sequence (Bryman 1988a, b), the components depicted in Figure 1.1 provide a useful model. The following stages are delineated by the model.

Theory

The starting-point for the process is a theoretical domain. Theories in the social sciences can vary between abstract general approaches (such as functionalism) and fairly low-level theories to explain specific phenomena (such as voting behaviour, delinquency, aggressiveness). By and large, the theories that are most likely to receive direct empirical attention are those which are at a fairly low level of generality. Merton (1967) referred to these as theories of the middle range, to denote theories that stood between general, abstract theories and empirical findings. Thus, Hirschi (1969), for example, formulated a 'control theory' of juvenile delinquency which proposes that delinquent acts are more likely when the child's bonds to

Figure 1.1 The research process

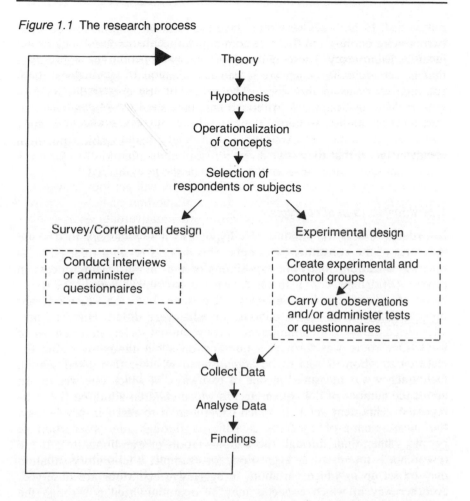

society are breached. This theory in large part derived from other theories and also from research findings relating to juvenile delinquency.

Hypothesis

Once a theory has been formulated, it is likely that researchers will want to test it. Does the theory hold water when faced with empirical evidence? However, it is rarely possible to test a theory as such. Instead, we are more likely to find that a hypothesis, which relates to a limited facet of the theory, will be deduced from the theory and submitted to a searching enquiry. Hirschi, for example, drawing upon his control theory, stipulates that children who are tied to conventional society (in the sense of adhering to conventional values and participating or aspiring to participate in conventional values) will be less likely to commit delinquent acts than those

3

not so tied. Hypotheses very often take the form of relationships between two or more entities – in this case commitment to conventional society and juvenile delinquency. These 'entities' are usually referred to as 'concepts' – that is, categories in which are stored our ideas and observations about common elements in the world. The nature of concepts is discussed in greater detail in Chapter 4. Although hypotheses have the advantage that they force researchers to think systematically about what they want to study and to structure their research plans accordingly, they exhibit a potential disadvantage in that they may divert a researcher's attention too far away from other interesting facets of the data he or she has amassed.

Operationalization of concepts

In order to assess the validity of a hypothesis it is necessary to develop measures of the constituent concepts. This process is often referred to as *operationalization*, following expositions of the measurement process in physics (Bridgman 1927). In effect, what is happening here is the translation of the concepts into variables – that is, attributes on which relevant objects (individuals, firms, nations, or whatever) differ. Hirschi operationalized the idea of commitment to conventional society in a number of ways. One route was through a question on a questionnaire asking the children to whom it was to be administered whether they liked school. Delinquency was measured in one of two ways, of which one was to ask about the number of delinquent acts to which children admitted (i.e. self-reported delinquent acts). In much experimental research in psychology, the measurement of concepts is achieved through the observation of people, rather than through the administration of questionnaires. If the researcher is interested in aggression, for example, a laboratory situation may be set up in which variations in aggressive behaviour are observed. Another way in which concepts may be operationalized is through the analysis of existing statistics, of which Durkheim's (1952/1898) classic analysis of suicide rates is an example. A number of issues to do with the process of devising measures of concepts and some of the properties that measures should possess are discussed in Chapter 4.

Selection of respondents or subjects

If a survey investigation is being undertaken, the researcher must find relevant people to whom the research instrument that has been devised (for example, self-administered questionnaire, interview schedule) should be administered. Hirschi, for example, randomly selected over 5,500 school-children from an area in California. The fact of random selection is important here because it reflects a commitment to the production of findings that can be generalized beyond the confines of those who participate in a study. It is rarely possible to contact all units in a population, so that a *sample* invariably has to be selected. In order to be able to generalize to a wider population, a *representative sample*, such as one that can be achieved through random sampling, will be required. Moreover, many of the statistical techniques to be covered in this book are *inferential statistics*, which allow the researcher to demonstrate the probability that the results deriving from a sample are likely to be found in the population from which the sample was taken, but only if a random sample has been selected. These issues are examined in Chapter 6.

Setting up a research design

There are two basic types of research design that are employed by psychologists and sociologists. The former tend to use *experimental* designs in which the researcher actively manipulates aspects of a setting, either in the laboratory or in a field situation, and observes the effects of that manipulation on experimental subjects. There must also be a 'control group' which acts as a point of comparison with the group of subjects who receive the experimental manipulation. With a *survey/correlational* design, the researcher does not manipulate any of the variables of interest and data relating to all variables are collected simultaneously. The term *correlation* also refers to a technique for analysing relationships between variables (see Chapter 8), but is used in the present context to denote a type of research design. The researcher does not always have a choice regarding which of the two designs can be adopted. Thus, for example, Hirschi could not *make* some children committed to school and others less committed and observe the effects on their propensity to commit delinquent acts. Some variables, like most of those studied by sociologists, are not capable of manipulation. However, there are areas of research in which topics and hypotheses are addressed with both types of research design (for example, the study of the effects of participation at work on job satisfaction and performance – see Locke and Schweiger 1979; Bryman 1986). It should be noted that in most cases, therefore, the nature of the research design – whether experimental or survey/correlational – is known at the outset of the sequence signified by Figure 1.1, so that research-design characteristics permeate and inform a number of stages of the research process. The nature of the research design has implications for the kinds of statistical manipulation that can be performed on the resulting data. The differences between the two designs is given greater attention in the next section.

Collect data

The researcher collects data at this stage, by interview, questionnaire, observation, or whatever. The technicalities of the issues pertinent to this stage are not usually associated with a book such as this. Readers should consult a textbook concerned with social and psychological research methods if they are unfamiliar with the relevant issues.

Analyse data

This stage connects very directly with the material covered in this book. At a minimum, the researcher is likely to want to describe his or her subjects in terms of the variables deriving from the study. The researcher might for example be interested in the proportion of children who claim to have committed no, just one, or two or more delinquent acts. The various ways of analysing and presenting the information relating to a single variable (sometimes called *univariate analysis*) are examined in Chapter 5. However, the analysis of a single variable is unlikely to suffice and the researcher will probably be interested in the connection between that variable and each of a number of other variables, i.e. *bivariate analysis*. The examination of connections among variables can take either of two forms. A researcher who has conducted an experiment may be interested in the extent to which experimental and control groups differ in some respect. The researcher might for example be interested in examining whether watching violent films increases aggressiveness. The experimental group (which watches the violent films) and the control group (which does not) can then be compared to see how far they differ. The techniques for examining differences are explored in Chapter 7. The researcher may be interested in relationships between variables – are two variables connected with each other so that they tend to vary together? Hirschi (1969: 121), for example, presents a table which shows how liking school and self-reported delinquent acts are interconnected. He found that whereas only 9 per cent of children who say they like school have committed two or more delinquent acts, 49 per cent of those who say they dislike school have committed as many delinquent acts. The ways in which relationships among pairs of variables can be elucidated can be found in Chapter 8. Very often the researcher will be interested in exploring connections among more than two variables, i.e. *multivariate analysis*. Chapter 9 examines such analysis in the context of the exploration of differences, while Chapter 10 looks at the multivariate analysis of relationships among more than two variables. The distinction between studying differences and studying relationships is not always clear-cut. We might find that boys are more likely than girls to commit delinquent acts. This finding could be taken to mean that boys and girls differ in terms of propensity to engage in delinquent acts or that there is a relationship between gender and delinquency.

Findings

If the analysis of the data suggests that a hypothesis is confirmed, this result can be fed back into the theory that prompted it. Future researchers can then concern themselves either with seeking to replicate the finding or with other ramifications of the theory. However, the refutation of a hypothesis can be just as important in that it may suggest that the theory is faulty or at the very least in need of revision. Sometimes, the hypothesis may be confirmed in some respects only. Thus, for example, a multivariate analysis may suggest that a relationship between two variables pertains only to some members of a sample, but not others (for example, women but not men, or younger but not older people). Such a finding will require a reformulation of the theory. Not all findings will necessarily relate directly to a hypothesis. With a social survey, for example, the researcher may collect data on topics whose relevance only becomes evident at a later juncture.

As suggested above, the sequence depicted in Figure 1.1 constitutes a model of the research process, which may not always be reproduced in reality. None the less, it does serve to pin-point the importance to the process of quantitative research of developing measures of concepts and the thorough analysis of subsequent data. One point that was not mentioned in the discussion is the *form* that the hypotheses and findings tend to assume. One of the main aims of much quantitative research in the social sciences is the demonstration of *causality* – that one variable has an impact upon another. The terms *independent variable* and *dependent variable* are often employed in this context. The former denotes a variable that has an impact upon the dependent variable. The latter, in other words, is deemed to be an effect of the independent variable. This causal imagery is widespread in the social sciences and a major role of multivariate analysis is the elucidation of such causal relationships (Bryman 1988a). The ease with which a researcher can establish cause-and-effect relationships is strongly affected by the nature of the research design and it is to this topic that we shall now turn.

Causality and research design

As suggested in the last paragraph, one of the chief preoccupations among quantitative researchers is to establish causality. This preoccupation in large part derives from a concern to establish findings similar to those of the natural sciences, which often take a causal form. Moreover, findings which establish cause and effect can have considerable practical importance: if we know that one thing affects another, we can manipulate the cause to produce an effect. In much the same way that our knowledge that smoking may cause a number of illnesses, such as lung cancer and heart

7

disease, the social scientist is able to provide potentially practical information by demonstrating causal relationships in appropriate settings.

To say that something causes something else is not to suggest that the dependent variable (the effect) is totally influenced by the independent variable (the cause). You do not necessarily contract a disease if you smoke and many of the diseases contracted by people who smoke afflict those who never smoke. 'Cause' here should be taken to mean that variation in the dependent variable is affected by variation in the independent variable. Those who smoke a lot are more likely than those who smoke less, who in turn are more likely than those who do not smoke at all, to contract a variety of diseases that are associated with smoking. Similarly, if we find that watching violence on television induces aggressive behaviour, we are not saying that only people who watch televised violence will behave aggressively, nor that only those people who behave aggressively watch violent television programmes. Causal relationships are invariably about the likelihood of an effect occurring in the light of particular levels of the cause: aggressive behaviour may be more likely to occur when a lot of television violence is watched and people who watch relatively little television violence may be less likely to behave aggressively.

Establishing causality

In order to establish a causal relationship, three criteria have to be fulfilled. First, it is necessary to establish that there is an apparent relationship between two variables. This means that it is necessary to demonstrate that the distribution of values of one variable corresponds to the distribution of values of another variable. Table 1.1 provides information for ten children on the number of aggressive acts they exhibit when they play in two groups

Table 1.1 Data on television violence and aggression

Child	Number of hours of violence watched on television per week	Number of aggressive acts recorded
1	9.50	9
2	9.25	8
3	8.75	7
4	8.25	7
5	8.00	6
6	5.50	4
7	5.25	4
8	4.75	5
9	4.50	3
10	4.00	3

of five for two hours per group. The point to note is that there is a relationship between the two variables in that the distribution of values for number of aggressive acts coincides with the distribution for the amount of televised violence watched – children who watch more violence exhibit more aggression than those who watch little violence. The relationship is not perfect: three pairs of children – 3 and 4, 6 and 7, and 9 and 10 – record the same number of aggressive acts, even though they watch different amounts of television violence. Moreover, 8 exhibits more aggression than 6 or 7, even though the latter watch more violence. None the less, a clear pattern is evident which suggests that there is a relationship between the two variables.

Second, it is necessary to demonstrate that the relationship is *non-spurious*. A spurious relationship occurs when there is not a 'true' relationship between two variables that appear to be connected. The variation exhibited by each variable is affected by a common variable. Imagine that the first five children are boys and the second five are girls. This would suggest that gender has a considerable impact on both variables. Boys are more likely than girls both to watch more television violence *and* to exhibit greater aggressiveness. There is still a slight tendency for watching more violence and aggression to be related for both boys and girls, but these tendencies are far less pronounced than for the ten children as a whole. In other words, gender affects each of the two variables. It is because boys are much more likely than girls both to watch more television violence and to behave aggressively that there is a spurious relationship, as illustrated by Figure 1.2.

Third, it is necessary to establish that the cause precedes the effect, i.e. the *time order* of the two related variables. In other words, we must establish that aggression is a consequence of watching televised violence and not the other way around. An effect simply cannot come before a cause. This may seem an extremely obvious criterion that is easy to demonstrate, but as

Figure 1.2 A spurious relationship

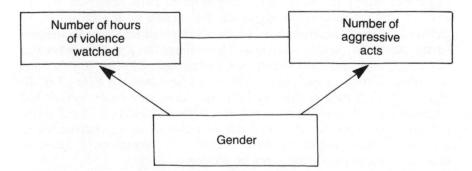

we will see, it constitutes a very considerable problem for non-experimental research designs.

Causality and experimental designs

A research design provides the basic structure within which an investigation takes place. While a number of different designs can be found, a basic distinction is that between experimental and non-experimental research designs, of which the survey/correlational is the most prominent. In an experiment, the elucidation of cause and effect is an explicit feature of the framework. The term *internal validity* is often employed as an attribute of research and indicates whether the causal findings deriving from an investigation are relatively unequivocal. An internally valid study is one which provides firm evidence of cause and effect. Experimental designs are especially strong in respect of internal validity; this attribute is scarcely surprising in view of the fact that they have been developed specifically in order to generate findings which indicate cause and effect.

If we wanted to establish that watching violence on television enhances aggression in children, we might conceive of the following study. We bring together a group of ten children. They are allowed to interact and play for two hours, during which the number of aggressive acts committed by each child is recorded by the observers, and the children are then exposed to a television programme with a great deal of violence. Such exposure is often called the experimental treatment. They are then allowed a further two-hour period of play and interaction. Aggressive behaviour is recorded in exactly the same way. What we have here is a sequence which runs

$$\text{Obs}_1 \ \text{Exp} \ \text{Obs}_2$$

where Obs_1 is the initial measurement of aggressive behaviour (often called the *pre-test*), Exp is the experimental treatment which allows the independent variable to be introduced, and Obs_2 is the subsequent measurement of aggression (often called the *post-test*).

Let us say that Obs_2 is 30 per cent higher than Obs_1, suggesting that aggressive behaviour has increased substantially. Does this mean that we can say that the increase in aggression was caused by the violence? We cannot make such an attribution because there are alternative explanations of the presumed causal connection. The children may well have become more aggressive over time simply as a consequence of being together and becoming irritated by each other. The researchers may not have given the children enough food or drink and this may have contributed to their bad humour. There is even the possibility that different observers were used for the pre- and post-tests who used different criteria of aggressiveness. So long as we cannot discount these alternative explanations, a definitive conclusion about causation cannot be proffered.

Anyone familiar with the natural sciences will know that an important facet of a properly conducted experiment is that it is controlled so that potentially contaminating factors are minimized. In order to control the contaminating factors that have been mentioned (and therefore to allow the alternative explanations to be rejected), a *control group* is required. This group has exactly the same cluster of experiences as the group which receives the first treatment – known as the *experimental group* – but it does not receive the experimental treatment. In the context of our imaginary television study, we now have two groups of children who are exposed to exactly the same conditions, except that one group watches the violent films (the experimental group) and the second group has no experimental treatment (the control group). This design is illustrated in Figure 1.3. The two groups' experiences have to be as similar as possible, so that only the experimental group's exposure to the experimental treatment distinguishes them.

It is also necessary to ensure that the members of the two groups are as similar as possible. This is achieved by taking a sample of children and *randomly assigning* them to either the experimental or the control group. If random assignment is not carried out, there is always the possibility that the differences between the two groups can be attributed to divergent personal or other characteristics. There may, for example, be more boys than girls in one group, or differences in the ethnic composition of the two groups. Such differences in personal or background characteristics would mean that the ensuing findings could not be validly attributed to the independent variable, and that factor alone.

Let us say that the difference between Obs_1 and Obs_2 is 30 per cent and between Obs_3 and Obs_4 is 28 per cent. If this were the case, we would conclude that the difference between the two groups is so small that it appears that the experimental treatment (Exp) has made no difference to the increase in aggression; in other words, aggression in the experimental group would probably have increased anyway. The frustration of being together too long or insufficient food or drink or some other factor

Figure 1.3 An experiment

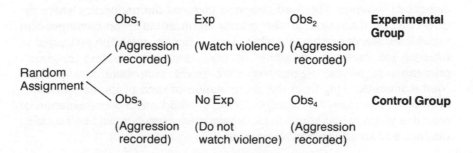

	Obs_1	Exp	Obs_2	**Experimental Group**
	(Aggression recorded)	(Watch violence)	(Aggression recorded)	
Random Assignment				
	Obs_3	No Exp	Obs_4	**Control Group**
	(Aggression recorded)	(Do not watch violence)	(Aggression recorded)	

probably accounts for the Obs_2–Obs_1 difference. However, if the difference between Obs_3 and Obs_4 were only 3 per cent, we would be much more prepared to say that watching violence has increased aggression in the experimental group. It would suggest that around 27 per cent of the increase in aggressive behaviour in the experimental group (i.e. $30 - 3$) can be attributed to the experimental treatment. Differences between experimental and control groups are not usually as clear-cut as in this illustration, since often the difference between the groups is fairly small. Statistical tests are necessary in this context to determine the probability of obtaining such a difference by chance. Such tests are described in Chapters 7 and 9.

In this imaginary investigation, the three criteria of causality are met, and therefore if we did find that the increase in the dependent variable were considerably greater for the experimental group than the control group we could have considerable confidence in saying that watching television violence caused greater aggression. First, a relationship is established by demonstrating that subjects watching television violence exhibited greater aggression than those who did not. Second, the combination of a control group and random assignment allows the possibility of the relationship being spurious to be eliminated, since other factors which may impinge on the two variables would apply equally to the two groups. Third, the time order of the variables is demonstrated by the increase in aggressive behaviour succeeding the experimental group's exposure to the television violence. Precisely because the independent variable is manipulated by the researcher, time order can be easily demonstrated, since the effects of the manipulation can be directly gauged. Thus, we could say confidently that Watching television violence → Aggressive behaviour, since the investigation exhibits a high degree of internal validity.

There is a variety of different types of experimental design. These are briefly summarized in Figure 1.4. In the first design, there is no pre-test, just a comparison between the experimental and control groups in terms of the dependent variable. With the second design, there is a number of groups. This is a frequent occurrence in the social sciences where one is more likely to be interested in different levels or types of the independent variable rather than simply its presence or absence. Thus, in the television-violence context, we could envisage four groups consisting of different degrees of violence. The third design, a *factorial* design, occurs where the researcher is interested in the effects of more than one independent variable on the dependent variable. The researcher might be interested in whether the presence of adults in close proximity reduces children's propensity to behave aggressively. We might then have four possible combinations deriving from the manipulation of each of the two independent variables. Thus, for example, Exp_{1+A} would mean a combination of watching violence and adults in close proximity; Exp_{1+B} would be watching violence and no adults in close proximity.

Figure 1.4 Three types of experimental design

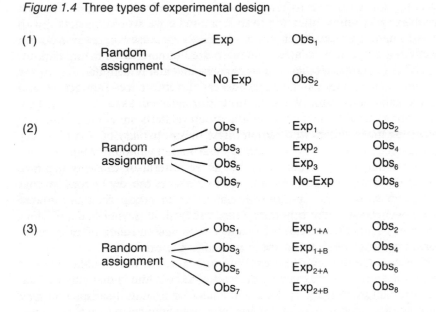

Survey design and causality

When a social survey is carried out, the nature of the research design is very different from the experiment. The survey usually entails the collection of data on a number of variables at a single juncture. The researcher might be interested in the relationship between people's political attitudes and behaviour on the one hand, and a number of other variables such as each respondent's occupation, social background, race, gender, age, and various non-political attitudes. However, none of these variables is manipulated as in the experiment. Indeed, many variables cannot be manipulated and their relationships with other variables can only be examined through a social survey. We cannot make some people old, others young, and still others middle-aged and then observe the effects of age on political attitudes. Moreover, not only are variables not manipulated in a social-survey study, data on variables are simultaneously collected so that it is not possible to establish a time order to the variables in question. In an experiment, a time order can be discerned in that the effect of the manipulated independent variable on the dependent variable is directly observed. The characteristics of surveys are not solely associated with research using interviews or questionnaires. Many studies using archival statistics, such as those collected by governments and organizations, exhibit the same characteristics, since data are often available in relation to a number of variables for a particular year.

Survey designs are often called *correlational* designs to denote the tendency for such research to be able to reveal relationships between variables and to draw attention to their limited capacity in connection with the elucidation of causal processes. Precisely because in survey research variables are not manipulated (and often are not capable of manipulation), the ability of the researcher to impute cause and effect is limited. Let us say that we collect data on manual workers' levels of job satisfaction and productivity in a firm. We may find, through the kinds of techniques examined in Chapter 8, that there is a strong relationship between the two, suggesting that workers who exhibit high levels of job satisfaction also have high levels of productivity. We can say that there is a relationship between the two variables (see Figure 1.5), but as we have seen, this is only a first step in the demonstration of causality. It is also necessary to confirm that the relationship is non-spurious. Could it be, for example, that workers who have been with the firm a long time are both more satisfied and more productive (see Figure 1.6)? The ways in which the possibility of non-spuriousness can be checked are examined in Chapter 10.

However, the third hurdle – establishing that the putative cause precedes the putative effect – is extremely difficult. The problem is that either of the two possibilities depicted in Figure 1.7 may be true. Job satisfaction may cause greater productivity, but it has long been recognized that the causal connection may work the other way around (i.e. if you are good at your job you often enjoy it more). Because data relating to each of the two variables have been simultaneously collected, it is not possible to arbitrate between the two versions of causality presented in Figure 1.7. One way of dealing with this problem is through a reconstruction of the likely causal order of the variables involved. Sometimes this process of inference can be fairly

Figure 1.5 A relationship between two variables

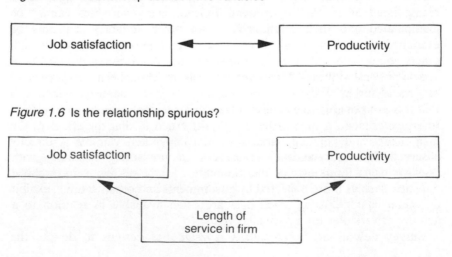

Figure 1.6 Is the relationship spurious?

Figure 1.7 Two possible causal interpretations of a relationship

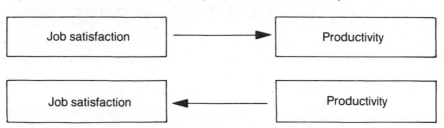

uncontroversial. If, for example, we find a relationship between race and number of years spent in formal schooling, we can say that the former affects the latter. However, this modelling of likely causal connections is more fraught when it is not obvious which variable precedes the other, as with the relationship between job satisfaction and productivity. When such difficulties arise, it may be necessary to include a second wave of data collection in relation to the same respondents in order to see, for example, whether the impact of job satisfaction on subsequent productivity is greater than the impact of productivity on subsequent job satisfaction. Such a design is known as a *panel design* (Cramer 1988), but is not very common in the social sciences. The bulk of the discussion in this book about non-experimental research will be concerned with the survey/correlational design in which data on variables are simultaneously collected.

The procedures involved in making causal inferences from survey data are examined in Chapter 10 in the context of the multivariate analysis of relationships among variables. The chief point to be gleaned from the preceding discussion is that the extraction of causal connections among variables can be undertaken with greater facility in the context of experimental research than when survey data are being analysed.

Exercises

1. What is the chief difference between univariate, bivariate, and multivariate quantitative data analysis?

2. Why is random assignment crucial to a true experimental design?

3. A researcher collects data by interview on a sample of households to find out if people who read 'quality' daily newspapers are more knowledgeable about politics than people who read 'tabloid' newspapers each day. The hunch was confirmed. People who read the quality newspapers were twice as likely to respond accurately to a series of questions designed to test their political knowledge. The researcher concludes that the quality dailies induce higher levels of political knowledge than the tabloids. Assess this reasoning.

Chapter two

Analysing data with computers: first steps with SPSS-X and SPSS/PC+

Since the different kinds of statistics to be described in this book will be carried out with one of the, if not the, most widely used and comprehensive statistical programs in the social sciences, SPSS, we will begin by outlining what this entails. The abbreviation SPSS stands for *Statistical Package for the Social Sciences*. This package of programs is available for both main-frame and personal computers. These programs are being continuously updated and so there are various versions in existence. The latest revision for the mainframe computer is known as SPSS-X Release 3.0 (1988), while that for the personal computer is called SPSS/PC+ Version 3.0 (1988). We shall refer to the mainframe program as SPSS-X, even though earlier releases of it are written as SPSS^X. Since the differences between SPSS-X Release 3.0 and SPSS/PC+ Version 3.0 are relatively minor, we shall discuss them together, drawing attention to their differences when they arise. To simplify the presentation, we will point out differences between the various releases of SPSS-X in the Appendix which is at the end of the book. Unless we need to be more specific, we shall refer to the program generally as SPSS. All the statistical tests described in this book can be carried out with both SPSS-X and SPSS/PC+, apart from two (rho and partial correlation) which are only available with SPSS-X. In addition, SPSS/PC+ Version 3.0 can only handle up to 500 variables at a time.

The great advantage of using a package like SPSS is that it will enable you to score and to analyse quantitative data very quickly and in many different ways once you have learned how. In other words, it will help you to eliminate those long hours spent working out scores, carrying out involved calculations, and making those inevitable mistakes that so frequently occur while doing this. It will also provide you with the oppor-tunity for using more complicated and often more appropriate statistical techniques which you would not have dreamt of attempting otherwise.

There is, of course, what may seem to be a strong initial disadvantage in using computer programs to analyse data and that is you will have to learn how to run these programs. The time spent doing this, however, will be much less than doing these same calculations by hand. In addition, you will have picked up some knowledge which should be of value to you in a world where the use of computers is fast becoming increasingly common. The ability to do things quickly and with little effort is also much more fun and often easier than you might at first imagine.

When mastering a new skill, like SPSS, it is inevitable that you will make mistakes which can be frustrating and off-putting. While this is something we all do, it may seem that we make more mistakes when learning to use a computer than we do carrying out other activities. The reason for this is that programs require instructions to be given in a very precise form and usually in a particular sequence in order for them to work. This precision may be less obvious or true of other everyday things that we do. It is worth remembering, however, that these errors will not harm the computer or its program in any way.

In order to make as few mistakes as possible, it is important at this stage to follow precisely the instructions laid down for the examples in this and subsequent chapters in terms of the characters and spaces that go to make up each line. Although 'bugs' do sometimes occur, errors are usually the result of something you have done and not the fault of the machine or the program. The program will tell you what the error is if there is something wrong with the form of the instructions you have given it, but not if you have told it to add up the wrong set of numbers. In other words, it questions the presentation but not the objectives of the instructions.

Gaining access to SPSS

To use SPSS, it is necessary to have access to it via a personal computer or a *terminal* connected to a mainframe computer. These are normally maintained by the Computer Centre in your institution, which will tell you where they are and how to use them. Both a computer terminal and a personal computer consist of a *keyboard* on which you type in your instructions and usually a video display unit (VDU) or television-like *screen* which shows you what you have typed. Other terminals have a *printer* instead of a screen, but these printing terminals are becoming less common. While being much slower in showing you what you have typed, printers are very helpful when you first learn to use a computer because they print out a record of everything you have done. A screen normally only displays 25 lines of information, which disappears as it scrolls from the top when the screen becomes full. This makes it more difficult to remember what you have typed. Regardless of which kind of terminal you use, the computer you are connected to will have a *high-speed* printer which you can instruct to print out any information you have stored in it. Indeed, if you want to keep a record of what you have done when using a screen, then this usually can be effected by typing in a few instructions to do this. Your Computer Centre should be able to tell you what these instructions

17

are. How to do this with SPSS/PC+ will be described later.

Keyboards are used to type or put in (hence the term *input*) the data that you want to analyse. If you have a small amount of data, it is most probably quicker to do this yourself. If, however, you are intending to collect and analyse a large amount of data, then it is more convenient to let the Computer Centre do this for you if it provides such a service. You also use the keyboard to type in or write the SPSS program that you want to run.

Since different makes of computers have different instructions or programs for operating them which also change from time to time, it is not possible in a book of this size to provide you with all the information you need to use them. Your Computer Centre will show you how to do this. However, you might find it helpful to have a general idea of how to operate a computer.

First, if you are using a mainframe computer, you have to register as a user at your Computer Centre just as you do when using a library or bank. They will give you an identification label or *ID* which may be your surname and initials, a *password* which you can change so that only you will know it, and some space to store information in, which is sometimes referred to as your *directory* or *file space*. Every time you want to use a terminal, you have to quote your ID followed by your password. This is often called *logging on* or *logging in*. The idea of the password is to prevent unauthorized people from using the computer and having access to your file space.

Second, you will have to learn how to store or to file information in this space as well as how to change it and get rid of or delete it. In other words, you will need to know how to use an *editor* or editing system which does this. The information is stored in *files* which will consist of your data and the SPSS programs you want to run. In order to work with or call them, it is necessary to give each of them a short name. The name should be of a form which helps you remember what is contained in the file to which it refers.

Third, you will need to learn the few commands necessary to run your SPSS program or job, to display the results on your screen, and to print them out if you wish to keep a hard copy of them. While this might seem like a lot to learn at first, you will soon get the hang of it. Since the instructions for editing files and running SPSS jobs are standard for SPSS/PC+, they will be described later to show you how to use this program. Although the instructions for operating a mainframe computer may be different, there may be a sufficient degree of similarity to give you some idea of what may be entailed when using another editor with SPSS-X.

The data file

Before you can analyse your data, you need to create a file which holds them. The data have to be put into a file space which consists of a large number of rows, comprising a maximum of eighty columns in many computers and in SPSS/PC+. Each column in a row can only take one character such as a single digit. The data for the same variable are always placed in the same column(s) in a row and a row always contains the data of the same object of analysis or *case*. Cases are often people, but can be any unit of interest such as families, schools, hospitals, regions, or nations.

To illustrate the way in which these files are created, we will use an imaginary set of data from a questionnaire study which is referred to as the Job Survey. The data relating to this study derive from two sources: a questionnaire study of employees who answer questions about themselves and a questionnaire study of their supervisors who answer questions relating to each of the employees. The questions asked are shown in Appendix 2.1 at the end of this chapter, while the coding of the information or data collected is presented in Table 2.1. The cases consist of people, usually called *subjects* by psychologists and *respondents* by sociologists. Although questionnaire data have been used as an example, it should be recognized that SPSS and the data-analysis procedures described in this book may be used with other forms of quantitative data, such as official statistics or observational measures.

Since it is easier to analyse data consisting of numbers rather than a mixture of numbers and other characters such as alphabetic letters, all of the variables or answers in the Job Survey have been coded as numbers. So, for instance, each of the five possible answers to the first question has been given a number varying from 1 to 5. If the respondent has put a tick against White/European, then this response is coded as 1. (Although the use of these categories may be questioned, as may many of the concepts in the social sciences, this kind of information is sometimes collected in surveys and is used here as an example of a categorical variable. We shall shorten the name of the first category to 'white' throughout the book to simplify matters.) It is preferable in designing questionnaires that, wherever possible, numbers should be clearly assigned to particular answers so that little else needs to be done to the data before it is typed in by someone else. Before multiple copies of the questionnaire are made, it is always worth checking with the person who types in this information that this has been adequately done.

It is also important to reserve a number for missing data, such as a failure to give a clear and unambiguous response, since we need to record this information. Numbers which represent real or non-missing data should not be used to code missing values. Thus, for example, since the answers to the first question on ethnic group in the Job Survey are coded 1 to 5, it is necessary to use any other number to identify a missing response. In this survey all missing data except that for absenteeism have been coded as zero since this value cannot be confused with the way that non-missing data are represented. Because some employees have not been absent from work

Table 2.1 The Job-Survey data

```
01  1 1  8300  29  01  4 0 3 4 4 2 4 2 2 2 2 3 2 2 3 0 1  07
02  2 1  7300  26  05  2 0 0 2 3 2 2 1 2 3 4 4 4 1 3 4 4  08
03  3 1  8900  40  05  4 4 4 4 1 2 1 2 2 2 1 2 3 1 4 3 4  00
04  3 1  8200  46  15  2 2 5 2 4 1 2 2 2 3 2 2 3 2 3 3 4  04
05  2 2  9300  63  36  4 3 4 4 1 2 3 3 3 4 5 5 4 1 3 5 3  00
06  1 1  8000  54  31  2 2 5 3 3 2 1 1 2 4 4 4 4 1 1 3 4  01
07  1 1  8300  29  02  0 3 3 2 3 2 2 3 2 3 5 4 2 2 3 5 2  00
08  3 1  8800  35  02  5 2 2 4 2 3 4 3 2 3 3 3 2 2 3 4 4  02
09  2 2  8800  33  04  3 3 1 2 4 2 3 4 1 2 2 3 2 2 2 1 1  05
10  2 2  6900  27  06  4 3 2 3 3 2 1 3 2 3 4 3 5 1 2 2 4  04
11  1 1  7100  29  04  2 2 4 1 4 2 1 1 2 5 4 3 4 2 2 2 3  08
12  2 1     0  19  02  1 1 5 2 4 1 1 1 1 3 4 3 3 1 3 2 3  04
13  4 1  9000  55  35  3 3 3 4 2 2 2 3 2 5 5 5 4 1 4 3 5  01
14  1 2  8500  29  01  2 3 4 2 4 2 2 3 1 4 3 4 4 1 1 2 2  00
15  3 1  9100  48  08  3 3 2 2 1 3 2 4 4 2 3 3 3 2 4 5 5  01
16  2 1  7900  32  07  3 3 4 2 2 2 3 1 2 4 2 2 2 2 2 2 3  04
17  1 1  8300  48  14  3 3 3 2 4 1 2 2 2 4 5 4 4 1 2 5 3  01
18  1 2  6700  18  01  2 2 4 2 4 2 3 2 2 5 5 5 1 1 2 3 3  06
19  3 2  7500  28  02  4 4 2 3 2 3 4 3 3 3 2 3 2 2 3 4 4  03
20  3 2  8800  37  01  3 2 3 3 3 3 2 1 2 5 4 4 5 1 1 4 1  03
21  1 1     0  43  16  1 4 4 3 3 3 2 3 3 3 2 4 4 2 4 5 2  06
22  1 1  8700  39  06  3 2 3 2 3 3 2 2 3 4 3 5 3 2 1 1 5  05
23  1 1  9000  53  05  1 4 3 4 4 3 2 2 3 5 4 2 1 3 3 5    13
24  2 2  8000  34  09  1 3 4 1 5 1 2 1 1 3 4 4 3 2 1 3 3  09
25  3 2  8500  43  17  4 3 4 5 3 3 1 3 2 3 2 4 4 1 3 5 2  02
26  1 1  7000  21  01  4 4 2 2 3 4 3 3 4 2 3 2 2 1 2 5 5  03
27  1 1  8100  50  28  3 2 3 3 4 2 1 1 2 5 5 5 4 1 2 2 4  08
28  1 2  6200  31  09  1 2 5 1 4 2 2 1 2 4 4 5 4 2 3 5 5  00
29  1 1  6800  31  12  3 3 4 3 3 3 2 2 3 2 3 1 2 1 3 5 4  06
30  2 2  8200  52  21  2 3 2 3 2 3 3 3 3 2 2 2 2 2 4 4 3  10
31  1 1  7200  54  12  3 5 3 3 3 3 2 3 2 4 3 4 4 2 4 4 2  99
32  3 2  6200  28  10  2 2 4 1 5 1 2 2 2 3 3 3 2 1 2 4 4  09
33  2 2  8300  50  23  4 4 3 4 3 4 2 3 4 3 3 3 3 2 3 4 5  05
34  2 2  8000  52  21  5 4 3 3 3 3 4 3 3 2 3 3 2 1 3 2 5  04
35  1 2  7500  40  21  1 1 3 4 3 3 2 3 2 2 3 2 2 1 2 2 3  06
36  2 1  5900  19  01  2 2 5 2 4 2 1 2 2 5 5 5 5 2 2 3 2  03
37  2 1  8800  38  04  5 4 1 4 3 5 3 3 3 2 1 2 1 2 4 4 4  08
38  2 1  9000  61  41  5 3 2 4 1 3 2 2 2 1 2 2 2 3 5 4    03
39  1 2  7800  37  08  3 2 4 2 3 2 3 3 2 4 4 5 1 3 4 4    08
40  2 1  6700  31  15  2 2 5 2 5 2 2 2 1 5 5 5 4 2 1 1 2  05
41  2 2  7500  43  21  4 3 2 2 2 3 4 2 3 3 3 3 3 1 1 4 2  00
42  3 1  6800  23  03  1 2 5 3 5 1 1 2 1 4 4 4 5 1 3 2 2  08
43  2 2  7000  27  05  1 1 4 1 4 1 1 1 2 4 5 4 4 2 1 2 1  09
44  1 1  7500  28  07  3 3 1 3 3 3 5 3 3 1 2 2 1 1 2 4 3  09
45  1 1  6600  00  10  1 1 4 1 4 2 2 2 2 4 2 5 5 1 4 1 3  10
46  3 1  6700  18  01  4 2 3 4 2 2 3 3 2 4 3 5 4 1 4 3 4  03
47  1 2 10300  48  23  3 4 3 3 3 2 2 3 2 2 1 3 2 2 4 4 3  08
48  1 2  6800  29  10  2 3 5 4 4 2 2 2 1 3 4 2 2 1 3 4 4  11
49  1 2  7300  42  10  2 2 3 3 3 2 2 1 2 5 5 5 5 2 1 4 4  00
50  1 1  9100  53  12  4 5 2 5 1 4 5 3 4 2 2 2 2 2 4 4 4  01
51  1 1  7600  32  12  3 2 4 1 4 3 2 2 3 3 3 4 2 1 2 3 2  01
52  1 2  6500  31  02  1 3 5 1 5 2 2 3 2 5 4 4 5 2 1 3 1  08
53  1 1  9500  55  19  5 4 3 5 3 5 4 3 3 3 4 3 1 3 4 3    00
54  3 2  7400  26  08  4 4 1 3 3 4 5 2 3 1 2 1 2 2 4 3 3  02
55  1 2  8600  53  22  3 4 2 3 1 3 4 4 3 2 1 2 2 1 3 5 5  00
```

56	1	1	7800	51	31	2	3	3	3	3	3	2	4	4	5	4	5	5	1	4	1	1	08
57	1	1	7700	48	23	3	1	4	3	4	2	2	2	2	5	5	4	5	1	1	3	2	06
58	1	2	6900	48	28	1	1	4	1	5	2	2	2	1	5	5	5	5	2	1	4	3	04
59	2	2	7900	62	40	1	2	3	2	5	2	2	3	2	5	4	4	5	2	1	1	5	07
60	2	1	8700	57	13	2	3	4	2	3	2	3	1	2	3	3	4	3	1	4	4	1	04
61	1	2	8900	42	20	5	4	2	2	2	3	3	3	3	2	1	2	4	2	3	3	3	02
62	1	1	7100	21	02	1	2	3	1	4	2	3	2	1	3	3	3	3	1	4	2	2	00
63	3	2	6400	26	08	3	1	3	2	4	1	2	1	1	2	3	3	2	1	4	1	1	04
64	1	2	6800	46	00	1	2	5	2	4	3	1	2	2	5	5	5	5	2	2	3	4	05
65	1	2	10500	59	21	4	3	2	4	2	2	2	3	3	2	3	2	2	2	4	5	1	04
66	4	2	7100	30	08	0	3	3	2	4	2	3	2	2	5	4	4	4	1	2	2	3	02
67	1	1	7300	29	8	3	2	2	3	3	2	3	2	1	5	3	4	3	2	1	4	5	10
68	3	1	6900	45	09	2	3	4	3	4	3	3	3	3	4	3	3	2	2	3	4	09
69	3	1	8000	53	30	3	2	5	3	2	2	1	2	2	4	5	3	4	2	2	1	4	02
70	1	1	6900	47	22	2	3	4	2	5	2	3	4	2	4	3	5	4	1	2	4	4	11

(i.e. zero days), missing data for absenteeism could not be coded as '0'. Instead, it is indicated by '99' since no employee has been away that long. Coding missing data as zero also makes it easier to take account of varying amounts of such data when a number of similar variables are combined, as we shall see later. Sometimes it might be necessary to distinguish different kinds of missing data, such as a 'Don't know' response from a 'Does not apply' one, in which case these two answers would be represented by different numbers.

It is advisable to give each subject an identifying number to be able to refer to them if necessary. This number should be placed in the first few columns of each row or line. Since there are seventy subjects, only columns 1 and 2 need to be used for this purpose. If there were 100 subjects, then the first three columns would be required to record this information as the largest number consists of three digits. One empty or blank space will be left between columns containing data for different variables to make the file easier to read, although it is not necessary to do this.

Since all the data for one subject can be fitted on to one line using this fixed format, only one line needs to be reserved for each subject in this instance and the data for the next subject can be put into the second line. If more than one line were required to record all the data for one subject, then you would use as many subsequent rows as were needed to do so. In this case, it may also be worth giving each of the lines of data for a particular subject an identifying number to help you read the information more readily, so that the first line would be coded 1, the second 2, and so on. Each line or row of data for a subject is known as a *record* in SPSS.

The first variable in our survey and our data file refers to the racial or ethnic origin of our respondents. Since this can only take one of six values (if we include the possibility that they might not have answered this question), then these data can be put into one column. If we leave a space between the subject's two-digit identification number and the one-digit number representing their ethnic group, then the data for this latter variable will be placed in column 4. Since the second variable of gender can also be coded as a single digit number, this information has been placed in column 6. The third variable of current gross annual income, however, requires five columns of space since two subjects (47 and 65) earned more than £10,000 and so this variable occupies columns 8 to 12 inclusive (please note that the comma and pound sign should not be included when entering the data).

A full listing of the variables and the columns they occupy is given later on in Table 2.2 when describing the SPSS program. The data file is named **jsr.dat** which is an abbreviation of 'job survey raw data'. Since SPSS accepts letters written in capitals or upper case (for example, JSR.DAT) and small or lower case (for example, jsr.dat), lower-case letters will be used to make typing easier for you.

The SPSS command file

To analyse your data with SPSS, you have to create or write a *command file*. This tells or commands SPSS what you want done with the data. Like the data file, the command file consists of a number of lines, which contain up to eighty columns or characters in most computers and operating systems. A command file for the Job Survey data can be found on p. 27. The simplest and most basic command file need consist of only two or three commands at the most. The first command, **data list**, informs SPSS how the data are arranged in that file. The second command, **missing values**, is only necessary if you have missing data, and states how the missing data are coded. After giving these commands, you may be in a position to tell SPSS what statistical tests or *procedures* you want carried out on your data.

SPSS names

The names used to refer to data files and any variables you wish to analyse within an SPSS command file have to meet certain specifications. They must be no longer than eight characters and must begin with an alphabetic character (A–Z), an @ (at), or a $ (dollar). They can contain numbers (0–9) or a # (hash) but no blank spaces are allowed. In addition certain words, known as *keywords*, cannot be used because they can only be interpreted as commands by SPSS. They include words such as **add**, **and**, **any**, **or**, and **to**, to give but a few examples. A full list of these keywords can be found in the index of the *SPSS-X User's Guide* and the *SPSS/PC+ Manual*. If you accidentally use one of these words as a name, you will be told of this in the output you receive. No keyword contains numbers so you can be certain that names which include numbers will always be recognized as such. It is important to remember that the same name cannot be used for different files or variables. Thus, for example, you could not use the name **satis** to refer to all four of the questions which measure job satisfaction. You would need to distinguish them in some way such as calling the answer to the first question **satis1**, the answer to the second one **satis2**, and so on.

Data list command

Whenever you wish to analyse some data, it is necessary to tell SPSS where your data are, what the names of the variables are, and in which columns they are to be found. In SPSS-X, you also need to state how many lines or **records** there are for each subject or case. All this is done with the **data list** command. To illustrate the use of this command, we will once again use the Job-Survey data.

This command can be divided into three parts. The first part comprises the two keywords **data list** which are used to identify this command. The second part specifies the data file to be looked at which in this example we have called **jsr.dat**. In SPSS-X we also need to indicate the number of lines or records of data for each subject, which as you may recall is one. These two parts are combined as follows:

data list file=jsr.dat records=1

Note that the 'd' of **data** is placed in the first column.

In SPSS/PC+, the **records=1** subcommand is omitted and the file name is enclosed in apostrophes:

data list file='jsr.dat'

If the file is stored on and read from a *floppy disk*, then the name of the *drive* used to do this needs to be indicated in the file name. So, for example, if the disk has been inserted into drive A, then the file name would be **'a:jsr.dat'**. A colon separates the name of the drive from that of the file.

The next part of this command lists the names of the variables you want to identify and the columns in which they are located. The beginning of each row of variable names needs to be indicated by a forward slash (*/*). This may be shown more clearly by starting each row on a new line. However, since this line represents a continuation of the command in the previous one, it is necessary in SPSS-X to convey this by placing it in column 2 and not column 1. If you put this information in column 1 by mistake, then SPSS-X would unsuccessfully try to read it as the start of a new command. Although this restriction does not apply to SPSS/PC+, it will be used to make clearer the beginning of each command and to ensure their compatability with SPSS-X.

Each variable is given a short name following the rules outlined above, which should be reread if you cannot remember them. The shortened names of the twenty-four variables of the survey and the columns they occupy in the data file are given in Table 2.2. Of course, it is possible to shorten them further. However, to make it easier for you to remember what we are referring to, we have kept them as long and as meaningful as possible.

Any variable to which you want to refer in your command file has to be listed in this command, together with the columns in which it is located. Since we will be referring to all of them, we will have to list them all. The name for the identification number of each subject has been shortened to **id** while that for the subject's ethnic group has been abbreviated to **ethnicgp**. If the data for a variable only occupy one column, as is the case for ethnic group, then simply list the column number, which is 4 in this instance. If the data, however, are located in two or more columns as they are for the

Table 2.2 The SPSS names and location of the Job-Survey variables

Variable name	SPSS name	Column location
Identification number	**id**	1–2
Ethnic group	**ethnicgp**	4
Gender	**gender**	6
Gross annual income	**income**	8–12
Age	**age**	14–15
Years worked	**years**	17–18
Organizational commitment	**commit**	20
Job-satisfaction scale		
Item 1	**satis1**	22
Item 2	**satis2**	24
Item 3	**satis3**	26
Item 4	**satis4**	28
Job-autonomy scale		
Item 1	**autonom1**	30
Item 2	**autonom2**	32
Item 3	**autonom3**	34
Item 4	**autonom4**	36
Job-routine scale		
Item 1	**routine1**	38
Item 2	**routine2**	40
Item 3	**routine3**	42
Item 4	**routine4**	44
Attendance at meeting	**attend**	46
Rated skill	**skill**	48
Rated productivity	**prody**	50
Rated quality	**qual**	52
Absenteeism	**absence**	54–55

subject's identification number, then give the number for the first and the last columns in which the data are to be found separated by a single dash or hyphen as in **1–2**. Following these rules, the relevant part of this command for these two variables is:

/id 1–2 ethnicgp 4

Where the data for two or more consecutive variables are located in exactly the same number of columns, it is permissible first to list these variables together and then to provide the first and last numbers of the columns in which all the data for these variables are to be found. In the present study, for example, the two variables of age (**age**) and years of working for the firm (**years**) are next to one another and the data for both of them occupy two columns. Consequently, these two variables can be listed together followed by the numbers of the first and last columns the data occupy. Since there is a space between each of the columns of data, it is necessary to take account of this by locating the data for each variable in three rather than two columns. As the two extra columns only contain blanks, they will not affect the values for the two variables. The first column, then, would be 13 and the last one 18. These two variables can be listed in the following way:

age years 13–18

One way of checking that the first and last columns have been correctly identified is to divide the number of columns specified (i.e. six) by the number of variables (i.e. two) to see if the result is a whole number (i.e. three). If the first column were incorrectly listed as 14 rather than 13, then the fact that 5 divided by 2 does not result in a whole number should alert you to your mistake. If you do not realize the mistake you have made, SPSS will draw your attention to it in the output it gives you.

Where the variables are similar in nature and are consecutively located, such as the series of items measuring job satisfaction, it may be useful to include as the last part of the name (the suffix) a numeral that corresponds to the number and position of such variables. In the Job Survey, for example, there are four consecutive items that assess job satisfaction. Consequently, these items have been named **satis1** to **satis4**. Where this is done, it is possible to refer to them in the **data list** command by only listing the names of the first and last variables and indicating that there is a sequence of them by separating the names with the keyword **to** as follows:

satis1 to satis4

The complete command for identifying the Job-Survey variables is:

/id 1–2 ethnicgp 4 gender 6 income 8–12 age years 13–18 commit
satis1 to satis4 autonom1 to autonom4 routine1 to routine4 attend
skill prody quality 19–52 absence 54–55.

With SPSS/PC+, it is necessary to end a command with a full stop. This will be generally included in the examples throughout the book to show where it occurs. It should be omitted when using SPSS-X.

Missing values

It is necessary to tell SPSS how you have coded data that are missing. If you do not do this, it will read the codes you have assigned to them as real or non-missing data. So, for example, if you have coded missing data for **age** as a zero and you do not inform SPSS that this is what you have done, then it will interpret a zero as someone who is not yet one year old.

The command for telling SPSS what number(s) indicate(s) missing data are the two keywords **missing values** followed by the variable name and the number(s) (in round brackets) that you have used to refer to missing values. If, for example, you wanted to indicate that the missing value for **ethnicgp** in the Job Survey is zero, then you would do this as follows:

missing values ethnicgp (0).

Where consecutive variables have been assigned the same missing value, it is only necessary to list the name of the first and last variables in that sequence. Thus, in the Job Survey, for instance, the missing values for the variables inclusively included between ethnic group and organizational commitment could be indicated in the following way:

missing values ethnicgp to commit (0).

Where different numbers have been used to indicate missing data for different variables, the variables have to be separately listed with their respective missing values. Since, for example, the missing data for absenteeism are coded as '99' rather than '0' as used for other variables, it has to be listed separately as follows:

missing values ethnicgp to commit (0) absence (99).

Only one to three values can be used in this command to code missing data for a single variable. If you have more than three, it is necessary to group some of them together into no more than three values using the **recode** command. You will be shown how to use this command in the next chapter.

Where a series of related variables may be combined to form a new variable for each subject, their missing values should not be given as these will be ignored when using the valuable **count** command. In the Job Survey, for example, job satisfaction has been assessed with four items in order to try and obtain a more reliable estimate of it. These four items will be combined to form one overall score of job satisfaction (**satis**) rather than four separate ones, if it can be shown that these four measure the same variable. Because of this possibility, the missing values for these items will not be given. The same is true of the subsequent eight items, four of which have been designed to tap job autonomy (**autonom**) and the other four job routine (**routine**). Consequently, the **missing values** command for this data file is:

missing values ethnicgp to commit attend to qual (0) absence (99).

Statistical procedures

At this stage, you may be ready to analyse your data. The rest of the book describes numerous ways in which you can do this. To show you what a simple command file, which will carry out a statistical analysis, looks like, we will ask SPSS to calculate the average or *mean* age of the sample. This can be done with a number of SPSS commands, but we shall use the one called **descriptives**. This is also called **condescriptive** in SPSS-X, which can be used as an alternative name or *alias*. This works out a number of other descriptive statistics as well. All we have to do is to add the name we have given this variable (which is **age**) after the word **descriptives**, making sure to leave one space between them:

descriptives age.

SPSS recognizes many keywords such as **descriptives** and **missing values** by their first three or four letters, so that if you mistype the subsequent letters, their functions will be still carried out.

Finish

In SPSS-X, the final command is **finish**, which tells SPSS-X that there are no more instructions to be read. In this case it is optional since there are no more commands to carry out. You might use this command in some situations to run just the first part of a longer command file. In SPSS/PC+, however, this command is used to end a session with SPSS/PC+.

The complete command file

For SPSS-X, the command file will have the following form:

data list file=jsr.dat records=1
  /id 1–2 ethnicgp 4 gender 6 income 8–12 age years 13–18 commit
  satis1 to satis4 autonom1 to autonom4 routine1 to routine4 attend
  skill prody qual 19–52 absence 54–55
missing values ethnicgp to commit attend to qual (0) absence (99)
descriptives age
finish

For SPSS/PC+, the command file is:

```
data list file='a:jsr.dat'
 /id 1-2 ethnicgp 4 gender 6 income 8-12 age years 13-18 commit
 satis1 to satis4 autonom1 to autonom4 routine1 to routine4 attend
 skill prody qual 19-52 absence 54-55.
descriptives age.
```

Once you have typed these lines of instructions into your file space, you have to save them as a file if you intend to run them altogether on SPSS-X, and to give this file a name. We shall call it **jsma.sps**, which is short for Job-Survey mean-age SPSS command file.

Running an SPSS command file

You are now ready to run this SPSS file or job. Since the instructions for doing this for SPSS-X vary according to the computer being used, we will not give them here. You need to find these out from your Computer Centre. The instructions for doing this for SPSS/PC+ will be outlined at the end of this chapter. For both SPSS-X and SPSS/PC+, you can run one command at a time. This is known as *interactive processing*, as opposed to *batch processing*, where the complete file is run. Since it is more difficult to recall what you have done with interactive processing, it is not recommended and will not be described.

The output

Every time you run an SPSS job, you will receive some *output* which will contain a copy of what you have done. This output is normally sent to your file space and appears as a new file, which you can read. In SPSS/PC+, it also appears on your screen. In addition, you can ask for and later collect a *hard copy* of it by having it printed on a high-speed printer. The output will always contain a copy of your command file as well as additional information.

The **data list** command in SPSS-X, for example, automatically produces a table immediately after it which states the number of records per case as well as the following information about each of the listed variables: the **VARIABLE** name, the **RECORD** number, the **START**ing and **END**ing columns, the **FORMAT** which is **F** for fixed, the **WIDTH** in number of columns, and the number of **DEC**imal places. To produce this table with SPSS/PC+, it is necessary to add the keywords **fixed** and **table** to the **data list** command:

```
data list file='a:jsr.dat' fixed table
```

Part of the table for the current job is reproduced in Table 2.3. This

Table 2.3 Segment of SPSS **data list** table

5 0 skill prody qual 19–52 absence 54–55.

THE ABOVE DATA LIST STATEMENT WILL READ 1 RECORDS FROM FILE JSRD

VARIABLE	REC	START	END	FORMAT	WIDTH	DEC
ID	1	1	2	F	2	0
ETHNICGP	1	4	4	F	1	0
GENDER	1	6	6	F	1	0
.	.	.	.	.	.	.
.	.	.	.	.	.	.
.	.	.	.	.	.	.
ABSENCE	1	54	55	F	2	0
END OF DATALIST TABLE.						

table is obviously useful to check the location of each variable.

Of more immediate interest is the calculation of the mean age which is presented in the following way on page 2 of the SPSS-X output:

NUMBER OF VALID OBSERVATIONS (LISTWISE) = 69.00
VARIABLE   MEAN STD DEV MINIMUM MAXIMUM VALID N LABEL
AGE   39.188   12.317   18.000   63.000   69

The mean age, we can see, is 39.188 years. The SPSS/PC+ output is very similar. One difference is that decimal places are rounded to two rather than three places, so that the mean age in the SPSS/PC+ output is 38.19.

Other information is present, some of which needs explaining. The **descriptives** command on its own also provides the standard deviation (see Chapter 5), the minimum age, the maximum age, and the number of cases (**VALID N**) on which this information is based. We will discuss whether and how to use labels in the next chapter since they are not essential to what we want to do. If we look at the ages in our Job-Survey data, then we can confirm that the minimum age is indeed 18 (for case numbers 18 and 46) while the maximum is 63 (for case number 5). We should also notice that the age for one of our subjects (case number 45) is missing, making the number of cases which provide valid data for this variable 69 and not 70.

Requesting particular descriptive statistics

If we just wanted the mean age and not the other statistics, then it would be possible to do this by using the subcommand **statistics** followed by a number which identifies the statistic you require. If you do not specify any particular statistics, you will obtain those given automatically or by *default* when using the **descriptives** command. These were, as we have just seen, the mean, the standard deviation, and the minimum and maximum values.

The statistics that the **descriptives** command gives and the numbers for selecting them are shown below, as well as the keywords which can be substituted for the numbers in SPSS-X:

statistic 1 or **mean**	Mean.	
statistic 2 or **semean**	Standard error of mean.	
statistic 5 or **stddev**	Standard deviation.	
statistic 6 or **variance**	Variance.	
statistic 7 or **kurtosis**	Kurtosis and standard error.	
statistic 8 or **skewness**	Skewness and standard error.	
statistic 9 or **range**	Range.	
statistic 10 or **minimum**	Minimum.	
statistic 11 or **maximum**	Maximum.	
statistic 12 or **sum**	Sum.	
statistic 13 or **default**	Mean, standard deviation, minimum, and maximum. These are the default statistics.	
satistics all	All the above statistics will be given.	

The keywords cannot be used with SPSS/PC+. What these statistics are will be described in Chapter 5.

To obtain just the mean age for our sample, we would add the sub-command **statistic 1** after the **descriptives** command:

descriptives age
 /statistic 1.

If we wanted only the mean and the standard deviation, then we would put the numbers **1** and **5** on the **statistics** subcommand:

descriptives age
 /statistic 1 5.

The output for the mean on its own would look like this:

NUMBER OF VALID OBSERVATIONS (LISTWISE) =   69.00
VARIABLE   MEAN VALID N LABEL
AGE   39.188   69

Missing cases

As we have seen, the age for one of the cases is missing, so that we have sixty-nine subjects instead of seventy. SPSS provides us with a number of ways of dealing with missing data. These vary somewhat for the different statistical procedural commands. For the **descriptives** one, we need only concern ourselves with two possibilities.

The default option, which is used if you do not specifically request an alternative, is to exclude cases on a *pairwise* or variable-by-variable basis. To illustrate this, it is helpful to introduce a second variable which will be income. We will ask SPSS to calculate the average income as well as the average age of our sample. We do this by listing both these variables on the **descriptives** command as follows:

descriptives age income.

The relevant output for this command is:

NUMBER OF VALID OBSERVATIONS (LISTWISE) = 67.00

VARIABLE	MEAN	STD DEV	MINIMUM	MAXIMUM	VALID N	LABEL
AGE	39.188	12.317	18.000	63.000	69	
INCOME	7819.118	997.947	5900.000	10500.000	68	

We see from this output that the number of valid cases for determining average income is 68, which is one less than that for calculating average age. If we look at the incomes in our Job-Survey data file, we will notice that the data for two of the subjects (cases 12 and 21) are missing, whereas age was missing for only one of them (case 45). The default option for dealing with missing data on the **descriptives** command is to work out the statistics for each variable based on the number of valid cases for that variable.

A second option is to exclude cases *listwise* whereby the statistics are based on those subjects who have no missing data on any of the variables listed on the **descriptives** command. Note that the number of such cases is always given in the output. When we only asked for the mean age, we were told that the listwise number of valid observations was sixty-nine. Since only one variable is being examined here, the listwise and the pairwise number of cases is the same. However, when we request statistics for two or more variables, the number of listwise and pairwise cases may be different as it was when we wanted both mean age and mean income. It is also worth stressing that the listwise option only refers to the variables mentioned on the **descriptives** command. So, although we have some other subjects with missing data (for example, cases 1 and 2 have some missing for the job-satisfaction items), they would not be excluded from the analysis because these variables were not listed on the **descriptives** command.

To request the listwise deletion or exclusion of subjects, we add the following subcommand immediately after the **descriptives** command:

descriptives age income
 /option 5.

The statistical output for this command is:

NUMBER OF VALID OBSERVATIONS (LISTWISE) = 67

VARIABLE	MEAN	STD DEV	MINIMUM	MAXIMUM	LABEL
AGE	39.433	12.242	18.000	63.000	
INCOME	7837.313	994.048	5900.000	10500.000	

Two things are worth noting about this output. The first is that the column listing the number of valid cases has disappeared since this is the same for both variables (i.e. 67) and the number of listwise cases is always stated initially. The second point to note is that the mean age and its standard deviation (39.433 and 12.242) are slightly different from the previous pairwise deletion analysis (39.188 and 12.317) because the data for two subjects (cases 12 and 21) have been dropped.

Finally, if we just want the listwise means for age and income, we simply add the two previous subcommands (in either order) immediately after the **descriptives** command:

```
descriptives age income
 /statistic 1
 /option 5.
```

Checking for and correcting mistakes

Edit

Because it is easy and common to make mistakes in setting up a command file and because some command files can take a relatively long time to run, it may be worth checking your file with the **edit** command which you place in the first line of your file. This command can only be used with SPSS-X since it is not available in SPSS/PC+. It looks for errors in the structure of your commands without carrying out any of them when you run the file. Since it may not be immediately obvious to you what your mistake is, we will present some examples of commands with errors in them and the *error* or *warning messages* SPSS reports. These messages will be printed also if you try to run these commands without **edit**.

Misspelling a previously defined variable

Assume that we have misspelt the variable **age** as **ag** on the **descriptives** command:

```
descriptives ag
```

If we do this with SPSS-X, the following error message will appear after this command has been displayed in the output:

```
  6   0 descriptives ag
> ERROR 701 on LINE 6, Column 16, TEXT: AG
> An undefined variable name, or a scratch or system variable was
> specified in a variable list which accepts only standard variables.
> Check spelling, and verify the existence of this variable.
> THIS COMMAND NOT EXECUTED
```

The message points out that an error is to be found in the text **ag** starting in column 16 of line 6 of the command file. Since we have not defined the variable **ag** in the **data list** command, SPSS does not recognize it.

The same error in SPSS/PC+ would produce the following message:

ERROR 507, Text: AG
SYNTAX ERROR--SPSS/PC+ expects a subcommand or variable name. Perhaps
a variable name is misspelled. Valid subcommands for this procedure
are OPTIONS and STATISTICS.
This command not executed.

Since SPSS/PC+ does not recognize **ag**, it does not know whether it is supposed to be a variable name or a subcommand. Consequently, it alerts the user to both possibilities.

Incorrect column number on *data list* command

Assume we have mistakenly typed 19 instead of 18 as the last column for the two variables of **age** and **years** worked for the firm on the **data list** command, using SPSS-X:

data list file=jsr.dat records=1
 /id 1–2 ethnicgp 4 gender 6 income 8–12 age years 13–19 commit
 satis1 to satis4 autonom1 to autonom4 routine1 to routine4 attend
 skill prody qual 19–52 absence 54–55

This is a good example of a single and simple mistake creating five further errors because of the knock-on effect it has on what follows it. Identifying and correcting this initial error will remove the others, so it is not as bad as it might seem initially.

The first error message appears as the **data file** command produces the table for the location of the first of the two variables, namely **age** (see Table 2.4). When the **data list** command cannot evenly divide the number of columns (i.e. seven) reserved for the two variables of **age** and **years** by two, it does not define their location or that of subsequent ones. As a result, error messages stating that these variables are undefined will be produced whenever these variables are encountered on further commands. This happened four times altogether, with **commit**, **attend**, and **qual** on the **missing values** command and **age** on the **descriptives** one. Note that the two other variables on the **missing values** command, **skill**, and **prody** were not described as being undefined because they were not explicitly listed on this command, although they were implied by the use of the keyword **to**. Since they were undefined, there was no record of them.

Table 2.4 First error message when column number on **data list** command is incorrect

VARIABLE	REC	START	END	FORMAT	WIDTH	DEC
ID	1	1	2	F	2	0
ETHNICGP	1	4	4	F	1	0
GENDER	1	6	6	F	1	0
INCOME	1	8	12	F	5	0

>ERROR 4143 LINE 2, COLUMN 52, TEXT: 13
> Column format was used on the DATA LIST command, but the number of
>columns specified is not evenly divisible by the number of
>variables specified.
> NO FURTHER COMMANDS WILL BE EXECUTED. ERROR SCAN CONTINUES.

The **missing values** command was also described as being incorrect because of the three unspecified variables on it (i.e. **commit, attend,** and **qual**):

> **ERROR 4816 LINE 5, COLUMN 50, TEXT: (**
> **The variable list on the MISSING VALUES command was incorrect.**

If the same mistake was made in SPSS/PC+, processing would stop after the first error message, which would read:

ERROR 67,   Text: COMMIT
INCORRECT COLUMN RANGE ON DATA LIST COMMAND—The number of
columns specified is not evenly divisible by the number of variables specified.
This command is not executed.

Not indenting the continuation of an SPSS-X command line

SPSS-X interprets a letter in the first column of a line as a new command. This does not apply to SPSS/PC+. When continuing an SPSS-X command line on to a second line, it is necessary to indent the subsequent lines by at least one space. Assume that we have not done this for the **data list** command, so that the forward slash falls into the first column:

```
data list file=jsr.dat records=1
/id 1–2 ethnicgp 4 gender 6 income 8–12 age years 13–18 commit
 satis1 to satis4 autonom1 to autonom4 routine1 to routine4 attend
 skill prody qual 19–52 absence 54–55
```

The following error message would appear after this last line in the output:

```
5    0    skill prody qual 19–52 absence 54–55
ERROR 1    LINE 2, COMMAND NAME: /ID
> Text appearing in the first column is not recognized as a command.
> Is it spelled correctly? If it was intended as a continuation of
> the previous command, the first column must be blank.
> NO FURTHER COMMANDS WILL BE EXECUTED.
> ERROR SCAN CONTINUES.
```

The message says that the name of a command is expected in line 4 of the command file and that the text appearing in the first two columns is not recognized as such.

The failure to understand correctly the **data list** command means that an *active* file containing the data and a *dictionary* saying what the variables are cannot be created. As a result, when the procedural command is encountered, a second error reporting this is conveyed:

```
6    0    descriptives age
> ERROR 4096
> No permanent dictionary has been defined. There are no variables
> defined in the above transformations that a procedure may access.
```

Correcting the first error will automatically remove the second one.

The wrong data file

Finally, assume that we have no file in our file space called **js.dat** but that we have mistakenly called the data file **js.dat** instead of **jsr.dat** when using SPSS-X so that the **data list** command reads:

```
data list file=js.dat
```

When we run the command file, we will receive two error messages in the resulting output. The first message will be displayed after the end of the **data list** command as follows:

```
1    0    data list file=js.dat records=1
> ERROR    4127    LINE    1,    COLUMN    16,    TEXT: JS.DAT
> The file specified in the DATA LIST command is unsuitable for
> input – probably because it does not exist.
> NO FURTHER COMMANDS WILL BE EXECUTED. ERROR SCAN CONTINUES.
```

The message tells us that there is an error in the text **js.dat** starting in column 16 of line 1 of the command file where the name of the data file is expected. It suggests quite correctly that this file most probably does not exist.

Once again, the command file does not create an active file and a dictionary because it cannot find the data file. The failure to do this brings about the same second error as before, which will disappear if we correctly specify the data file:

```
7    0    descriptives age
> ERROR       4096
> No permanent dictionary has been defined. There are no variables
> defined in the above transformations that a procedure may access.
```

If you have a file in your file space called **js.dat** but which is not the one you wanted to refer to, then **edit** will not pick up this error. However, if you run the command file without **edit**, then what happens will depend on the information in this file. If the file contains numerical data but not those you wanted to analyse, then you might only realize your mistake if the results do not make sense to you. If, on the other hand, the data file contained alphabetic characters such as commands when the command file expected numbers, you would receive a warning the first eighty times this occurred. These would be shown after the first procedural command and after some information on the amount of memory needed to carry out this command.

In our example where the procedural command is a **descriptives** one and the first word of the data file is **data** instead of numbers, the following warnings would be shown:

```
6    0    descriptives age
> WARNING    652
> An invalid numeric field has been found.
> The result has been set to the system-missing value.
SOURCE COMMAND NUMBER -          1
, STARTING COLUMN NUMBER - 1, CONTENTS OF FIELD: da
> WARNING 652
> An invalid numeric field has been found.
> The result has been set to the system-missing value.
SOURCE COMMAND NUMBER -   1
, STARTING COLUMN NUMBER - 4, CONTENTS OF FIELD: a
```

What these warnings mean is where SPSS-X comes across an alphabetic character when it is expecting a number, it interprets this as a missing value. This occurs when the variables on the **data list** command (**SOURCE COMMAND NUMBER - 2**) are being processed. When it reads the data for the first variable, **ID**, which start in column 1 and end in column 2, it finds the letters **da**. It therefore sets this information as missing. It does the same when it reads the data for the second variable, which is in column 4 and which is **a**.

If we made the same mistake in SPSS/PC+, so that the **data list** command reads **data list file='a:js.dat'**, we would receive the following error message:

```
ERROR    355, TEXT: a:js.dat
FILE CANNOT BE OPENED—Check spelling and directory name. IF the file does exist,
try increasing the FILES specification in CONFIG.SYS.
This command not executed.
```

Hopefully, these examples of the kinds of mistakes which are easily and commonly made will help you to work out what you may have done wrong. As we have seen, it is sometimes only necessary to correct the first mistake, since the others may be a consequence of it.

Editing in SPSS/PC+

We will briefly describe here how to get started with SPSS/PC+, which we shall assume is already installed on a personal computer to which you have access. After switching on the machine, you may need to log in with the appropriate code when the prompt appears. After a while, another prompt will be shown. If you do not have any control over who uses the personal computer on which you are working, you may want to store your work on a floppy disk. This is inserted into a slot called a drive and needs to be formatted if new. Now type **spsspc**, which will invoke the program. A split screen (with two windows) will appear. We need only concern ourselves with the bottom half of it which is blank and which we shall use to type in and edit information. To do this, we need to call the *editor* by holding down the key with ALT on it and press the key with E (for 'edit') on it. You will notice that the screen *cursor* (the point on the screen which shows you where you are on it) changes from a flashing block to an underscore. In addition, the border of the top left half of the screen changes from lines to dots. These changes should help to remind you that you are in the editor. This editor is called Review in SPSS/PC+.

To analyse some data, you need to create a file to store them. If you have a large amount of data, you may be able to have this done for you by a local Data Preparation Centre. Keep this data file on a floppy disk and make a second or back-up copy. Alternatively, you can transfer it, using an appropriate program, from the mainframe computer where it is held to the personal computer you are using. Otherwise, you need to type it in yourself. To store or save the information you have typed, press the *function* key with F9 on it. At the bottom of the screen the phrase **write whole file** will be highlighted. To save or write this data file, press the Return key. You must give the data file a name, otherwise it will be called **scratch.pad** and will be wiped clean every time you create a new file. The name of the file should consist of a prefix or stem of up to eight characters and a suffix or extension of up to three characters. It is helpful if the extension refers to the kind of file it is. In this case, it is the data file for the Job Survey, which we could call **jsr.dat** (or **jsr1.dat** if you have more than one of them). If you want to keep a copy of the data file on a floppy disk (which is in, say, drive A:), simply prefix the name with an **a:**, as in **a:jsr.dat**. It is advisable to do this if you wish to use that file on subsequent sessions.

Having saved the data file, now write the command file. If we want to calculate the mean age of the subjects in the Job Survey, this would be:

```
data list file='a:jsr.dat'
 /age 14–15.
missing values age (0).
descriptives age
 /statistic 1.
```

If the data file is stored on a *fixed disk* (C:) of the personal computer, there is no need to specify the drive name, i.e. **file='jsr:dat'**.

To run this command file, move the cursor to the top line of the file (i.e. the line with **data list**) by pressing the cursor key with the upward arrow on it (↑). Now press the function key F10 and then the Return key. The analysis will proceed with the results being displayed on the full screen. If the 'MORE' message appears in the top right corner of the screen, press any key to display more output. If you want to carry out further commands, type them in at the bottom of the command file. Run them by moving the cursor to the first line of the new command, press the F10 function key and the Return key. If there is a mistake in your command file, processing will stop, and your file will reappear with the cursor on the line with the error. The error can be corrected and the file run again with the cursor on the corrected line by pressing the function key F10 and the Return key. To save this command file, press the F9 function key, the Return key, and type in an appropriate name such as **jsma.sps**. The extension **sps** reminds us that it is an SPSS command file. To insert a file you have already created into the editor, press the F3 function key, move the cursor to highlight the phrase **insert file** at the bottom of the screen, press the Return key, and type in the name of the file you want to edit or run. If you have created a number of files, you may have forgotten one or more of their names. To remind yourself of what they are, list them by pressing the F1 function key. Move the cursor to highlight the phrase **file list** at the bottom of the screen and press the Return key. To list any files stored on a floppy disk, type the name of the drive (for example **a**) followed by a colon, an asterisk, full stop, and another asterisk before pressing the Return key:

a:*.*

The output produced by SPSS/PC+ will be saved on a file called **spss.lis**. You can print this out when you leave SPSS/PC+ by using the appropriate command. However, when you return to SPSS/PC+, this file will have been wiped clean. Should you wish to edit or save it, insert it into the editor, make any necessary changes and then save it by using the F9 function key. Make sure you rename this file by replacing the stem **spss** with another name. Once again, you can keep a copy of this output file by storing it on a floppy disk. To leave SPSS/PC+, type **finish**, press the function key F10 and the Return key.

The following keys will move the cursor quickly within a file. Press the Control key and the key with the leftward pointing arrow on it (←) to shift the cursor to the start of the line it is on. To move it to the end of the line, press the Control key and the one with the rightward pointing arrow on it (→). To move it to the top of the file, press the Control and the Home key, while to move it to the bottom of the file, press the Control and the End key. To move the cursor up or down one or more lines, respectively press the cursor key with the upward and downward pointing arrow on it. To shift the cursor one or more characters to the left or to the right, respectively press the cursor key with the leftward and the rightward pointing arrow on it.

The following keys will delete information from a file. To delete one or more previous characters, press the backspace key. The Delete key removes the character the cursor is currently on. To delete the whole line the cursor is on, press either the ALT or the function F4 key together with the key with D on it. To remove a number of lines at once, move the cursor to the first (or the last) line you want deleted, press the F7 and then the Return key. Now move the cursor to the last (or the first) line you want to delete, pressing the F7 key again. You have now marked or defined the area you want removed. To delete it, press the function key F8 and then the D key.

Finally, if you want to cancel a command, press the Escape key immediately afterwards.

Exercises

1. You need to collect information on the religious affiliation of your respondents. You have thought of the following options: Agnostic, Atheist, Buddhist, Catholic, Hindu, Jewish, Muslim, Protestant and Taoist. Which further category has to be included?

2. You want to record this information in a data file to be stored in a computer. How would you code this information?

3. Looking through your completed questionnaires, you notice that on one of them no answer has been given to this question. What are you going to put in your data file for this person?

4. Suppose that on another questionnaire two categories had been ticked by the respondent. How would you deal with this situation?

5. The first two of your sample of fifty subjects describe themselves as agnostic and the second two as atheists. The ages of these four subjects are 25, 47, 33, and 18. How would you arrange this information in your data file?

6. If data are available for all the options of the religious-affiliation question, how many columns would be needed to store this information?

7. How does SPSS know to what the numbers in the data file refer?

8. How many columns to a line are there in most computers for listing data or commands?

9. Write an SPSS-X **data list** command for the first three variables in the data displayed in Table 7.7 (p. 125), using the variable names provided (for example, **id**, **attend1**, and **qual1**) and leaving one blank column between those reserved for the values of each of the variables. There is one line of data for each subject and the data file is called **ps.dat**. The numbers at the end of the names refer to three consecutive months, while the letters stand for **attend**ance at the firm's meeting, and rated **qual**ity of work.

10. Write the equivalent **data list** command for SPSS/PC+.

11. Write an SPSS-X command for all ten variables in Table 7.7, using the names provided and leaving one blank between the columns of data as before.

12. What is the maximum number of characters that can be used for the name of a variable in SPSS?

Appendix 2.1: The Job-Survey questions

Employee questionnaire

This questionnaire is designed to find out a few things about yourself and your job. Please answer the questions truthfully. There are no right or wrong answers.

	Col	Code
1. To which of the following racial or ethnic groups do you belong? (Tick one)	4	
____White/European		1
____Asian		2
____West Indian		3
____African		4
____Other		5
2. Are you male or fem	6	
____Male		1
____Female		2
3. What is your current annual income before tax and other deductions?	8–12	
£ _____		
4. What was your age last birthday (in years)?	14–15	
_____ years		
5. How many years have you worked for this firm?	17–18	
_____ years		

6. Please indicate whether you (1) strongly disagree, (2) disagree, (3) are undecided, (4) agree, or (5) strongly agree with each of the following statements. Circle one answer only for each statement.

		SD	D	U	A	SA	
(a)	I would not leave this firm even if another employer could offer me a little more money	1	2	3	4	5	20
(b)	My job is like a hobby to me	1	2	3	4	5	22
(c)	Most of the time I have to force myself to go to work	1	2	3	4	5	24
(d)	Most days I am enthusiastic about my work	1	2	3	4	5	26
(e)	My job is pretty uninteresting	1	2	3	4	5	28
(f)	I am allowed to do my job as I choose	1	2	3	4	5	30
(g)	I am able to make my own decisions about how I do my job	1	2	3	4	5	32
(h)	People in my section of the firm are left to do their work as they please	1	2	3	4	5	34
(i)	I do not have to consult my supervisor if I want to perform my work slightly differently	1	2	3	4	5	36
(j)	I do my job in much the same way every day	1	2	3	4	5	38
(k)	There is little variety in my work	1	2	3	4	5	40
(l)	My job is repetitious	1	2	3	4	5	42
(m)	Very few aspects of my job change from day to day	1	2	3	4	5	44

7. Did you attend the firm's meeting this month?   46

                                          ____Yes   1
                                          ____No   2

Supervisor questionnaire

I would be grateful if you could answer the following questions about one of the people for whom you act as supervisor – [Name of Employee]

1. Please describe the skill level of work that this person performs. Which of the following descriptions best fits his/ her work? (Tick one)   48

                                      ____Unskilled   1
                                      ____Semi-skilled   2
                                      ____Fairly skilled   3
                                      ____Highly skilled   4

2. How would you rate his/her productivity? (Tick one)   50
                                    ____Very poor   1
                                    ____Poor   2
                                    ____Average   3
                                    ____Good   4
                                    ____Very good   5

3. How would rate the quality of his/her work?   52
(Tick one)
                                    ____Very poor   1
                                    ____Poor   2
                                    ____Average   3
                                    ____Good   4
                                    ____Very good   5

4. How many days has he/she been absent in the last
twelve months?   54–5
                                    _____ days

Chapter three

Analysing data with computers: further steps with SPSS-X and SPSS/PC+

Now that you know how to set up a basic SPSS command file, we can introduce you to some further commands which you may find very useful. These commands will enable you to do the following: select certain cases (such as all white men under the age of 40) for separate analyses; create new variables (such as scoring an attitude or personality scale) and new data files (to contain them); provide fuller labels for your variables; and add comments to remind yourself what you have done. SPSS can also carry out other operations which are not described in this book such as combining files in various ways. If you want to do things which are not mentioned here, then consult the *SPSS-X User's Guide* or *SPSS/PC+ Manual.*

Selecting cases

To select cases with certain characteristics, you use the **select if** command followed by a logical expression indicating what you want to do. A logical expression is one which is true, false, or unknown. If you wanted to find out, for example, the average age of only the men in the Job-Survey sample, you could use the command file described in the previous chapter with the following three lines placed after the **data list** and **missing values** commands:

select if (gender eq 1).
descriptives age
 /statistic 1.

The logical expression is enclosed in parentheses, although these are optional in SPSS-X. The variable to be used is listed together with the keyword **eq** (which stands for 'equals') and the code for males which is '1'. This **select if** command will go through the data file picking only those cases where **gender** is equal to 1, resulting in the following statistical output:

NUMBER OF VALID OBSERVATIONS (LISTWISE) = 38.00
VARIABLE   MEAN VALID N LABEL
AGE   39.21   38

This **select if** command will continue to select only males if you request further statistical procedures. If you want to carry out additional statistical analyses on the whole sample or on females, it is necessary to precede it with the **temporary** command in SPSS-X:

temporary
select if (gender eq 1)

If you do this, the **select if** command will only be in effect for the next procedural command. If you omit the **temporary** command and then go on to ask for the average age of females, you will find that there are no such cases since at this stage there are only males left in the sample. This problem would arise, for example, if the following set of commands were inadvertently used:

select if (gender eq 1)
descriptives age
statistic 1
select if (gender eq 2)
descriptives age
statistic 1

The message you would receive for the females would be:

STATISTICS CAN NOT BE COMPUTED FOR ANY OF THE REQUESTED
VARIABLES. ALL VARIABLES WERE EITHER MISSING, ALPHANUMERIC, OR
HAD NUMERIC
c VALUES EXCEEDING 10,000,000,000,000.

The **temporary** command can also be used with data transformation commands (**compute**, **recode**, **if**, and **count**) and data labelling commands (**variable labels**, **value labels**, and **missing values**). The use of these commands (apart from **missing values**, which has already been described) will be outlined later on in this chapter. As in this instance, the **temporary** command only operates for the next procedural command.

In SPSS/PC+, on the other hand, it is necessary to use the **process if** command to select cases temporarily:

process if (gender eq 1).

Since this command does not accept logical operators such as 'and' and 'or' (see below), it is only possible to select cases temporarily using one value of one variable.

Relational operators

A relational operator like **eq** compares the value on its left (for example, **gender**) with that on its right (for example, **1**). There are six such operators, which can be represented by the following keywords (with a blank space on either side) or symbols (with or without such spaces):

eq	**=**	**equal to**
ne	**< >**	**not equal to**
lt	**<**	**less than**
le	**<=**	**less than or equal to**
gt	**>**	**greater than**
ge	**>**	**greater than or equal to**

The question of which is the most appropriate operator to use in selecting cases will depend on the selection criteria. To select cases under 40 years of age, we could use **lt**:

select if (age lt 40).

It would also, of course, have been possible to use **le** with age 39 in this instance since we are dealing with whole numbers:

select if (age le 39).

To select non-whites, we could use **< >** with **1** since whites are coded '1':

select if (ethnicgp < > 1).

Combining logical relations

We can combine logical expressions (except when using **process if** in SPSS/PC+) with the logical operators **and** and **or**. We can, for example, select white men under 40 with the following command:

select if (ethnicgp=1 and gender=1 and age < 40).

An ampersand (**&**) can be substituted for **and** and a vertical (**l**) or broken vertical (**¦**) bar for **or**.

To select people of only West Indian and African origin, we would have to use the **or** logical operator:

select if (ethnicgp=3 or ethnicgp=4).

Note that it is necessary to repeat the full logical relation. It is *not* permissible to abbreviate this command as:

select if (ethnicgp=3 or 4).

An alternative way of doing the same thing in SPSS-X (but which is not possible in SPSS/PC+) is to use the **any** logical function where any case with a value of either 3 or 4 for the variable **ethnicgp** is selected:

select if any (ethnicgp,3,4)

The variable and the values to be selected are placed in parentheses.

To select people between the ages of 30 and 40 inclusive, we can use the expression:

select if (age ge 30 and age le 40).

Here, we have to use the **and** logical operator. If we used **or**, we would in effect be selecting the whole sample since everybody is either above 30 or below 40 years of age.

Another way of selecting people aged 30 to 40 inclusively in SPSS-X (but not in SPSS/PC+) is to use the **range** logical function where any case with a value in the range of 30 to 40 for the variable **age** is selected:

select if range (age,30,40)

Recoding the values of variables

Sometimes it is necessary to change or to **recode** the values of some variables. Thus, for example, it is recommended that the wording of questions which go to make up a scale or index should be varied in such a way that people who say yes to everything (*yeasayers*) or no (*naysayers*) do not end up with an extreme score. To illustrate this, we have worded two of the four questions assessing job satisfaction in the Job Survey ('6c. Most of the time I have to force myself to go to work' and '6e. My job is pretty uninteresting') in the opposite direction from the other two ('6b. My job is like a hobby to me' and '6d. Most days I am enthusiastic about my work'). These questions are answered in terms of a 5-point scale ranging from 1 ('strongly disagree') to 5 ('strongly agree'). While we could reverse the numbers for the two negatively worded items (6c and 6e) on the questionnaire, this would draw the attention of our respondents to what we were trying to accomplish. It is simpler to reverse the coding when we come to analyse the data. Since we want to indicate greater job satisfaction with a higher number, we will recode the answers to the two negatively worded questions, so that 1 becomes 5, 2 becomes 4, 4 becomes 2, and 5 becomes 1. We can do this in the following way with the **recode** command where 6c is referred to as **satis2** and 6e as **satis4**:

recode satis2 satis4 (1=5) (2=4) (4=2) (5=1).

The variables to be recoded must already be defined, so this command comes after **data list**. The variable names precede the values to be changed. The values for each case are recoded from left to right and are only changed once so that when 1 is initially recoded as 5 (1=5) in the above example, it is not subsequently reconverted as 1 (5=1) at the end of the command.

The values to be changed must always be placed in parentheses. There can only be one value to the right of the equals sign, whereas there can be any number to its left. If, for example, we wished to form a 3-point scale with only one agree, one disagree, and one undecided answer, we could do this in the following way:

recode satis1 to satis4 (1,2=1) (3=2) (4,5=3).

If we then wanted to recode the two negatively worded items, we could do this by adding this request following a forward slash on the previous command:

recode satis1 to satis4 (1,2=1) (3=2) (4,5=3)/satis2 satis4 (1=3) (3=1).

A number of other useful keywords are available for recoding values. The keyword **thru** specifies a range of values. We could, for example, recode ethnic group into whites (code unchanged) and non-whites (recoded as 2) with this word:

recode ethnicgp (2 thru 5=2).

We could also do this using the keyword **else** where all the values not explicitly mentioned are recoded as a single one:

recode ethnicgp (else=2).

The keywords **highest** and **lowest** (abbreviated as **hi** and **lo**) can be used to indicate the highest and lowest values of a variable without determining what these are, provided there are no missing value(s). We could, for example, use these words to categorize our sample into those 40 years old or above and those below:

recode age (lo thru 39=1) (40 thru hi=2).

If we had ages which were not whole numbers and which fell between 39 and 40, such as 39.9, they would not be recoded. To avoid this problem, we would use overlapping end-points:

recode age (lo thru 40=1) (40 thru hi=2).

In this example all people aged 40 and less would be coded as 1. Since values are recoded consecutively and once only, age 40 will not also be recoded as 2.

Using **recode** for a variable permanently changes its values, making it impossible to check the original values used in that command file. If we wanted to check or to retain these, we could store the recoded values as a new variable with the keyword **into** in SPSS-X. We could keep, for example, the 3-point recoded values of the job-satisfaction items as the new variables **rsatis1** to **rsatis4**:

recode satis1 to satis4 (1,2=1) (3=2) (4,5=3) into rsatis1 to rsatis4

To do this in SPSS/PC+, we would first have to create the new variables **rsatis1** to **rsatis4** with the **compute** command (see appropriate section below) as follows, before recoding them:

compute rsatis1=satis1.
compute rsatis2=satis2.
compute rsatis3=satis3.
compute rsatis4=satis4.
recode rsatis1 to rsatis4 (1,2=1) (3=2) (4,5=3).

If some of the values of a variable were to remain unchanged as a new variable, then we could use the keywords **else** and **copy** to accomplish this in SPSS-X (but not in SPSS/PC+, where there is no **copy** keyword). Thus, for instance, to form a revised ethnic-group variable where Africans are recoded as being in the same category as West Indians, while the others stay unchanged, we could use the following command:

recode ethnicgp (3=2) (else=copy) into rethncgp

(Note that the variable name must be no longer than eight characters, so we have dropped the **i**.)

Checking recoded values and new variables

It is always good practice to check what you have done, particularly when you are learning a new skill. So far, we have asked you to accept on trust what we have said about recoding values. Let us now see whether some of these examples do what we have described. To check this, we use the command **list**. **List** on its own will display the permanent and temporary values of all the variables for every subject on the **data list** command in the order they are listed on this command. To select variables, we use the subcommand **variables**, followed by a space or an equals sign together with the names of the variables we want to look at. So, to check the original and new values of the ethnic-group variable, we use the following command which comes, of course, after the **recode** command:

list variables ethnicgp rethncgp.

We need only ask for the recoding of one case for each of the four ethnic groups to check the operation of this command. We could, therefore, look through the data on ethnic group and select the first representative of each category (i.e. cases 1,2,3, and 13) as appropriate examples using a **select if** command:

select if (id=1 or id=2 or id=3 or id=13).
compute rethncgp=ethnicgp.
recode rethncgp (1=1) (2,3=2) (4=4).
list variables id ethnicgp rethnicgp.

These commands immediately follow the **missing values** command. We have also requested the identification or case number of each person. The relevant output is:

ID	ETHNICGP	RETHNCGP
1	1	1.00
2	2	2.00
3	3	2.00
13	4	4.00

NUMBER OF CASES READ = 4   NUMBER OF CASES LISTED = 4

As we can see, values 1, 2 and 4 remain the same, while 3 is recoded as 2.

Computing a new variable

Sometimes we want to create a new variable – for example, we have used four items to assess what may be slightly different aspects of job satisfaction. Rather than treat these items as separate measures, it may be preferable and reasonable to combine them into one index. To do this, we can use the **compute** command to create a new variable **satis** by adding together **satis1** and **satis4**. Before doing this, however, we have to remember to recode two of the items (**satis2** and **satis4**) because the answers to them are scored in the reverse way. The two commands, then, which are needed for creating the new variable **satis** are:

```
recode satis2 satis4 (1=5) (2=4) (4=2) (5=1).
compute satis=satis1+satis2+satis3+satis4.
```

To check that this does what we want, we will try this out on the first three cases in the data file since it would be redundant to do this on all seventy individuals. To select these cases, we can use the following command:

```
select if (id le 3).
```

We would insert this command after the **missing values** one but before the **recode** and **compute** ones to save the computer having to make these transformations for all the cases. We also need to ask it to list the relevant variables, which are **id**, **satis1** to **satis4**, and the new variable **satis**. Consequently, the four commands needing to be placed after **missing values** are:

```
select if (id le 3).
recode satis2 satis4 (1=5) (2=4) (4=2) (5=1).
compute satis=satis1+satis2+satis3+satis4.
list variables id satis1 to satis4 satis.
```

The relevant output for these commands are:

ID	SATIS1	SATIS2	SATIS3	SATIS4	SATIS
1	0	3	4	2	9.00
2	0	0	2	3	5.00
3	4	2	4	5	15.00

As we can see, the new variable **satis** is the sum of the four items.

An alternative way of computing a total score in SPSS-X (which is not available in SPSS/PC+) is to use the **sum** function, which will add together the values of the variables enclosed in parentheses after it:

compute satis=sum(satis1,satis2,satis3,satis4)

Other arithmetic operations available with **compute** are subtraction ($-$), multiplication (∗), division (/) and exponentiation (∗∗).

Missing data and computing scores to form new measures

This section may be difficult for some readers to follow and, if so, can be skipped. It describes how new measures can be created by adding scores together, such as the responses to the four **satis** questions.

As we have seen, the **satis1** score for the first subject and the **satis1** and **satis2** scores for the second subject are missing. In research, it is quite common for some scores to be missing. Subjects may omit to answer questions, they may circle two different answers to the same question, the experimenter may forget to record a response, and so on. It is important to consider carefully how you are going to deal with missing data. If many of the data for one particular variable are missing, this suggests that there are problems with its measurement which need to be sorted out. Thus, for example, it may be a question which does not apply to most people, in which case it is best omitted. If many scores for an individual are missing, it is most probably best to omit this person from the sample since there may be problems with the way in which these data were collected. Thus, for example, it could be that the subject was not paying attention to the task at hand.

When computing scores to form a new measure, a rule of thumb is sometimes applied to the treatment of missing data such that if 10 per cent or more of them are missing for that index, the index itself is then defined as missing for that subject. If we applied this principle to the two subjects in this case, no score for job satisfaction would be computed for them, although they would have scores for job routine and autonomy. To operate this rule, we would first have to count the number of missing values to see whether they exceeded 10 per cent. We would then have to set the job-satisfaction total score as missing for subjects with more than this number of items missing, which in this case is if one or more of the items are absent.

To count the number of missing values, we use the **count** command where the number of job-satisfaction items (**satis1** to **satis4**) which have a value of zero are counted to form a new variable called **numissat** (number of **mis**sing **sati**s):

count numissat=satis1= to satis4 (0).

To set the job-satisfaction total score as missing for subjects with one or more of their answers to the four items as missing, we use the **if** command in which the job-satisfaction total score is coded as zero (**satis=0**) when the newly computed count score (**numissat**) is greater than or equal to one (**ge 1**):

if (numissat ge 1) satis=0.

Since we now have a new variable (**satis**) which can have missing values, we have to indicate this with the **missing values** command:

missing values satis (0).

The full set of commands for computing the job-satisfaction total score where it would be assigned as missing if one or more of the four individual scores constituting it were missing would be:

compute satis=satis1+satis2+satis3+satis4.
count numissat=satis1 to satis4 (0).
if (numissat ge 1) satis=0.
missing values satis (0).

These four commands would set the **satis** score as zero for the first two subjects.

When computing scores to form an index, we may want to form an average total score by dividing the total score by the number of available individual scores. One such situation is where we have a variable which is made up of more than ten items and we want to assign it as missing when the scores for 10 per cent or more of its items are not available. Suppose we have a variable which is made up of 100 items. If ten or more of the scores for these items are missing, this variable will be coded as zero. If nine or fewer of them are missing, we have to take account of the fact that the total score may be based on numbers of items ranging from 91 to 100. We can control for this by using the average rather than the total score, which is obtained by dividing the total score by the number of items for which data are available. One advantage of doing this is that the averaged scores now correspond to the answers on the Job-Survey questionnaire, so that an average score of 4.17 on job satisfaction means that that person generally answers 'agree' to the job-satisfaction items.

To illustrate how this can be done, we will use the four **satis** items. With only four items, we cannot use a cut-off point of 10 per cent for exclusion as missing. Therefore, we will adopt a more lenient criterion of 50 per cent. If 50 per cent or more (i.e. two or more) of the scores for the job-satisfaction items are missing, we will code that variable for subjects as missing. To do this, we will first of all compute the total score (**satis**) for the four items. Since the missing values have been set as zero, they will not affect the total. We will then compute a new variable (**nuvasat**) which will count the number of values which are not zero to determine how many valid scores there are. If there are three or more such scores (**if nuvasat ge 3**), we will average them by dividing the total with the number of valid scores (**satis/nuvasat**). If there are two or less (**if nuvasat le 2**), we will assign the variable as missing. The six commands to do this are:

```
recode satis2 satis4 (1=5) (2=4) (4=2) (5=1).
compute satis=satis1+satis2+satis3+satis4.
count nuvasat=satis1 to satis4 (1 thru 5).
if (nuvasat ge 3) satis=satis/nuvasat.
if (nuvasat le 2) satis=0.
missing values satis (0).
```

It is also possible to work out the average score for a specified number of non-missing or valid scores with the **mean** function in SPSS-X (but not SPSS/PC+). This number is placed immediately after the word **mean** which in this case is 2 and is listed as **mean.2**. This command will compute a mean if two or more of the four items are valid. Since we have not done so already, it is necessary to state what a valid score is by using the **missing values** command. The three commands which compute the mean for job satisfaction if two or more of the items are not missing are:

```
recode satis2 satis4 (1=5) (2=4) (4=2) (5=1)
missing values satis1 to satis4 (0)
compute satis=mean.2(satis1,satis2,satis3,satis4)
```

If we want the mean value to be displayed as a zero when it is missing, then it is necessary to add the following command which records assigned missing values (**sysmis**) as zeroes:

```
recode satis (sysmis=0)
```

Creating a new file

If we intend to carry out a series of analyses on this new variable, it saves considerable time if a new file is also created to contain all the variables we wish to work on. If we do not do this, we have to compute the new variable each time we want to run an analysis. Since we wish to form three new variables (job satisfaction, job routine, and job autonomy total scores) from the Job Survey, we are going to produce a second data file, which we shall call **jss.dat** (for **j**ob **s**urvey **s**cored **dat**a). We will use the following commands to create these variables:

```
missing values ethnicgp to commit attend to qual (0) absence (99).
recode satis2 satis4 (1=5) (2=4) (4=2) (5=1).
compute satis=satis1+satis2+satis3+satis4.
count numissat=satis1 to satis4 (0).
if (numissat ge 1) satis=0.
compute autonom=autonom1+autonom2+autonom3+autonom4.
count numisaut=autonom1 to autonom4 (0).
if (numisaut ge 1) autonom=0.
compute routine=routine1+routine2+routine3+routine4.
count nimisrou+routine1 to routine4 (0).
if (nimisrou ge 1) routine=0.
missing values satis autonom routine (0).
```

Since we know that there are no missing data for the items of the other two scales, it is not necessary to count them in this case. Although it is easy to determine if there are any missing values in data sets with which we are unfamiliar by using the **frequencies** command (see below), it does no harm to be cautious and assume that there may be some, as we have done here.

There are two kinds of data file which can be created using SPSS. The first is a *system* file in which the data and other descriptive information such as the variable names, their location, and their missing values are stored in binary form. The advantages of this file are that it is quicker for the computer to read and it is not necessary to have a **data list** and **missing values** command. Its disadvantage is that it is not possible to read it since the information is in binary form. The second kind of file is a *tabular* one which takes the same form as the original data file we created. We will describe how to set up both kinds of files.

Tabular files

We shall set up a tabular file which has one free column between the data for each variable to make it easier to read. To do this with SPSS-X, we have to add an empty column to those variables which do not have one. If we look at the **data list** command of the file we are using to create these three new variables, we will see that the location of the first two variables (**ethnicgp** and **gender**) is specified as a single column (4 and 6) since they can only take single-digit figures (i.e. 0–9). Column 5 is the empty one used to separate them. If we write another file which contains these two variables, they will be placed next to one another without the intervening space. To create this space, we use the **formats** command. This lists the names of the variables whose formats are to change and what these new formats are to be. The new format is described in parentheses after the variable(s) to which it applies. The information to be placed in brackets is the character **f** together with a description of the new format in terms of the total number of columns it is to occupy followed by a full stop and the number of columns which are to be assigned as decimals. Since the original data for **ethnicgp** and **gender** are in the form of a single whole digit, the new format will be **(f2.0)**. The command specifying this takes the following form:

formats ethnicgp gender (f2.0)

Since it is also necessary to reformat **income**, the three new variables, and **absence**, the full command is:

formats ethnicgp gender (f2.0) income (f6.0) satis autonom
 routine (f3.0) absence (f3.0)

Two commands are needed to create a new file which are placed after the **formats** one. The first command is **write**, which specifies the name of the file to be created with the subcommand **outfile=**. It can also be used to request a copy of the format of the table in your printout with the sub-command **table**. This is very useful for setting up the **data list** command which is required for this new data file. The **write** command takes the following form:

write outfile=jss.dat table

If we only want a selection of the original variables to be stored in the new data file, we specify their names. We want to keep all the original ones apart from the individual items which were used to form the three total scores. Since we have no use for the count of the number of missing items (for example, **numissat**), we shall also omit this from the list. However, we have to add three new variables. So the variables we list as wanting to keep are:

/id ethnicgp gender income age years commit satis autonom
 routine attend skill prody qual absence

If we wanted to list some of these variables on a second line, or if we could not fit all their values on one line, we would start the second line with a forward slash (*/*). We could also indicate that we had two lines or records per subject by starting each line with the subject's **id** and the number of the line enclosed in apostrophes or quotation marks (**'1'** and **'2'**).

The second command is **execute**. Without this no table will be produced.

So the commands needed to produce this tabular data file are:

formats ethnicgp gender (f2.0) income (f6.0) satis autonom
 routine (f3.0) absence (f3.0)
write outfile=jss.dat table
 /id ethnicgp gender income age years commit satis autonom
 routine attend skill prody qual absence
execute

Once this new data file has been created, we can set up the following command file to carry out various statistical analyses:

```
data list file=jss.dat records=1
 /id ethnicgp gender 1-6 income 7-12 age years 13-18 commit 19-20
 satis autonom routine 21-29 attend skill prody qual 30-37
 absence 38-40
missing values ethnicgp to qual (0) absence (99)
```

To produce a similar tabular data file in SPSS/PC+, first format the data. Since one empty column is automatically placed before the data for each variable, it is necessary to ensure that the format of all the variables you want to keep corresponds to the number of columns they occupy, as follows:

```
formats id(f2.0) ethnicgp gender(f1.0) income(f5.0)
 age years(f2.0) commit(f1.0) satis autonom routine(f2.0)
 attend skill prody qual (f1.0) absence(f2.0).
```

The **write** command simply lists the names of the variables to be included:

```
write id ethnicgp gender income age years commit satis
 autonom routine attend skill prody qual absence.
```

When these commands are run, an SPSS procedure output file called **SPSS.PRC** is produced, which needs to be renamed and saved. We shall call this file **jss.dat**, which in this example is stored on a floppy disk in drive A.

To analyse these data, we need the following commands:

```
data list file='a:jss.dat'.
 /id 1-3 ethnicgp gender 4-7 income 8-13 age years 14-19
 commit 20-21 satis autonom routine 22-30 attend skill prody
 qual 31-38 absence 39-41.
missing values ethnicgp to qual (0) absence (99).
```

Because an empty column has also been placed before the **id** variable, all the column numbers have been shifted forward by one.

System file

To create a system file in SPSS-X, we omit the **formats** command since we will not be able to read the file as it is written in binary format. We also require a **save** command which names the system file to be created with the subcommand **outfile=**:

```
save outfile=jss.sys
```

To remind ourselves that this is a system file, we will add the suffix or extension **.sys** to the prefix or stem **jss**.

As before we can specify which variables we want to retain by using the **keep** subcommand which will be the same ones as we kept previously:

/keep id ethnicgp gender income age years commit satis autonom
routine attend skill prody qual absence

So the commands needed to create this system file are:

save outfile=jss.sys
 /keep id ethnicgp gender income age years commit satis autonom
 routine attend skill prody qual absence

To use this data file for subsequent analyses, we create a command file which begins with the **get** command, the **file=** subcommand, and the name of the file to be analysed:

get file=jss.sys

No **data list** or **missing values** commands are required since these have already been stored on the system file.

In SPSS/PC+, the **save** command is used also to create a system file, with the name of this file in single quotes:

save outfile='a:jss.sys'

However, unlike SPSS-X, variables are kept by indicating those which are to be excluded. This is done with the subcommand **drop**. To retain the same variables as those in the previous SPSS-X system file, we would use the following subcommand:

/drop satis1 to satis4 numissat autonom1 to autonom4 numissaut
routine1 to routine4 numissrou.

To call up this file for subsequent analyses, the **get** command is used:

get file='a:jss.sys'.

In this case the system file is stored on a floppy disk in drive A.

Titles, comments, and labels

Finally, you might find the following commands useful to help remind you what you have done.

Titles and subtitles

At the top of each page of your output, SPSS automatically places a heading which includes the date, a title which gives the name of the system being used (which is SPSS/PC+ in SPSS/PC+), and the page number. This title can be replaced with another one and a further subtitle on subsequent pages with the **title** and **subtitle** commands. The title occupies the first line on the page of output and the subtitle the second one, which can be omitted if you wish. Each can be changed independently of the other and can contain no more than fifty-eight characters in SPSS/PC+ and sixty in SPSS-X. The **subtitle** command is useful for describing the output of different statistical procedures where it should be placed before the procedure whose output it refers to and not within it. If we wanted to remind ourselves that a command file or job was being run to produce a file containing the scored data of the Job Survey, we could place the following two lines at the start of the command file:

Title "Job Survey Data".
Subtitle "Program used to create the JSSD file".

Comments

Comments can also be inserted at any point in your command file. There are two ways of doing this in SPSS-X. First, you can start a new line with the **comment** command or an asterisk (*) and type a message for as many lines as you like, starting each new line with a blank space:

Comment Command lines for scoring
  job satisfaction

Second, you can insert a short comment within the symbols **/*** and **/*** on one command line, as in:

count numissat=satis1 to satis4 (0) /* number of missing satis/*

The first slash should be preceded by a blank and the comment cannot be continued over two or more lines.

In SPSS/PC+, only the asterisk can be used to insert a comment:

* Command lines for scoring
  job satisfaction.

Variable labels

Only being allowed to use eight characters to describe a variable may make it difficult to remember what it is later on. The **variable labels** command can be used to specify longer labels (including blanks) which will be used to describe the variables in the output generated by most of the statistical procedures (but not, for example, factor analysis). The label must be preceded by the variable name and a blank space, and must be enclosed within apostrophes or quotation marks. Their maximum length is 120 characters in SPSS-X and 60 in SPSS/PC+, although most procedures print fewer characters than this. It is usually most convenient to place this command near to where the variable names are introduced, such as after the **data list** or **missing values** command. Beginning each line with a new variable makes them easier to read. To illustrate its use, the following variable names were given labels:

```
variable labels ethnicgp 'ethnic group'
  years 'years worked'
  commit 'organizational commitment'
  satis1 'job satisfaction item 1'
  satis2 'job satisfaction item 2'
  satis3 'job satisfaction item 3'
  satis4 'job satisfaction item 4'
  skill 'rated skill'
  prody 'rated productivity'
  absence 'days absent'.
```

Variables such as **gender**, **income**, and **age** have not been given a label since their names are already self-explanatory in this case.

Value labels

The values that variables can take can also be specified with the **value labels** command and will be displayed in output produced by statistical procedures. Like **variable labels**, they are stored in system files. They follow the variable name and the value to which they refer and are enclosed within apostrophes or quotation marks. Their maximum length is sixty characters in SPSS/PC+ and SPSS-X but many procedures print fewer than their maximum. A new variable is preceded by a forwards slash. To give the same labels to the same variables, list all the variables first and follow them with the values and their labels. The value and its label must be on the same line. To make the variables easier to read, start a new variable on a new line. The following variables and their values have been labelled:

```
value labels ethnicgp 0 'not reported' 1 'white' 2 'asian'
    3 'west indian' 4 'african' 5 'other'
  /gender 1 'male' 2 'female'
  /commit to autonom4 0 'not reported' 1 'strongly disagree'
    2 'disagree' 3 'undecided' 4 'agree' 5 'strongly agree'.
```

The output shown in Table 3.1 illustrates the use of these last two commands to count how frequent the values are for **satis1** (variable and value labelled), **autonom1** (value labelled only), and **qual** (neither):

```
frequencies variables=satis1 autonom1 qual.
```

To run this, the only commands which need to precede it are the **data list**, the **variable**, and the **value label** ones.

Table 3.1 **Frequencies** SPSS/PC+ output with and without **variable** and **value labels** (Job Survey)

SATIS1   job/satisfaction item 1

Value label	Value	Frequency	Per cent	Valid Per cent	Cum. Per cent
not reported	0	2	2.9	2.9	2.9
strongly disagree	1	7	10.0	10.0	12.9
disagree	2	22	31.4	31.4	44.3
undecided	3	24	34.3	34.3	78.6
agree	4	13	18.6	18.6	97.1
strongly agree	5	2	2.9	2.9	100.0
	Total	70	100.0	100.0	

Valid cases   70   Missing cases   0

AUTONOM1

Value label	Value	Frequency	Per cent	Valid Per cent	Cum. Per cent
strongly disagree	1	8	11.4	11.4	11.4
disagree	2	34	48.6	48.6	60.0
undecided	3	21	30.0	30.0	90.0
agree	4	5	7.1	7.1	97.1
strongly agree	5	2	2.9	2.9	100.0
	Total	70	100.0	100.0	

Valid cases   70   Missing cases   0

QUAL

Value label	Value	Frequency	Per cent	Valid Per cent	Cum. Per cent
	1	9	12.9	12.9	12.9
	2	12	17.1	17.1	30.0
	3	17	24.3	24.3	54.3
	4	21	30.0	30.0	84.3
	5	11	15.7	15.7	100.0
	Total	70	100.0	100.0	

Valid cases   70   Missing cases   0

The **frequency** command also gives the percentage of values in each category, and the valid and cumulative percentages based on the number of valid cases. Since we did not assign zero values for **satis1** as missing, we have no missing cases.

Exercises

1. What is the appropriate SPSS command for selecting men and women who are of African origin in the Job-Survey data?

2. Write an SPSS command to select women of Asian or West Indian origin who are 25 years old or younger in the Job-Survey data.

3. What SPSS command would you use to select subjects who had no missing job-satisfaction scores in the Job-Survey data?

4. If you wanted temporarily to select Asian men from the Job-Survey data, what SPSS-X command would you use?

5. What would the appropriate SPSS/PC+ command be for temporarily selecting Asian men from the Job-Survey data?

6. Recode the Job-Survey variable **skill** so that there are only two categories (unskilled/semi-skilled vs. fairly/highly skilled).

7. Recode the variable **income** into three groups of those earning less than £5,000, between £5,000 and under £10,000, and £10,000 and over, and where missing values are assigned as zero.

8. Using the arithmetic operator *, express the variable **weeks** as **days** – in other words, convert the number of weeks into the number of days.

9. The variable name **patpre** refers to how depressed the patient feels before treatment. Provide the SPSS command which will give this variable the label of **pretest depression-patient**.

10. The three values (1, 2, and 3) of a variable called **treat** respectively refer to the 'control', 'therapy', and 'drug' conditions in a study comparing the effectiveness of no treatment (control), psychotherapy (therapy), and drugs (drug) in treating depression. Write an SPSS command which will attach the appropriate labels in apostrophes to the three values.

11. Write the minimum command file necessary for computing the frequencies of **satis1** with missing values assigned as zero and providing variable and value labels.

12. Prepare a command file for analysing the data file **'jss.dat'**, which includes the following commands: title, subtitle, data list, missing values, variable labels, and value labels.

Chapter four

Concepts and their measurement

As suggested in Chapter 1, concepts form a linchpin in the process of social research. Hypotheses contain concepts which are the products of our reflections on the world. Concepts express common elements in the world to which we give a name. We may notice that some people have an orientation in which they dislike people of a different race from their own, often attributing to other races derogatory characteristics. Still others are highly supportive of racial groups, perhaps seeing them as enhancing the 'host' culture through instilling new elements into it and hence enriching it. Yet others are merely tolerant, having no strong views one way or the other about people of other racial groups. In other words, we get a sense that people exhibit a variety of positions in regard to racial groups. We may want to suggest that there is a common theme to these attitudes, even though the attitudes themselves may be mutually antagonistic. What seems to bind these dispositions together is that they reflect different positions in regard to 'racial prejudice'. In giving the various dispositions that may be held regarding persons of another race a name, we are treating it as a concept, an entity over and above the observations about racial hostility and supportiveness that prompted the formulation of a name for those observations. Racial prejudice has acquired a certain abstractness, so that it transcends the reflections that prompted its formulation. Accordingly, the concept of racial prejudice becomes something that others can use to inform their own reflections about the social world. In this way, hypotheses can be formulated which postulate connections between racial prejudice and other concepts, such as that it will be related to social class or to authoritarianism.

Once formulated, a concept and the concepts with which it is purportedly associated, such as social class and authoritarianism, will need to be *operationally defined*, in order for systematic research to be conducted in relation to it. An operational definition specifies the procedures (operations) that will permit differences between individuals in respect of the concept(s) concerned to be precisely specified. What we are in reality talking about here is *measurement* – that is, the assignment of numbers to the units of analysis – be they people, organizations, or nations – to which a concept refers. Measurement allows small differences between units to be specified. We can say that someone who actively speaks out against members of other races is racially prejudiced, while someone who actively supports them is the obverse of this, but it is difficult to specify precisely the different positions that people may hold in between these extremes. Measurement assists in the specification of such differences by allowing systematic differences between people to be stipulated.

In order to provide operational definitions of concepts, *indicators* are required which will stand for those concepts. It may be that a single indicator will suffice in the measurement of a concept, but in many instances it will not. Thus, for example, would it be sufficient to measure 'religious commitment' by conducting a survey in which people are asked how often they attend church services? Clearly it would not, since church attendance is but one way in which an individual's commitment to his or her religion may be expressed. It does not cover personal devotions, behaving as a religious person should in secular activities, being know-ledgeable about one's faith, or how far they adhere to central tenets of faith (Glock and Stark 1965). These reflections strongly imply that more than one indicator is likely to be required to measure many concepts; otherwise our findings may be open to the argument that we have only tapped one facet of the concept in question.

If more than one indicator of a concept can be envisaged, it may be necessary to test hypotheses with each of the indicators. Imagine a hypothesis in which 'organizational size' was a concept. We might measure (i.e. operationally define) this concept by the number of employees in a firm, its turnover, or its net assets. While these three prospective indicators are likely to be interconnected, they will not be perfectly related (Child 1973), so that hypotheses about organizational size may need to be tested for each of the indicators. Similarly, if religious commitment is to be measured, it may be necessary to employ indicators which reflect all of the facets of such commitment in addition to church attendance. Thus, for example, individuals may be asked how far they endorse central aspects of their faith in order to establish how far they adhere to the beliefs associated with their faith.

When questionnaires are employed to measure concepts, as in the case of religious commitment, researchers often favour multiple-item measures. In the Job-Survey data, **satis** is an example of a multiple-item measure. It entails asking individuals their positions in relation to a number of indicators, which stand for one concept. Similarly, there are four indicators of both **autonom** and **routine**. One could test a hypothesis with each of the indicators. However, if one wanted to use the Job-Survey data to examine a hypothesis relating to **satis** and **autonom**, each of which contains four questions, sixteen separate tests would be required. The procedure for analysing such multiple-item measures is to aggregate each individual's response in relation to each question and to treat the overall measure as a scale in relation to which each unit of analysis has a score. In the case of **satis**, **autonom**, and **routine**, the scaling procedure is *Likert scaling*, which is a popular approach to the creation of multiple-item measures. With Likert scaling, individuals are presented with a number of statements which appear to relate to a common theme; they then indicate their degree of agreement or disagreement on a five- or seven-point range. The answer to each constituent question (often called an *item*) is scored, for example from 1 for Strongly Disagree to 5 for Strongly Agree if the range of answers is in terms of five points. The individual scores are added up to form an overall score for each respondent. Multiple-item scales can be very long; the four **satis** questions are taken from an often-used scale developed by Brayfield and Rothe (1951) which comprised eighteen questions.

These multiple-item scales are popular for various reasons. First, a number of items is more likely to capture the totality of a broad concept like job satisfaction than a single question. Second, we can draw finer distinctions between people. The **satis** measure comprises four questions which are scored from 1 to 5, so that respondents' overall scores can vary between 4 and 20. If only one question was asked, the variation would be between 1 and 5 – a considerably narrower range of potential variation. Third, if a question is misunderstood by a respondent, when only one question is asked that respondent will not be appropriately classified; if a few questions are asked, a misunderstood question can be offset by those which are properly understood.

It is common to speak of measures as *variables*, to denote the fact that units of analysis differ with respect to the concept in question. If there is no variation in a measure, it is a *constant*. It is fairly unusual to find concepts whose measures are constants. On the whole, the social sciences are concerned with variables and with expressing and analysing the variation that variables exhibit. When *univariate analysis* is carried out, we want to know how individuals are distributed in relation to a single variable. Thus, for example, we may want to know how many cases can be found in each of the categories or levels of the measure in question, or we may be interested in what the average response is, and so on. With *bivariate analysis* we are interested in the connections between two variables at a time. Thus, for example, we may want to know whether the variation in **satis** is associated with variation in another variable like **autonom** or whether men and women differ in regard to **satis**. In each case, it is variation that is of interest.

Types of variable

One of the most important features of an understanding of statistical operations is an appreciation of when it is permissible to employ particular tests. Central to this appreciation is an ability to recognize the different forms that variables take, because statistical tests presume certain kinds of variable, a point that will be returned to again and again in later chapters.

The majority of writers on statistics draw upon a distinction developed by Stevens (1946) between nominal, ordinal, and interval/ratio scales or levels of measurement. First, *nominal* (sometimes called *categorical*) scales entail the classification of individuals in terms of a concept. In the Job-Survey data, the variable **ethnicgp**, which classifies respondents in terms of five categories – white, Asian, West Indian, African, and Other – is an example of a nominal variable. Individuals can be allocated to each category, but the measure does no more than this and there is not a great deal more that we can say about it as a measure. We cannot order the categories in any way, for example.

This inability contrasts with *ordinal variables*, in which individuals are categorized but the categories can be ordered in terms of 'more' and 'less' of the concept in question. In the Job-Survey data, **skill**, **prody**, and **qual** are all ordinal variables. If we take the first of these, **skill**, we can see that people are not merely categorized into each of four categories – highly skilled, fairly skilled, semi-skilled, and unskilled – since we can see that someone who is fairly skilled is at a higher point on the scale than someone who is semi-skilled. We cannot make the same inference with **ethnicgp** since we cannot order the categories that it comprises. Although we can order the categories comprising **skill**, we are still limited in the things that we can say about it. Thus, for example, we cannot say that the skill differ-ence between being highly skilled and fairly skilled is the same as the skill difference between being fairly skilled and semi-skilled. All we can say is that those rated as highly skilled have more skill than those rated as fairly skilled, who in turn have greater skill than the semi-skilled, and so on. Moreover, in coding semi-skilled as 2 and highly skilled as 4, we cannot say that people rated as highly skilled are twice as skilled as those rated as semi-skilled. In other words, care should be taken in attributing to the categories of an ordinal scale an arithmetic quality that the scoring seems to imply.

With *interval/ratio variables*, we can say quite a lot more about the arithmetic qualities. In fact, this category subsumes two types of variable – interval and ratio. Both types exhibit the quality that differences between categories are identical – for example, someone aged 20 is one year older than someone aged 19, and someone aged 50 is one year older than someone aged 49. In each case, the difference between the categories is identical – one year. A scale is called an interval scale because the intervals between categories are identical. Ratio measures have a fixed zero point. Thus **age**, **absence**, and **income** have logical zero points. This quality means that one can say that somebody who is aged 40 is twice as old as someone aged 20. Similarly, someone who has been absent from work six times a year has been absent three times as often as someone who has been absent twice. However, the distinction between interval and ratio scales is often not examined by writers because in the social sciences, true interval variables frequently are also ratio variables (for example, income, age). In this book, the term *interval variable* will sometimes be employed to embrace ratio variables as well.

Interval/ratio variables are recognized to be the highest level of measurement because there is more that can be said about them than with the other two types. Moreover, a wider variety of statistical tests and procedures is available to interval/ratio variables. It should be noted that if an interval/ratio variable like age is grouped into categories – such as 20–29, 30–39, 40–49, 50–59, and so on – it becomes an ordinal variable. We cannot really say that the difference between someone in the 40–49 group and someone in the 50–59 group is the same as the difference between someone in the 20–29 group and someone in the 30–39 group, since we no longer know the points within the groupings at which people are located. On the other hand, such groupings of individuals are sometimes useful for the presentation and easy assimilation of information. It should be noted, too, that the position of *dichotomous* variables within the threefold classification of types of variable is somewhat ambiguous. With such variables, there are only two categories, such as male and female for the variable **gender**. A dichotomy is usually thought of as a nominal variable, but sometimes it can be considered an ordinal variable. When, for example, there is an inherent ordering to the dichotomy, such as passing and failing, the characteristics of an ordinal variable seem to be present.

Strictly speaking, measures like **satis**, **autonom**, and **routine**, which derive from multiple-item scales, are ordinal variables. Thus, for example, we do not know whether the difference between a score of 20 on the **satis** scale and a score of 18 is the same as the difference between 10 and 8. This poses a problem for researchers since the inability to treat such variables as interval means that methods of analysis like correlation and regression (see Chapter 8), which are both powerful and popular, could not be used in their connection since these techniques presume the employment of interval variables. On the other hand, most of the multiple-item measures created by researchers are treated by them as though they are interval variables because these measures permit a large number of categories to be stipulated. When a variable allows only a small number of ordered categories, as in the case of **commit**, **prody**, **skill**, and **qual** in the Job-Survey data, each of which comprises only either four or five categories, it would be unreasonable in most analysts' eyes to treat them as interval variables. When the number of categories is considerably greater, as in the case of **satis**, **autonom**, and **routine**, each of which can assume sixteen categories from 5 to 20, the case for treating them as interval variables is more compelling.

Certainly, there seems to be a trend in the direction of this more liberal treatment of multiple-item scales as having the qualities of interval variables. On the other hand, many purists would demur from this position. Moreover, there does not appear to be a rule of thumb which allows the analyst to specify when a variable is definitely ordinal and when interval. None the less, in this book it is proposed to reflect much of current practice and to treat multiple-item measures such as **satis**, **autonom**, and **routine** as though they were interval scales. Labovitz (1970) goes further in suggesting that almost all ordinal variables can and should be treated as interval variables. He argues that the amount of error that can occur is minimal, especially in relation to the considerable advantages that can accrue to the analyst as a result of using techniques of analysis like correlation and regression which are both powerful and relatively easy to interpret. However, this view is controversial (Labovitz 1971) and whereas many researchers would accept the treatment of variables like **satis** as interval, they would cavil about variables like **commit**, **skill**, **prody**, and **qual**. Table 4.1 summarizes the main characteristics of the types of scale discussed in this section, along with examples from the Job-Survey data.

Dimensions of concepts

When a concept is very broad, serious consideration needs to be given to the possibility that it comprises underlying dimensions which reflect

Table 4.1 Types of variable

Type	Description	Example in Job-Survey data
Nominal	A classification of objects (people, firms, nations, etc.) into discrete categories.	**ethnicgp**
Ordinal	The categories associated with a variable can be rank-ordered. Objects can be ordered in terms of a criterion from highest to lowest.	**commit** **skill** **prody** **qual**
Interval (a)	With 'true' interval variables, categories associated with a variable can be rank-ordered, as with an ordinal variable, but the distances between categories are equal.	**income** **age** **years** **absence**
Interval (b)	Variables which strictly speaking are ordinal, but which have a large number of categories, such as multiple-item questionnaire measures. These variables are assumed to have similar properties to 'true' interval variables.	**satis** **routine** **autonom**
Dichotomous	A variable that comprises only two categories.	**gender** **attend**

different aspects of the concept in question. Very often it is possible to specify those dimensions on *a priori* grounds, so that possible dimensions are established in advance of the formation of indicators of the concept. There is much to recommend deliberation about the possibility of such underlying dimensions, since it encourages systematic reflection on the nature of the concept that is to be measured.

Lazarsfeld's (1958) approach to the measurement of concepts viewed the search for underlying dimensions as an important ingredient. Figure 4.1 illustrates the steps that he envisaged. Initially, the researcher forms an image from a theoretical domain. This image reflects a number of common characteristics, as in the previous example of job satisfaction which denotes the tendency for people to have a distinctive range of experiences in relation to their jobs. Similarly, Hall (1968) developed the idea of 'professionalism' as a consequence of his view that members of professions have a distinctive constellation of attitudes to the nature of their work. In each case, out of this *imagery* stage, we see a concept starting to form. At the next stage, *concept specification* takes place, whereby the concept is developed to show whether it comprises different aspects or dimensions. This stage allows the complexity of the concept to be recognized. In Hall's case, five dimensions of professionalism were proposed:

(1) *The use of the professional organization as a major reference.* This means that the professional organization and other members of the same profession are the chief source of ideas and judgements for the professional in the context of his or her work.

(2) *A belief in service to the public.* According to this aspect, the profession is regarded as indispensable to society.

(3) *Belief in self-regulation.* This notion implies that the work of a professional can and should only be judged by other members of the profession, because only they are qualified to make appropriate judgements.

(4) *A sense of calling to the field.* The professional is someone who is dedicated to his or her work and would probably want to be a member of the profession even if material rewards were less.

(5) *Autonomy.* This final dimension suggests that professionals ought to be able to make decisions and judgements without pressures from either clients, the organizations in which they work, or any other non-members of the profession.

Not only is the concept-specification stage useful in order to reflect and to capture the full complexity of concepts, it also serves as a means of bridging the general formulation of concepts and their measurement, since the establishment of dimensions reduces the abstractness of concepts.

The next stage is the *selection of indicators*, in which the researcher searches for indicators of each of the dimensions. In Hall's case, ten indicators of each dimension were selected. Each indicator entailed a statement in relation to which respondents had to answer whether they believed that it agreed Very Well, Well, Poorly, or Very Poorly in the light of how they felt and behaved as members of their profession. A neutral category was also provided. Figure 4.1 provides both the five dimensions of professionalism and one of the ten indicators for each dimension. Finally, Lazarsfeld proposed that the indicators need to be brought together through the *formation of indices* or *scales*. This stage can entail either of two possibilities. An overall scale could be formed which comprised all indicators relating to all dimensions. However, more frequently, separate scales are formulated for each dimension. Thus, in Hall's research, the indicators relating to each dimension were combined to form scales, so that we end up with five separate scales of professionalism. As Hall shows, different professions exhibit different 'profiles' in respect of these dimensions – one may emerge as having high scores for dimensions 2, 3, and 5, moderate for 1, and low for 4, whereas other professions will emerge with different combinations.

In order to check whether the indicators bunch in the ways proposed by an *a priori* specification of dimensions, *factor analysis*, a technique that will be examined in Chapter 11, is often employed. Factor analysis allows the researcher to check whether, for example, all of the ten indicators developed to measure 'autonomy' are really related to each other and not to indicators that are supposed to measure other dimensions. We might find that an indicator that is supposed to measure autonomy seems to be associated with many of the various indicators of 'belief in service to the public', while one or two of the latter might be related to indicators which are supposed to denote 'belief in self-regulation', and so on. In fact, when such factor analysis has been conducted in relation to Hall's professionalism scale, the correspondence between the five dimensions and their putative indicators has been shown to be poor (Snizek 1972; Bryman 1985). However, the chief point that should be recognized in the foregoing discussion is that the specification of dimensions for concepts is often an important step in the development of an operational definition.

Some measurement is carried out in psychology and sociology with little (if any) attention to the quest for dimensions of concepts. Thus, for example, the eighteen-item measure of job satisfaction developed by Brayfield and Rothe (1951), which was mentioned above, does not specify dimensions, though it is possible to employ factor analysis to search for *de facto* ones. The chief point that can be gleaned from this section is that the search for dimensions can provide an important aid to understanding the nature of concepts and that when established on the basis of *a priori* reasoning can be an important step in moving from the complexity and abstractness of many concepts to possible measures of them.

Figure 4.1 Concepts, dimensions, and measurement

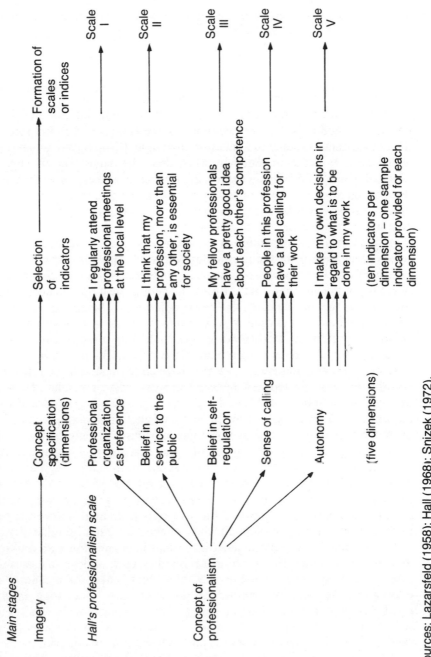

Main stages

Imagery →

Concept
specification
(dimensions)

→ Selection
of
indicators

→ Formation of
scales
or indices

Hall's professionalism scale

Professional
organization
as reference

I regularly attend
professional meetings
at the local level

→ Scale
I

Belief in
service to the
public

I think that my
profession, more than
any other, is essential
for society

→ Scale
II

Concept of
professionalism

Belief in self-
regulation

My fellow professionals
have a pretty good idea
about each other's competence

→ Scale
III

Sense of calling

People in this profession
have a real calling for
their work

→ Scale
IV

Autonomy

I make my own decisions in
regard to what is to be
done in my work

→ Scale
V

(five dimensions)

(ten indicators per
dimension – one sample
indicator provided for each
dimension)

Sources: Lazarsfeld (1958); Hall (1968); Snizek (1972).

Validity and reliability of measures

It is generally accepted that when a concept has been operationally defined, in that a measure of it has been proposed, the ensuing measurement device should be both reliable and valid.

Reliability

The reliability of a measure refers to its consistency. This notion is often taken to entail two separate aspects – external and internal reliability. External reliability is the more common of the two meanings and refers to the degree of consistency of a measure over time. If you have kitchen scales which register different weights every time the same bag of sugar is weighed, you would have an externally unreliable measure of weight, since the amount fluctuates over time in spite of the fact that there should be no differences between the occasions that the item is weighed. Similarly, if you administered a personality test to a group of people, re-administered it shortly afterwards, and found a poor correspondence between the two *waves* of measurement, the personality test would probably be regarded as externally unreliable because it seems to fluctuate. When assessing external reliability in this manner, that is by administering a test on two occasions to the same group of subjects, *test–retest reliability* is being examined. We would anticipate that people who scored high on the test initially will also do so when retested; in other words, we would expect the relative position of each person's score to remain relatively constant. The problem with such a procedure is that intervening events between the test and the retest may account for any discrepancy between the two sets of results. Thus, for example, if the job satisfaction of a group of workers is gauged and three months later is reassessed, it might be found that, in general, respondents exhibit higher levels of satisfaction than previously. It may be that in the intervening period they have received a pay increase or a change to their working practices, or some grievance that had been simmering before has been resolved by the time job satisfaction is retested. Also, if the test and retest are too close in time, subjects may recollect earlier answers, so that an artificial consistency between the two tests is created. However, test–retest reliability is one of the main ways of checking external reliability.

Internal reliability is particularly important in connection with multiple-item scales. It raises the question of whether each scale is measuring a single idea and hence whether the items that make up the scale are internally consistent. A number of procedures for estimating internal reliability exist, two of which can be readily computed with SPSS. First, *split-half reliability* divides the items in a scale into two groups (either randomly or on an odd–even basis) and examines the relationship between respondents' scores for the two halves. Thus, the Brayfield–Rothe job-satisfaction measure, which contains eighteen items, would be divided into two groups of nine, and the relationship between respondents' scores for the two halves would be estimated. A coefficient is generated, which can be interpreted in the same way as Pearson's correlation coefficient (see Chapter 8), in that it varies between 0 and 1 and the nearer the result is to 1 – and preferably at or over 0.8 – the more internally reliable is the scale. Secondly, the currently widely used *Cronbach's alpha* essentially calculates the average of all possible split-half reliability coefficients. Again, the rule of thumb is that the result should be 0.8 or above. This rule is also generally used in relation to test–retest reliability. When a concept and its associated measure are deemed to comprise underlying dimensions, it is normal to calculate reliability estimates for each of the constituent dimensions rather than for the measure as a whole. Indeed, if a factor analysis confirms that a measure comprises a number of dimensions the overall scale will probably exhibit a low level of internal reliability, since the split-half reliability coefficients may be lower as a result.

Both split-half and alpha estimates of reliability can be easily calculated with SPSS. With SPSS/PC+, these routines are available only on the Advanced Statistics module. It is necessary to ensure that all items are coded in the same direction. Thus, in the case of **satis** it is necessary to ensure that the reverse items (such as **satis2** and **satis4**) have been coded so that agreement is indicative of lack of job satisfaction. In order to generate a reliability test of the four items which make up **satis**, the following format would be required:

```
reliability variables=satis1 to satis4
 /scale (testscore)=satis1 to satis4
 /model=alpha.
```

The full stop after **alpha** should be omitted if SPSS-X is being used. More than one test for reliability can be carried out, by including further items in the first line and inserting a second **scale** subcommand. The following would produce alpha coefficients for both **satis** and **routine**:

```
reliability variables=satis1 to satis4 routine1 to routine4
 /scale (testscore)=satis1 to satis4
 /scale (testscore)=routine1 to routine4
 /model=alpha.
```

If split-half coefficients were required, **split** should be substituted for **alpha** in either of the two command files, i.e. after **model=**.

Two other aspects of reliability, that is in addition to internal and external reliability, ought to be mentioned. First, when material is being coded for themes, the reliability of the coding scheme should be tested. This problem can occur when a researcher needs to code people's answers to interview questions that have not been pre-coded, in order to search for general underlying themes to answers or when a content analysis of newspaper articles is conducted to elucidate ways in which news topics tend to be handled. When such exercises are carried out, more than one coder should be used and an estimate of *inter-coder reliability* should be provided to ensure that the coding scheme is being consistently interpreted by coders. This exercise would entail gauging the degree to which coders agree on the coding of themes deriving from the material being examined. Second, when the researcher is classifying behaviour an estimate of *inter-observer reliability* should be provided. If, for example, aggressive behaviour is being observed, an estimate of inter-observer reliability should be presented to ensure that the criteria of aggressiveness are being consistently interpreted. Methods of bivariate analysis (see Chapter 8) can be used to measure inter-coder and inter-observer reliability. A discussion of some methods which have been devised specifically for the assessment of inter-coder or inter-observer reliability can be found in Jackson (1983).

Validity

The question of validity draws attention to how far a measure really measures the concept that it purports to measure. How do we know that our measure of job satisfaction is really getting at job satisfaction and not at something else? At the very minimum, a researcher who develops a new measure should establish that it has *face validity* – that is, that the measure apparently reflects the content of the concept in question.

The researcher might seek also to gauge the *concurrent validity* of the concept. Here the researcher employs a criterion on which people are known to differ and which is relevant to the concept in question. Thus, for example, some people are more often absent from work (other than through illness) than others. In order to establish the concurrent validity of our job-satisfaction measure we may see how far people who are satisfied with their jobs are less likely than those who are not satisfied to be absent from work. If a lack of correspondence were found, such as frequent absentees being just as likely to be satisfied as not satisfied, we might be tempted to question whether our measure were really addressing job satisfaction. Another possible test for the validity of a new measure is *predictive validity*, whereby the researcher uses a future criterion measure, rather than a contemporaneous one as in the case of concurrent validity. With predictive validity, the researcher would take later levels of absenteeism as the criterion against which the validity of job satisfaction would be examined.

Some writers advocate that the researcher should also estimate the *construct validity* of a measure (Cronbach and Meehl 1955). Here, the researcher is encouraged to deduce hypotheses from a theory that is relevant to the concept. Drawing upon ideas about the impact of technology on the experience of work (for example, Blauner 1964), the researcher might anticipate that people who are satisfied with their jobs are less likely to work on routine jobs; those who are not satisfied are more likely to work on routine jobs. Accordingly, we could investigate this theoretical deduction by examining the relationship between job satisfaction and job routine. On the other hand, some caution is required in interpreting the absence of a relationship between job satisfaction and job routine in this example. First, the theory or the deduction that is made from it may be faulty. Second, the measure of job routine could be an invalid measure of the concept.

All of the approaches to the investigation of validity that have been discussed up to now are designed to establish what Campbell and Fiske (1959) refer to as *convergent validity*. In each case, the researcher is concerned to demonstrate that the measure harmonizes with another measure. Campbell and Fiske argue that this process usually does not go far enough in that the researcher should really be using different measures of the same concept to see how far there is convergence. Thus, for example, in addition to devising a questionnaire-based measure of job routine, a researcher could use observers to rate the characteristics of jobs in order to distinguish between degrees of routineness in jobs in the firm (for example, Jenkins *et al.* 1975). Convergent validity would entail demonstrating a convergence between the two measures, although it is difficult to interpret a lack of convergence since either of the two measures could be faulty. Many of the examples of convergent validation that have appeared since Campbell and Fiske's (1959) article have not involved different *methods*, but have employed different questionnaire research instruments (Bryman 1989). Thus, for example, two questionnaire-based measures of job routine might be used, rather than two different methods. Campbell and Fiske went even further in suggesting that a measure should also exhibit *discriminant validity*. The investigation of discriminant validity implies that one should also search for *low* levels of correspondence between a measure and other measures which are supposed to represent other concepts. Although discriminant validity is an important facet of the validity of a measure, it is probably more important for the student to focus upon the various aspects of convergent validation that have been discussed. In order to investigate both the various types of convergent validity and discriminant validity, the various techniques covered in Chapter 8, which are concerned with relationships between pairs of variables, can be employed.

Exercises

1. Which of the following answers is true? A Likert scale is (a) a test for validity; (b) an approach to generating multiple-item measures; (c) a test for reliability; or (d) a method for generating dimensions of concepts?

2. When operationalizing a concept, why might it be useful to consider the possibility that it comprises a number of dimensions?

3. A researcher uses a fourfold scheme for classifying the social class of individuals: upper middle class, lower middle class, upper working class, lower working class. Is this a nominal, an ordinal, an interval, or a dichotomous variable?

4. In the Job-Survey data, is **absence** a nominal, an ordinal, an interval, or a dichotomous variable?

5. Is test–retest reliability a test of internal or external reliability?

6. What SPSS commands would you require in order to generate a measure of Cronbach's alpha for **autonom**?

7. Following on from Question 6, would this be a test of internal or external reliability?

8. A researcher develops a new multiple-item measure of 'political conservatism'. He/she administers the measure to a sample of individuals and also asks them how they voted at the last general election in order to validate the new measure. The researcher relates respondents' scores to how they voted. Which of the following is the researcher assessing: (a) the measure's concurrent validity; (b) the measure's predictive validity; or (c) the measure's discriminant validity?

Chapter five

Summarizing data

When researchers are confronted with a bulk of data relating to each of a number of variables, they are faced with the task of summarizing the information that has been amassed. If large amounts of data can be summarized, it becomes possible to detect patterns and tendencies that would otherwise be obscured. It is fairly easy to detect a pattern in a variable when, say, we have data on ten cases. Once we go beyond about twenty, however, it becomes difficult for the eye to catch patterns and trends unless the data are treated in some way. Moreover, when we want to present our collected data to an audience, it would be extremely difficult for readers to take in the relevant information. This chapter is concerned with the various procedures that may be employed to summarize a variable.

Frequency distributions

Imagine we have data on fifty-six students regarding which faculty they belong to at a university (see Table 5.1). The university has only four faculties: engineering, pure sciences, arts, and social sciences. Even though fifty-six is not a large number on which to have data, it is not particularly easy to see how students are distributed across the faculties. A first step that might be considered when summarizing data relating to a nominal variable such as this (since each faculty constitutes a discrete category) is the construction of a *frequency distribution* or *frequency table*. The idea of a frequency distribution is to tell us the number of cases in each category. By 'frequency' is simply meant the number of times that something occurs. Very often we also need to compute percentages, which tell us the proportion of cases contained within each frequency, i.e. *relative frequency*. In Table 5.2, the number 11 is the frequency relating to the arts category, i.e. there are eleven arts students in the sample, which is 20 per cent of the total number of students.

The procedure for generating a frequency distribution with SPSS will be addressed in a later section, but in the mean time it should be realized that all that is happening in the construction of a frequency table is that the

Table 5.1 The faculty membership of fifty-six students (imaginary data)

Case No.	Faculty	Case No.	Faculty
1	Arts	29	Eng
2	PS	30	SS
3	SS	31	PS
4	Eng	32	SS
5	Eng	33	Arts
6	SS	34	SS
7	Arts	35	Eng
8	PS	36	PS
9	Eng	37	Eng
10	SS	38	SS
11	SS	39	Arts
12	PS	40	SS
13	Eng	41	Eng
14	Arts	42	PS
15	Eng	43	SS
16	PS	44	PS
17	SS	45	Eng
18	Eng	46	Arts
19	PS	47	Eng
20	Arts	48	PS
21	Eng	49	Eng
22	Eng	50	Arts
23	PS	51	SS
24	Arts	52	Eng
25	Eng	53	Arts
26	PS	54	Eng
27	Arts	55	SS
28	PS	56	SS

Eng = Engineering   PS = Pure Sciences   SS = Social Sciences

number of cases in each category is added up. Additional information in the form of the percentage that the number of cases in each category constitutes is usually provided. This provides information about the *relative frequency* of the occurrence of each category of a variable. It gives a good indication of the relative preponderance of each category in the sample. Table 5.2 provides the frequency table for the data in Table 5.1. Percentages have been rounded up or down to a whole number (using the simple rule that 0.5 and above are rounded up and below 0.5 are rounded down) to make the table easier to read. The letter *n* is often employed to refer to the number of cases in each category (i.e. the frequency). An alternative way of presenting a frequency table for the data summarized in Table 5.2 is to omit the frequencies for each category and to present only the relative percentages. This approach reduces the amount of information that the reader must absorb. When this option is taken, it is necessary to

Table 5.2 Frequency table for data on faculty membership

	n	*Per cent*
Engineering	18	32
Pure Sciences	13	23
Arts	11	20
Social Sciences	14	25
Total	56	100

provide the total number of cases (i.e. $n=56$) beneath the column of percentages.

Table 5.2 can readily be adapted to provide a diagrammatic version of the data. Such diagrams are usually called *bar charts* or *bar diagrams* and are often preferred to tables because they are more easily assimilated. A bar chart presents a column for the number or percentage of cases relating to each category. Figure 5.1 presents a bar chart for the data in Table 5.1 in terms of the number of cases. On the horizontal axis the name of each category is presented. There is no need to order them in any way (for example, short to long bars). The bars should not touch each other but should be kept clearly separate. It should be realized that the bar chart does not provide more information than Table 5.2; indeed, some information is lost – the percentages. Its main advantage is the ease with which it can be interpreted, a characteristic that may be especially useful when data are being presented to people who may be unfamiliar with statistical material.

When a variable is at the interval level, the data will have to be grouped in order to be presented in a frequency table. The number of cases in each grouping must then be calculated. As an example, the Job-Survey data on **income** may be examined. We have data on sixty-eight individuals (two are missing), but if the data are not grouped there are thirty-three categories which are far too many for a frequency table. Moreover, the frequencies in each category would be far too small. In Table 5.3, a frequency table is presented of the data on **income**. Six categories are employed. In constructing categories such as these a number of points should be borne in mind. First, it is sometimes suggested that the number of categories should be between six and twenty, since too few or too many categories can distort the shape of the distribution of the underlying variable (for example, Bohrnstedt and Knoke 1982). However, it is not necessarily the case that the number of categories will affect the shape of the distribution. Also, when there are relatively few cases the number of categories will have to fall below six in order for there to be a reasonable number of cases in each category. On the other hand, a large number of categories will not be easy for the reader to assimilate and in this regard Bohrnstedt and Knoke's rule

Figure 5.1 Bar chart of data on faculty membership

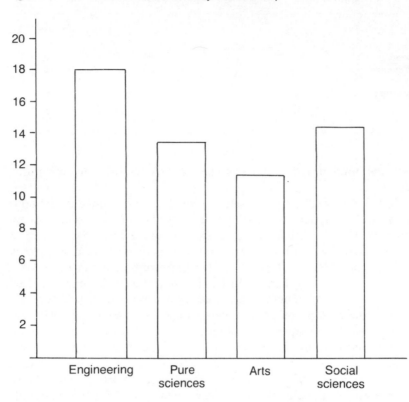

of thumb that the upper limit should be twenty categories seems slightly high. Second, the categories must be discrete. You should never group so that you have categories like: 6,000 or less; 6,000–7,000; 7,000–8,000; and so on. To which categories would incomes of £6,000 and £7,000 belong? Categories must be discrete, as in Table 5.3, so that there can be no uncertainty regarding to which category a case should be allocated. Note that in Table 5.3, the reader's attention is drawn to the fact that there are two missing cases. The presence of two missing cases raises the question of whether percentages should be calculated in terms of all seventy cases in the Job-Survey sample or the sixty-eight on whom we have income data. Most writers prefer the latter since the inclusion of all cases in the base for the calculation of the percentage can result in misleading inter-pretations, especially when there might be a large number of missing cases in connection with a particular variable.

The information in Table 5.3 can be usefully presented diagrammatically as a *histogram*. A histogram is like a bar chart, except that the bars are in contact with each other to reflect the continuous nature of the categories of

Table 5.3 Frequency table for income data (Job-Survey data)

£	n	Per cent
up to 5,999	1	1.5
6,000–6,999	16	23.6
7,000–7,999	20	29.4
8,000–8,999	22	32.3
9,000–9,999	7	10.3
10,000 and over	2	3.0
	68	100.0

Note: Two cases are missing.

Figure 5.2 Histogram for income data (Job-Survey data)

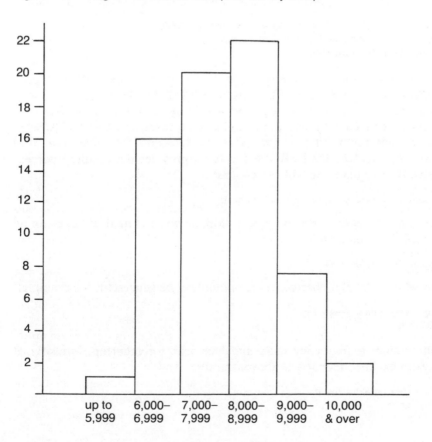

the variable in question. Figure 5.2 presents a histogram for the **income** data. Its advantages are the same as those for the bar chart.

If an ordinal variable is being analysed, grouping of categories is rarely necessary. In the case of the Job-Survey data, a variable like **skill**, which can assume only four categories, will not need to be grouped. The number of cases in each of the four categories can simply be added up and the percentages computed. A histogram can be used to display such data since the categories of the variable are ordered.

Using SPSS to produce frequency tables and histograms

In order to generate a frequency table for the variable **income** in the Job-Survey data the following command should be used:

frequencies variables=income.

Remember to omit the full stop if SPSS-X is being used. This command will provide the output in Table 5.4. Note that this table requires the income data to be grouped, which can be done through **recode**, as follows:

**recode income (1 thru 5999=1) (6000 thru 6999=2) (7000
thru 7999=3) (8000 thru 8999=4) (9000 thru
9999=5) (10000 thru hi=6).**

Table 5.4 provides three percentages: the frequency associated with each category as a percentage of all cases (**PERCENT**); the frequency associated with each category as a percentage of all cases on which data exist (**VALID PERCENT**); and the cumulative percentage (**CUM PERCENT**) which adds the valid percentages as you descend the table. For most purposes, the **VALID PERCENT** column provides the required percentages. If more than one table is required

frequencies variables=income age skill to qual.

will generate tables for **income**, **age**, **skill**, **prody**, and **qual**. If tables for all variables are required

frequencies variables=all.

should be used. Bar charts and histograms can be generated: for example,

**frequencies variables=ethnicgp
/barchart.**

will produce a frequency table and bar chart for **ethnicgp**. Similarly, if **income** has been recoded as above, the command

**frequencies variables=income
/histogram.**

Table 5.4 Frequency table and histogram for income data (SPSS-X output)

INCOME VALUE LABEL	VALUE	FREQUENCY	PER CENT	VALID PER CENT	CUM PER CENT
up to 5999	1	1	1.4	1.5	1.5
6000 to 6999	2	16	22.9	23.5	25.0
7000 to 7999	3	20	28.6	29.4	54.4
8000 to 8999	4	22	31.4	32.4	86.8
9000 to 9999	5	7	10.0	10.3	97.1
10000 and over	6	2	2.9	2.9	100.0
	0	2	2.9	MISSING	
	TOTAL	70	100.0	100.0	

```
                                          .50  OCCURRENCES
COUNT   VALUE  ONE  SYMBOL  EQUALS  APPROXIMATELY

   1    1.00   **
  16    2.00   ****************************************
  20    3.00   **************************************************
  22    4.00   ******************************************************
   7    5.00   ****************
   2    6.00   ****
               I.........I.........I.........I.........I.........I
               0         5        10        15        20        25
                         HISTOGRAM FREQUENCY


VALID CASES     68      MISSING CASES    2
```

will provide a frequency table and histogram based on the sixfold recoding mentioned above (see Table 5.4).

Measuring central tendency

One of the most important ways of summarizing a distribution of values for a variable is to establish its *central tendency* – the typical value in a distribution. Where, for example, do values in a distribution tend to concentrate? To many readers this may mean trying to find the 'average' of a distribution of values. However, statisticians are referring to a number of different measures when they talk about averages. Three measures of average (i.e. central tendency) are usually discussed in textbooks: the arithmetic mean, the median, and the mode.

The arithmetic mean

The arithmetic mean is a method for measuring the average of a distribution which conforms to most people's notion of what an average is. Consider the following distribution of values:

12 10 7 9 8 15 2 19 7 10 8 16

The arithmetic mean consists of adding up all of the values (i.e. 123) and dividing by the number of values (i.e. 12), which results in an arithmetic mean of 10.25. It is this kind of calculation which results in such seemingly bizarre statements as 'The average number of children is 2.37.' However, the arithmetic mean, which is often symbolized as $\bar{x}$, is by far the most commonly used method of gauging central tendency. Many of the statistical tests encountered later in this book are directly concerned with comparing means deriving from different samples or groups of cases (for example, analysis of variance – see Chapter 7). The arithmetic mean is easy to understand and to interpret, which heightens its appeal. Its chief limitation is that it is vulnerable to extreme values, in that it may be unduly affected by very high or very low values which can respectively increase or decrease its magnitude. This is particularly likely to occur when there are relatively few values; when there are many values, it would take a very extreme value to distort the arithmetic mean. Thus, for example, if the number 59 is substituted for 19 in the previous distribution of twelve values, the mean would be 13.58, rather than 10.25, which constitutes a substantial difference and could be taken to be a poor representation of the distribution as a whole.

The median

The median is the mid-point in a distribution of values. It splits a distribution of values in half. Imagine that the values in a distribution are arrayed from low to high – for example, 2, 4, 7, 9, 10: in this example, the median is the middle value, i.e. 7. When there is an even number of values, the average of the two middle values is taken. Thus, in the former group of twelve values, to calculate the mean we need to array them as follows

2 7 7 8 8 <u>9 10</u> 10 12 15 16 19.

Thus, in this array of twelve values, we take the two underlined values – the sixth and seventh – and divide their sum by 2, i.e. $(9+10)/2 = 9.5$. This is slightly lower than the arithmetic mean of 10.25, which is almost certainly due to the presence of three fairly large values at the upper end – 15, 16, 19. If we had the value 59 instead of 19, although we know that the mean would be higher at 13.58, the median would be unaffected, because it emphasizes the middle of the distribution and ignores the ends. For this reason, many writers suggest that when there is an outlying value which may distort the mean, the median should be considered because it will engender a more representative indication of the central tendency of a group of values. As a further example, consider Table 5.5 which provides the numbers of undergraduates in UK universities. Here we have an extreme outlying value (the University of London), which is three times the next highest value. The mean for this distribution is 5,240 and the median is a considerably lower value of 4,407. If London is excluded, the mean falls by over 500 to 4,711, while the median at 4,296 is relatively unaffected. The median changes slightly because the mid-point of the distribution alters when one value is removed. However, the median does not change a great deal because it ignores the extremes of the distribution. This example illustrates fairly well the mean's vulnerability to extreme values, as well as the median's comparative insensitivity. On the other hand, the median is less intuitively easy to understand and it does not use all of the values in a distribution in order for it to be calculated. Moreover, the mean's vulnerability to distortion as a consequence of extreme values is less when there is a large number of cases.

The mode

This final indicator of central tendency is rarely used in research reports, but is often mentioned in textbooks. The mode is simply the value that occurs most frequently in a distribution. In the foregoing array of twelve values, there are three modes – 7, 8, and 10. Unlike the mean, which can only be used in relation to interval variables, the mode can be employed at any measurement level. The median can be employed in relation to interval and ordinal, but not nominal, variables. Thus, although the mode appears more flexible, it is infrequently used, in part because it does not use all of the values of a distribution and is not easy to interpret when there is a number of modes.

Table 5.5 Numbers of undergraduates in universities in the UK, 1980–1

England	Undergraduates
Aston	4,467
Bath	2,970
Birmingham	7,379
Bradford	4,447
Bristol	6,206
Brunel	2,398
Cambridge	9,520
City	2,370
Durham	4,157
East Anglia	3,745
Essex	2,491
Exeter	4,418
Hull	4,902
Keele	2,496
Kent	3,519
Lancaster	4,050
Leeds	9,157
Leicester	4,024
Liverpool	6,861
London	30,620
Loughborough	4,729
Manchester Institute of Science and Technology	3,222
Manchester University	9,513
Newcastle	6,600
Nottingham	6,099
Oxford	9,381
Reading	4,666
Salford	4,184
Sheffield	6,846
Southampton	5,207
Surrey	2,806
Sussex	3,608
Warwick	4,407
York	2,849
Wales	
Aberystwyth University College	2,714
Bangor University College	2,459
Cardiff University College	4,617
Swansea University College	3,367
University of Wales Institute of Science and Technology	2,599
Scotland	
Aberdeen	4,977
Dundee	2,688
Edinburgh	8,561
Glasgow	9,065
Heriot-Watt	2,882
St Andrews	3,146
Stirling	2,702
Strathclyde	5,669
Northern Ireland	
Queen's University, Belfast	5,483
University of Ulster, Coleraine	1,538

Measuring dispersion

In addition to being interested in the typical or representative score for a distribution of values, researchers are usually interested in the amount of variation shown by that distribution. This is what is meant by *dispersion* – how widely spread a distribution is. Dispersion can provide us with important information – for example, we may find two roughly comparable firms in which the mean income of manual workers is identical. However, in one firm the salaries of these workers are more widely spread, with both considerably lower and higher salaries than in the other firm. Thus, although the mean income is the same, one firm exhibits much greater dispersion in incomes than the other. This is important information that can usefully be employed to add to measures of central tendency.

The most obvious measure of dispersion is to take the highest and lowest value in a distribution and to subtract the latter from the former. This is known as the *range.* While easy to understand, it suffers from the disadvantage of being susceptible to distortion from extreme values. This point can be illustrated by the imaginary data in Table 5.6, which shows the marks

Table 5.6 Results of a test of mathematical ability for the students of two teachers (imaginary data)

	Teacher (A)	Teacher (B)
	65	57
	70	49
	66	46
	59	79
	57	72
	62	54
	66	66
	71	65
	58	63
	67	76
	61	45
	68	95
	63	62
	65	68
	71	50
	69	53
	67	58
	74	65
	72	69
	60	72
Arithmetic Mean	65.55	63.2
Standard Deviation	4.91	12.37
Median	66	64

out of 100 achieved on a mathematics test by two classes of twenty students, each of which was taught by a different teacher. The two classes exhibit similar means, but the patterns of the two distributions of values are highly dissimilar. Teacher A's class has a fairly bunched distribution, whereas that of Teacher B's class is much more dispersed. Whereas the lowest mark attained in Teacher A's class is 57, the lowest for Teacher B is 45. Indeed, there are eight marks in Teacher B's class that are below 57. However, whereas the highest mark in Teacher A's class is 74, three of Teacher B's class exceed this figure – one with a very high 95. Although the latter distribution is more dispersed, the calculation of the range seems to exaggerate its dispersion. The range for Teacher A is 74–57, i.e. a range of 17. For Teacher B, the range is 95–45, i.e. 50. This exaggerates the amount of dispersion since all but three of the values are between 72 and 45, implying a range of 27 for the majority of the values.

One solution to this problem is to eliminate the extreme values. The *inter-quartile range*, for example, is sometimes recommended in this connection (see Figure 5.3). This entails arraying a range of values in ascending order. The array is divided into four equal portions, so that the lowest 25 per cent are in the first portion and the highest 25 per cent are in the last portion. These portions are used to generate quartiles. Take the earlier array from which the median was calculated.

$$2\ 7\ 7\ 8\ 8\ 9\ 10\ 10\ 12\ 15\ 16\ 19$$

↑		↑
1st		3rd
Quartile		Quartile

The first quartile (Q1) will be between 7 and 8 and is calculated as $([3 \times 7]+8)/4$, i.e. 7.25. The third quartile (Q3) will be $(12+[3 \times 15])/4$, i.e.

Figure 5.3 The inter-quartile range

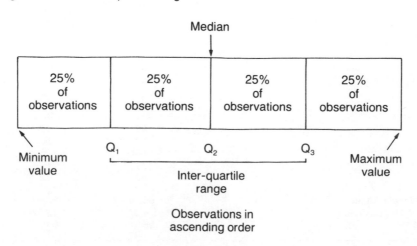

14.25. Therefore the inter-quartile range is the difference between the third and first quartiles, i.e. 14.25—7.25=7. As Figure 5.3 indicates, the median is the second quartile, but is not a component of the calculation of the inter-quartile range. The main advantage of this measure of dispersion is that it eliminates extreme values, but its chief limitation is that in ignoring 50 per cent of the values in a distribution, it loses a lot of information. A compromise is the *decile range*, which divides a distribution into ten portions (deciles) and, in a similar manner to the inter-quartile range, eliminates the highest and lowest portions. In this case, only 20 per cent of the distribution is lost.

By far the most commonly used method of summarizing dispersion is the *standard deviation*. In essence, the standard deviation calculates the average amount of deviation from the mean. Its calculation is somewhat more complicated than this definition implies. A further description of the standard deviation can be found in Chapter 7. The standard deviation reflects the degree to which the values in a distribution differ from the arithmetic mean. The standard deviation is usually presented in tandem with the mean, since it is difficult to determine its meaning in the absence of the mean.

We can compare the two distributions in Table 5.6. Although the means are very similar, the standard deviation for Teacher B's class (12.37) is much larger than that for Teacher A (4.91). Thus, the standard deviation permits the direct comparison of degrees of dispersal for comparable samples and measures. A further advantage is that it employs all of the values in a distribution. It summarizes in a single value the amount of dispersion in a distribution, which, when used in conjunction with the mean, is easy to interpret. The standard deviation can be affected by extreme values, but since its calculation is affected by the number of cases, the distortion is less pronounced than with the range. On the other hand, the possibility of distortion from extreme values must be borne in mind. None the less, unless there are very good reasons for not wanting to use the standard deviation, it should be used whenever a measure of dispersion is required. It is routinely reported in research reports and widely recognized as the main measure of dispersion.

This consideration of dispersion has tended to emphasize interval variables. The standard deviation can only be employed in relation to such variables. The range and inter-quartile range can be used in relation to ordinal variables, but this does not normally happen, while tests for dispersion in nominal variables are also infrequently used. Probably the best ways of examining dispersion for nominal and ordinal variables is through bar charts, histograms, and frequency tables.

Measuring central tendency and dispersion with SPSS

There are various routes to generating information about dispersion and central tendency. The subcommands associated with **frequencies** provide the bulk of descriptive statistics normally used. If the subcommand

/statistics default.

is provided after the **frequencies** command, the mean, standard deviation, minimum, and maximum will be produced. In addition, other measures of central tendency or dispersion can be specified. Thus,

frequencies variables=age years
 /statistics median mode range default.

will provide the default and other statistics indicated in the **statistics** subcommand for each of the variables specified in the **frequencies** command. If quartiles or deciles are required to calculate the inter-quartile or inter-decile ranges, the following command will provide the values for the *n*tile for each variable specified in a frequencies subcommand:

frequencies variables=age/ntiles=4.

This will provide the first, second, and third quartiles. If deciles are required, **10** should be substituted for **4** in the previous command.

There are yet other routes to the calculation of the mean and standard deviation, such as through the **statistics** subcommand which follows the routine for calculating Pearson's correlation coefficient (see Chapter 8). However, it is recommended to start out with **frequencies**. This command produces important information which is necessary at an early stage in the analysis of a set of data, since it provides a sense of the nature of the distribution of the variables to be analysed. To use more advanced statistical procedures at the outset in order to generate such basic information as mean and standard deviations would be virtually a case of running before learning to walk.

Stems and leaves, boxes and whiskers

In 1977, John Tukey published a highly influential book entitled *Exploratory Data Analysis*, which sought to introduce readers to a variety of techniques he had developed which emphasize simple arithmetic computation and diagrammatic displays of data. Although the approach he advocates is antithetical to many of the techniques conventionally employed by data analysts, including the bulk of techniques examined in this book, some of Tukey's displays can be usefully appended to more orthodox procedures. Two diagrammatic presentations of data are very relevant to the present discussion – the *stem and leaf display* and the *box and whisker plot* (sometimes called the *boxplot*).

The stem and leaf display

The stem and leaf display is an extremely simple means of presenting data on an interval variable in a manner similar to a histogram, but without the loss of information that a histogram necessarily entails. It can be easily constructed by hand, although arguably this would be more difficult with very large amounts of data. Figure 5.4 provides the data on undergraduates at UK universities which were presented in Table 5.5. The display has two main components. First, there are the digits to the left of the vertical line which make up the stem. These constitute the starting parts for presenting each value in a distribution. Each of the digits that form the stem represents thousands of students. Thus, the first digit on the stem is 1, which stands for 1,000 students. To the right of the stem are the leaves, each of which represents an item of data which is linked to the stem. Thus, the 5 to the right of the 1 refers to the lowest value in the distribution, namely 1,500. It should be noted that it is common for the last digit or digits in displays (often called 'trailing digits') to be dropped in this way. The next lowest is 2,370, which will be entered as 2,300. This will appear on the line starting with 2, so that the leaf will be 3. It is important to ensure that all of the leaves – the digits to the right of the stem – are vertically aligned. It is not necessary for the leaves to be ordered in magnitude, i.e. from 0 to 9, but it is easier to read. If there had been a university with 12,000 students, that is with no universities having values in the 10,000s or 11,000s, we would still have inserted a 10 and an 11 on the stem, but there would have been no leaves following it. However, the extremely outlying value should be

Figure 5.4 Stem and leaf diagram on undergraduates in the UK

1	5											
2	3	3	4	4	4	5	6	7	7	8	8	8	9
3	1	2	3	5	6	7						
4	0	0	1	1	4	4	4	4	6	6	7	9	9
5	2	4	6									
6	0	2	6	8	8							
7	3											
8	5											
9	0	1	3	5	5							

HI	30,620

Units = '000

separately indicated as in Figure 5.5. The unit of measurement, which in this case was '000s, should be clearly stated on a display.

The stem and leaf display provides a similar presentation to a histogram, in that it gives a sense of the shape of the distribution (such as whether values tend to be bunched at one end), the degree of dispersion, and whether there are outlying values. However, unlike the histogram it retains all the information, so that values can be directly examined to see whether particular ones tend to predominate.

The box and whisker plot

Figure 5.5 provides the skeletal outline of a box and whisker plot. The box comprises the middle 50 per cent of observations. Thus, the lower end of the box, in terms of the measure to which it refers, is the first quartile and the upper end is the third quartile. In other words, the box comprises the inter-quartile range. The line in the box is the median. The broken lines (the whiskers) extend downwards to the lowest value in the distribution and upwards to the largest value *excluding outliers*, i.e. extreme values, which are separately indicated and labelled. It has a number of advantages. Like the stem and leaf display, the box and whisker plot provides information about the shape and dispersion of a distribution – for example, is

Figure 5.5 Box and whisker plot

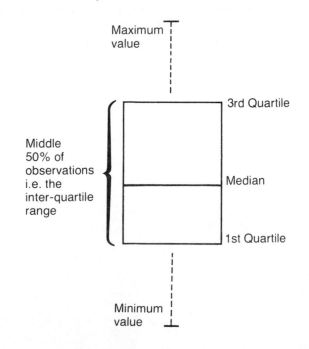

the box closer to one end or is it near the middle? The former would denote that values tend to bunch at one end. Unlike the stem and leaf display, the box and whisker plot provides an indication of central tendency, through the location of the median. This provides further information about the shape of the distribution, since it raises the question of whether the median is closer to one end of the box. On the other hand, the box and whisker plot does not retain information like the stem and leaf display. Figure 5.6 provides a box and whisker plot of the data from Table 5.5.

Both of these exploratory data-analysis techniques can be recommended as providing useful first steps in gaining a feel for data when you first start to analyse them. Should they be used as alternatives to histograms and other more common diagrammatic approaches? Here they suffer from the disadvantage of not being well known. The stem and leaf diagram is probably the easier of the two to assimilate, since the box and whisker diagram requires an understanding of quartiles and the median. If used in relation to audiences who are likely to be unfamiliar with these techniques, they may generate some discomfort even if a full explanation is provided. On the other hand, for audiences who are (or should be) familiar with these ideas, they have much to recommend them.

Figure 5.6 Box and whisker plot of undergraduates in the UK

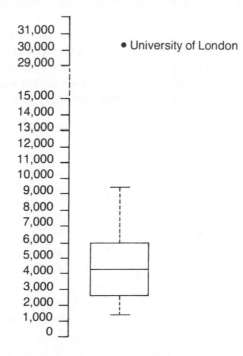

Generating stem and leaf displays and box and whisker plots with SPSS

The route to generating these two types of diagram is through the **manova** command which is described in Chapter 9. It is not necessary to understand this command in order to produce a stem and leaf display of **income**, the following commands should be used:

manova income
 /plot=boxplots.

With SPSS/PC+, the **manova** command is only available with the Advanced Statistics option. If a stem and leaf display is required, **stemleaf** should be substituted for **boxplots** after **plot=**.

The shape of a distribution

On a number of occasions, reference has been made to the shape of a distribution. Thus, for example, values in a distribution may tend to cluster at one end of the distribution or in the middle. In this section, we will be more specific about the idea of shape and introduce some ideas that are central to some aspects of data analysis to be encountered in later chapters.

Statisticians recognize a host of different possible distribution curves. By far the most important is the *normal distribution.* The normal distribution is a bell-shaped curve. It can take a number of different forms depending upon the degree to which the data are dispersed. Two examples of normal-distribution curves are presented in Figure 5.7. The term 'normal' is potentially very misleading, because perfectly normal distributions are very rarely found in reality. However, the values of a variable may approximate to a normal distribution and when they do, we tend to think of them as having the properties of a normal distribution. Many of the most common statistical techniques used by social scientists presume that the variables being

Figure 5.7 Two normal distributions

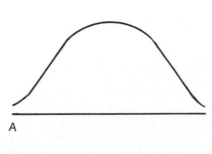
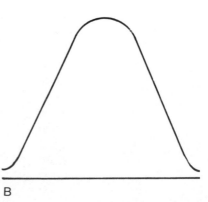

A   B

analysed are nearly normally distributed (see the discussion of parametric and non-parametric tests in Chapter 7).

The normal distribution should be thought of as subsuming all of the cases which it describes beneath its curve. Fifty per cent will lie on one side of the arithmetic mean; the other 50 per cent on the other side (see Figure 5.8). The median value will be identical to the mean: this is why the curve peaks at the mean. As the curve implies, most values will be close to the mean. However, the tapering off at either side indicates that as we move in either direction away from the mean, fewer and fewer cases are found. Only a small proportion will be found at its outer reaches. People's heights illustrate this fairly well. The mean height for an adult woman in the UK is 5ft 3½ ins (160.9 cm). If women's heights are normally distributed, we would expect that most women would cluster around this mean. Very few will be very short or very tall. We know that women's heights have these properties, though whether they are perfectly normally distributed is another matter.

The normal distribution displays some interesting properties that have been determined by statisticians. These properties are illustrated in Figure 5.9. In a perfectly normal distribution,

(1) 68.26 per cent of cases will be within one standard deviation of the mean;
(2) 95.44 per cent of cases will be within two standard deviations of the mean;
(3) 99.7 per cent of cases will be within three standard deviations of the mean.

Thus, if we have a variable which is very close to being normally distributed, we can say that if the mean is 20 and the standard deviation is 1.5, 95.44 per cent of cases will lie between 17 and 23 (i.e. $20 \pm 2 \times 1.5$). Turning this point around slightly, we can assert that there is a 95.44 per

Figure 5.8 The normal distribution and the mean

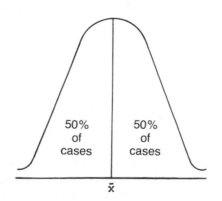

50%
of
cases

50%
of
cases

$\bar{x}$

Figure 5.9 Properties of the normal distribution

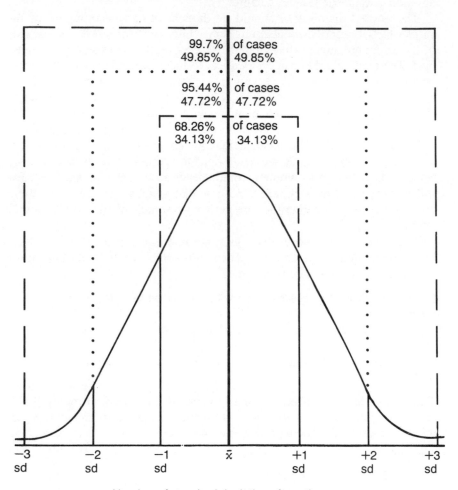

Number of standard deviations from the mean

cent probability that a case will lie between 17 and 23. Likewise, 99.7 per cent of cases will lie between 15.5 and 24.5 (i.e. 20 ± 3 × 1.5). Thus, we can be 99.7 per cent certain that the value relating to a particular case will lie between 15.5 and 24.5.

The data in Table 5.5 can be used to illustrate these ideas further. Ignoring the fact that we have all of the mathematics scores for the students of these two teachers for a moment, if we know the mean and standard deviation for each of the two distributions, assuming normality we can work out the likelihood of cases falling within particular regions of the mean. With teacher A's students, 68.26 per cent of cases will fall within

±4.91 (the standard deviation) of 65.55 (the mean). In other words, we can be 68.26 per cent certain that a student will have gained a mark of between 60.64 and 70.46. The range of probable marks for Teacher B's students is much wider, largely because the standard deviation of 12.37 is much larger. For teacher B's class, there is a 68.26 per cent probability of gaining a mark of between 50.83 and 75.77. Table 5.7 presents the ranges of marks for one, two, and three standard deviations from the mean for each teacher. The larger standard deviation for Teacher B's class means that for each standard deviation from the mean we must tolerate a wider range of probable marks.

It should be noted that as we try to attain greater certainty about the likely value of a particular case, the range of possible error increases from 1 × the standard deviation to 3 × the standard deviation. For teacher A, we can be 68.26 per cent certain that a score will lie between 70.46 and 60.64; but if we aimed for 99.7 per cent certainty, we must accept a wider band of possible scores, i.e. between 80.28 and 50.82. As we shall see in the context of the discussion of statistical significance in Chapter 6, these properties of the normal distribution are extremely useful and important when the researcher wants to make inferences about populations from data relating to samples.

It is important to realize that some variables will not follow the shape of the normal-distribution curve. In some cases, they may depart very strikingly from it. This tendency is most clearly evident when the values in a distribution are *skewed* – that is, they tend to cluster at either end. When this occurs, the mean and median no longer coincide. These ideas are illustrated in Figure 5.10. The left-hand diagram shows a curve that is *positively skewed* in that cases tend to cluster to the left and there is a long 'tail' to the right. In the right-hand diagram, the curve is *negatively skewed.* Another kind of departure is when a distribution possesses more than one peak. The stem and leaf display in Figure 5.5 suggests that the number of students in UK universities may exhibit more than one peak.

Table 5.7 Probable mathematics marks (from data in Table 5.6)

	One standard deviation from the mean 68.26% of cases will fall between:	Two standard deviations from the mean 95.44% of cases will fall between:	Three standard deviations from the mean 99.7% of cases will fall between:
Teacher A	70.46 and 60.64	75.37 and 55.73	80.28 and 50.82
Teacher B	75.57 and 50.83	87.94 and 48.46	100.31 and 26.09

Figure 5.10 Positively and negatively skewed distributions

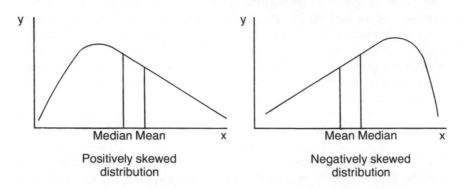

Positively skewed
distribution

Negatively skewed
distribution

Although there is a recognition that some variables in the social sciences do not exhibit the characteristics of a normal curve and that therefore we often have to treat variables as though they were normally distributed, when there is a very marked discrepancy from a normal distribution, such as in the two cases in Figure 5.10, some caution is required. Thus, for example, many writers would argue that it would not be appropriate to apply certain kinds of statistical test to variables which are profoundly skewed when that test presumes normally distributed data. Very often, skewness or other pronounced departures from a normal distribution can be established from the examination of a frequency table or of a histogram. SPSS provides a measure of skewness, which can be acquired through the statistics subcommand following a **frequencies** command. Thus

/statistics median mode range skewness default.

would allow the test for skewness to be added to the measures of central tendency and dispersion encountered previously. If there is no skew, or in other words if the variable is normally distributed, a value of zero or nearly zero will be registered. If there is a negative value, the data are negatively skewed; if the value is positive, the data are positively skewed. On the other hand, this test is not easy to interpret and there is much to be said for a visual inspection of data to discern excessive skew. This can be done through a frequency table, or through a diagrammatic presentation, such as a histogram or stem and leaf display.

Exercises

1. What SPSS commands would you need in order to generate a frequency table for **prody** (Job-Survey data), along with percentages, mean, median, and standard deviation?

2. Run the job for the commands from Question 1. What percentage of respondents are in the 'poor' category?

3. What problem would you anticipate if you used the mean and range as measures of central tendency and dispersion respectively for the variable 'size of firm' in Table 8.11?

4. Which of the following should *not* be used to represent an interval variable: (a) a box and whisker plot; (b) a stem and leaf display; (c) a bar chart; or (d) a histogram?

5. What SPSS commands would you need to calculate the standard deviation and inter-quartile range for **income** (Job-Survey data)?

6. What is the inter-quartile range for **satis**?

7. Why might the standard deviation be a superior measure of dispersion to the inter-quartile range?

8. Taking **satis** again, what is the likely range of **satis** scores that lie within two standard deviations of the mean? What percentage of cases is likely to lie within this range?

Chapter six

Sampling and statistical significance

In this chapter, we will be encountering some issues which are fundamental to an appreciation of how people (or whatever is the unit of analysis) should be selected for inclusion in a study and of how it is possible to generalize to the population from which people are selected. These two related issues are concerned with *sampling* and the *statistical significance* of results. In examining sampling we will be examining the procedures for selecting people so that they are representative of the population from which they are selected. The topic of statistical significance raises the issue of how confident we can be that findings relating to a sample of individuals will also be found in the population from which the sample was selected.

Sampling

The issue of sampling is important because it is rarely the case that we have sufficient time and resources to conduct research on all of those individuals who could potentially be included in a study. Two points of clarification are relevant at this early stage. We talk about sampling from a *population* in the introduction to this chapter. It should be recognized that when we sample, it is not necessarily people who are being sampled. We can just as legitimately sample other units of analysis such as organizations, schools, local authorities, and so on. Second, by a 'population' is meant a discrete group of units of analysis and not just populations in the conventional sense, such as the population of England and Wales. Populations can be populations of towns, of particular groups (for example, all accountants in the UK), of individuals in a firm, or of firms themselves. When we sample, we are selecting units of analysis from a clearly defined population.

Clearly, some populations can be very large and it is unlikely that all of the units in a population can be included because of the considerable time and cost that such an exercise would entail. Sometimes, they can be sufficiently small for all units to be contacted; or if they are not too large, it may be possible to carry out postal questionnaire or telephone-interview surveys on a whole population. On the other hand, researchers are very often faced with the need to sample. By and large, researchers will want to form a *representative sample* – that is, a sample that can be treated as though it were the population. It is rare that perfectly representative samples can be created, but the chances of forming a representative sample can be considerably enhanced by *probability sampling*. The distinction between probability and non-probability sampling is a basic distinction in discussions of sampling. With probability sampling, each unit of a population has a specifiable probability of inclusion in a sample. In the basic forms of probability sampling, such as simple random samples (see below), each unit will have an equal probability of inclusion.

As an example of non-probability sampling procedure, consider the following scenario. An interviewer is asked to obtain answers to interview questions for fifty people – twenty-five of each gender. She positions herself in a shopping area in town at 9.00 a.m. on a Monday and starts interviewing people one by one. Will a representative sample be acquired? While it is not impossible that the sample is representative, there are too many doubts about its representativeness: for example, most people who work will not be shopping, she may have chosen people to be interviewed who were well-dressed, and some people may be more likely to use shops by which she positions herself than others. In other words, there is a strong chance that the sample is not representative of the people of the town. If the sample is unrepresentative, then our ability to generalize our findings to the population from which it was selected is sharply curtailed. If we do generalize, our inferences may be incorrect. If the sample is heavily biased towards people who do not work, who appeal to the interviewer because of their appearance, and who only shop in certain retail outlets, it is likely to be a poor representation of the wider population.

By contrast, probability sampling permits the selection of a sample that should be representative. The following is a discussion of the main types of probability sample that are likely to be encountered.

Simple random sample

The simple random sample is the most basic type of probability sample. Each unit in the population has an equal probability of inclusion in the sample. Like all forms of probability sample, it requires a *sampling frame*, which provides a complete listing of all the units in a population. Let us say that we want a representative sample of 200 non-manual employees from a firm which has 600 non-manual employees. The sample is often denoted as n and the population as N. A sampling frame is constructed which lists the 600 non-manual employees. Each employee is allocated a number between 1 and N (i.e. 600). Each employee has a probability of n/N of being included in the sample, i.e. one in three. Individuals will be selected for inclusion on a random basis to ensure that human choice is eliminated from decisions about who should be included and who excluded.

Each individual in the sampling frame is allocated a number 1 to N. The idea is to select *n* from this list. To ensure that the process is random, a table of random numbers should be consulted. These tables are usually in columns of five-digit numbers: for example, the figures might be

26938
37025
00352

Since we need to select a number of individuals which is in three digits (i.e. 200), only three digits in each five-digit random number should be considered. Let us say that we take the last three digits in each random number, that is we exclude the first two from consideration. The first case for inclusion would be that numbered 938. However, since the population is only 600, we cannot have a case numbered 938, so this figure is ignored and we proceed to the next random number. The figure 37025 implies that the case numbered 025 will be the first case for inclusion. The person numbered 025 will be the first sampled case. The next will be the person numbered 352, and so on. The process continues until *n* (i.e. 200) units have been selected.

By relying on a random process for the selection of individuals, the possibility of bias in the selection procedure is largely eliminated and the chance of generating a representative sample is enhanced. Sometimes, a *systematic sample* is selected rather than a simple random sample. With a systematic sample the selection of individuals is undertaken directly from the sampling frame and without the need to connect random numbers and cases. In the previous example, a random start between 1 and 3 would be made. Let us say that the number is 1. The first case on the sampling frame would be included. Then, every third case would be selected, since one in three must be sampled. Thus, the fourth, seventh, tenth, thirteenth, and so on would be selected. The chief advantage of the systematic sample over the simple random sample is that it obviates the need to plough through a table of random numbers and to tie in each number with a corresponding case. This procedure can be particularly time-consuming when a large sample must be selected. However, in order to select a systematic sample, the researcher must ensure that there is no inherent ordering to the list of cases in the sampling frame, since this would distort the ensuing sample and would probably mean that it was not representative.

Stratified sampling

Stratified sampling is commonly used by social scientists because it can lend an extra ingredient of precision to a simple random or systematic sample. When selecting a stratified sample, the researcher divides the population into strata. The strata must be categories of a criterion. Thus, for example, the population may be stratified according to the criterion of gender, in which case two strata – male and female – will be generated. Alternatively, the criterion may be department in the firm, resulting in possibly five strata: production, marketing, personnel, accounting, and research and development. Provided that the information is readily available, people are grouped into the strata. A simple random or systematic sample is then taken from the listing in each stratum. It is important for the stratifying criterion to be relevant to the issues in which the researcher is interested; it should not be undertaken for its own sake. The researcher may be interested in how the attitudes of non-manual employees is affected by the department to which they are attached in the firm. The advantage of stratified sampling is that it offers the possibility of greater accuracy, by ensuring that the groups that are created by a stratifying criterion are represented in the same proportions as in the population.

Table 6.1 provides an illustration of the idea of a stratified sample. The table provides the numbers of non-manual personnel in each department in the first column and the number of each department (i.e. stratum) that would be selected on a one-in-three basis. The important point to note is that the proportions of personnel from each department in the sample are the same as in the population. The largest department – production – has 35 per cent of all non-manual employees in the firm and 35 per cent of non-manual employees in the sample. A simple random or systematic sample without stratification *might* have achieved the same result, but a stratified sample greatly enhances the likelihood of the proper representation of strata in the sample. Two or more stratifying criteria can be employed in tandem. If, for example, the researcher were interested in the effects of gender on job attitudes, as well as belonging to different departments, we would then have ten strata (five departments × two sexes) – that is, men and women in production, men and women in marketing, and so

Table 6.1 Devising a stratified random sample: non-manual employees in a firm

Department	Population N	Sample n
Production	210	70
Marketing	120	40
Personnel	63	21
Accounting	162	54
Research and development	45	15
Total	600	200

on. A one-in-three sample would then be taken from each of the ten strata.

If the numbers in some strata are likely to be small, it may be necessary to sample disproportionately. Thus, for example, we may sample two in three of those in Research and Development. This would mean that thirty, rather than fifteen, would be sampled from this department. However, to compensate the extra fifteen individuals that are sampled in Research and Development, slightly less than one in three for Production and Accounting may need to be sampled. When this occurs, it has to be recognized that the sample is differentially weighted relative to the population, so that estimates of the sample mean will have to be corrected to reflect this weighting.

Multistage cluster sampling

One disadvantage of the probability samples covered so far is that they do not deal very well with geographically dispersed populations. If we took a simple random sample of all chartered accountants in the UK or indeed of the population of the UK itself, the resulting sample will be highly scattered. If the aim were to conduct an interview survey, interviewers would spend a great deal of time and money travelling to their respondents. A *multistage cluster sample* is a probability sampling procedure that allows such geographically dispersed populations to be adequately covered, while simultaneously saving interviewer time and travel costs.

Initially, the researcher samples clusters, that is areas of the geographical region being covered. The case of seeking to sample households in a very large city can be taken as an example of the procedure. At the first stage, all of the electoral wards in the city would be ascribed a number 1 to N and a simple random sample of wards selected. At the second stage, a simple random sample of streets in each ward might be taken. At the third stage, a simple random sample of households in the sampled streets would be selected from the list of addresses in the electoral rolls for the relevant wards. By concentrating interviewers in small regions of the city, much time and travel costs can be saved. Very often, stratification accompanies the sampling of clusters. Thus, for example, wards might be categorized in terms of an indicator of economic prosperity (for example, high, medium, and low) like the percentage of heads of household in professional and managerial jobs. Stratification will ensure that clusters are properly represented in terms of this criterion.

Sampling problems

One of the most frequently asked questions in the context of sampling is 'How large should a sample be?'. In reality, there can only be a few guidelines to answering this question, rather than a single definitive response.

First, the researcher almost always works within time and resource constraints, so that decisions about sample size must always recognize these boundaries. There is no point in working out an ideal sample size for a project if you have nowhere near the amount of resources required to bring it into effect. Second, the larger the sample the greater the accuracy. Contrary to expectations, the size of the sample relative to the size of the population (in other words n/N) is rarely relevant to the issue of a sample's accuracy. This means that *sampling error* – differences between the sample and the population which are due to sampling – can be reduced by increasing sampling size. However, after a certain level, increases in accuracy tend to tail off as sample size increases, so that greater accuracy becomes economically unacceptable.

Third, the problem of non-response should be borne in mind. Most sample surveys attract a certain amount of non-response. Thus, it is likely that only some of the 200 non-manual employees we sample will agree to participate in the research. If it is our aim to ensure as far as possible that 200 employees are interviewed and if we think that there may be a 20 per cent rate of non-response, it may be advisable to select 250 individuals, on the grounds that approximately fifty will be non-respondents. Finally, the researcher should bear in mind the kind of analysis he or she intends to undertake. If, for example, the researcher intends to examine the relationship between department in the firm and attitudes to white-collar unions, a table in which department is cross-tabulated against attitude can be envisaged. If 'attitude to white-collar unions' comprises four answers and since 'department' comprises five categories, a table of twenty 'cells' would be engendered (see discussion of contingency tables and cross-tabulation in Chapter 8). In order for there to be an adequate number of cases in each cell a fairly large sample will be required. Consequently, considerations of sample size should be sensitive to the kinds of analysis that will be subsequently required.

The issue of non-response draws attention to the fact that a well-crafted sample can be jeopardized by the failure of individuals to participate. The problem is that respondents and non-respondents may differ from each other in certain respects, so that respondents may not be representative of the population. Sometimes, researchers try to discern whether respondents are disproportionately drawn from particular groups, such as whether men are clearly more inclined not to participate than women. However, such tests can only be conducted in relation to fairly superficial characteristics like gender; deeper differences, such as attitudinal ones, cannot be readily tested. In addition, some members of a sample may not be contactable, because they have moved or are on holiday. Moreover, even when a questionnaire is answered, there may still be questions which, by design or error, are not answered. Each of these three elements – non-response, inability to contact, and missing information for certain variables – may be sources of bias, since we do not know how representative those who do respond to each variable are of the population.

Finally, although social scientists are well aware of the advantages of probability-sampling procedures, a great deal of research does not derive from probability samples. In a review of 126 articles in the field of organization studies which were based on correlation research, Mitchell (1985) found that only twenty-one were based on probability samples. The rest used *convenience samples* – that is, samples which are either 'chosen' by the investigator or which choose themselves (for example, volunteers). However, when it is borne in mind that response rates to sample surveys are often quite low and are declining (Goyder 1988), the difference between research based on random samples and convenience samples in terms of their relative representativeness is not always as great as is sometimes implied. None the less, many of the statistical tests and procedures to be encountered later in this book assume that the data derive from a random sample. The point being made here is that this requirement is often not fulfilled and that even when a random sample has been used, factors like non-response may adversely affect its representativeness.

Statistical significance

How do we know if a sample is typical or representative of the population from which it has been drawn? To find this out we need to be able to describe the nature of the sample and the population. This is done in terms of the distributions of their values. Thus, for example, if we wanted to find out whether the proportion of men to women in our sample was similar to that in some specified population, we would compare the two proportions. The main tests for tackling such problems are described in Chapters 7 and 9. It should be noted that the same principle lies behind all statistical tests including those concerned with describing the relationship between two or more variables. Here, the basic idea underlying them will be outlined.

To do this we will take the simple case of wanting to discover whether a coin was unbiased in the sense that it lands heads and tails an equal number of times. The number of times we tossed the coin would constitute the sample while the population would be the outcomes we would theoretically expect if the coin were unbiased. If we flipped the coin just once, then the probability of it turning up heads is once every two throws or 0.5. In other words, we would have to toss it at least twice to determine if both possibilities occur. If we were to do this, however, there would be four possible theoretical outcomes as shown in Table 6.2: (1) a tail followed by a head; (2) a head followed by a tail; (3) two tails; and (4) two heads.

What happens on each throw is *independent* of, or not affected by, the outcome of any other throw. If the coin were unbiased, then each of the four outcomes would be equally probable. In other words, the probability

Table 6.2 The four possible outcomes of tossing a coin twice

	Possible outcomes	Probability (p)
(1)	Tail (T), Head (H)	0.25
(2)	Head (H), Tail (T)	0.25 } = 0.5
(3)	Tail (T), Tail (T)	0.25
(4)	Head (H), Head (H)	0.25

of obtaining either two tails or two heads (but not both possibilities) is one in four or 0.25, while that of obtaining a head and a tail is two in four, or 0.5. The probability of obtaining a head and a tail (0.5) is greater than that of two tails (0.25) or two heads (0.25) but is the same as that for two tails and two heads combined (0.25 + 0.25). From this it should be clear that it is not possible to draw conclusions about a coin being unbiased from so few throws or such a small sample. This is because the frequency of improbable events is much greater with small samples. Consequently, it is much more difficult with such samples to determine whether they come from a certain population.

If we plot or draw the distribution of the probability of obtaining the same proportion of heads to tails as shown in Figure 6.1, then it will take the shape of an inverted 'V'. This shape will contain all the possible outcomes which will add up to 1 (0.25 + 0.25 + 0.25 + 0.25 = 1).

Theoretically, the more often we throw the coin, the more similar the distribution of the possible outcomes will be to an inverted 'U' or normal distribution. Suppose, for example, we threw the same coin six times (or, what amounts to the same thing, six coins once). If we did this, there would be sixty-four possible outcomes. These are shown in Table 6.3.

The total number of outcomes can be calculated by multiplying the number of possible outcomes on each occasion (2) by those of the other occasions ($2 \times 2 \times 2 \times 2 \times 2 \times 2 = 64$). The probability of obtaining six heads or six tails in a row (but not both) would be one in sixty-four or about 0.016. Since there are six possible ways in which one head and five tails can be obtained, the probability of achieving this is six out of sixty-four or about 0.10 (i.e. 0.016 × 6). The distribution of the probability of obtaining different sequences of the same number of tails and heads grouped together (for example, the six sequences of finding five tails and a head) is presented in Figure 6.2.

It should be clear from this discussion that we can never be 100 per cent certain that the coin is unbiased, because even if we threw it 1,000 times, there is a very small chance that it will turn up all heads or all tails on every one of those throws. So what we do is to set a criterion or cut-off point at or beyond which we assume that the coin will be judged to be biased. This point is arbitrary and is referred to as the *significance level.* It is usually set

Figure 6.1 The distribution of similar theoretical outcomes of tossing a coin twice

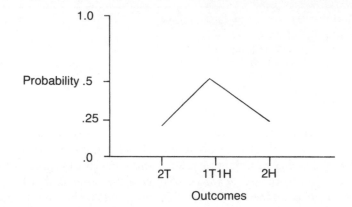

at a probability or *p* level of 0.05 or five times out of a hundred. Since the coin can be biased in one of two ways, i.e. in favour of either heads or tails, this 5 per cent is shared equally between these two possibilities. This means, in effect, that the probability of the coin being biased towards heads will be 0.025 and that the probability of its bias towards tails will also be 0.025. In other words, if it turns up heads or tails six times in a row, then the probability of both these outcomes occurring would be about 0.032 (i.e. 0.016 + 0.016), which is below the probability of 0.05. If either of these two events happened we would accept that the coin was biased. If, however, it landed tails once and heads five times, or heads once and tails five times, there are six ways in which either of these two outcomes could happen. Consequently, the probability of either one happening is six out of sixty-four or about 0.10. The probability of both outcomes occurring is about 0.2 (i.e. 0.10 + 0.10). In this case, we would have to accept that the coin was unbiased since this probability level is above the criterion of 0.05.

Because we can never be 100 per cent certain that the coin is either biased or unbiased, we can make one of two kinds of errors. The first kind is to decide that the coin is biased when it is not. This is known as a *Type I error* and is sometimes referred to as α (alpha). Thus, for example, as we have seen, an unbiased coin may land heads six times in a row. The second kind of error is to judge the coin to be unbiased when it is biased. This is called a *Type II error* and is represented by β (beta). It is possible, for instance, for a biased coin to come up tails once and heads five times. We can reduce the possibility of making a Type I error by accepting a lower level of significance, say 0.01 instead of 0.05; but doing this increases the probability of making a Type II error. In other words, the probability of a Type I error is inversely related to that of a Type II one. The more likely we are to make a Type I error, the less likely we are to commit a Type II error.

Table 6.3 \Theoretical outcomes of tossing a coin sixty-four times and the probabilities of similar outcomes

	Theoretical outcomes	Probability		Theoretical outcomes	Probability
1	TTTTTT	0.016	64	HHHHHH	0.016
2	TTTTTH		63	HHHHHT	
3	TTTTHT		62	HHHHTH	
4	TTTHTT	0.096	61	HHHTHH	0.096
5	TTHTTT		60	HHTHHH	
6	THTTTT		59	HTHHHH	
7	HTTTTT		58	THHHHH	
8	TTTTHH		57	HHHHTT	
9	TTTHHT		56	HHHTTH	
10	TTHHTT		55	HHTTHH	
11	TTTHTH		54	HHHTHT	
12	TTHTHT		53	HHTHTH	
13	TTHTTH		52	HHTHHT	
14	THTHTT		51	HTHTHH	
15	THHTTT	0.234	50	HTTHHH	0.234
16	THTTTH		49	HTHHHT	
17	THTTHT		48	HTHHTH	
18	HTTHTT		47	THHTHH	
19	HTTTHT		46	THHHTH	
20	HTHTTT		45	THTHHH	
21	HTTTTH		44	THHHHT	
22	HHTTTT		43	TTHHHH	
23	TTTHHH		42	HHHTTT	
24	TTHHHT		41	HHTTTH	
25	TTHHTH		40	HHTTHT	
26	TTHTHH		39	HHTHTT	
27	THTHTH		38	HTHTHT	
28	THTHHT		37	HTHTTH	0.313
29	THHTTH		36	HTTHHT	
30	THHTHT		35	HTTHTH	
31	THTTHH		34	HTHHTT	
32	THHHTT		33	HTTTHH	

At this stage, it is useful to discuss briefly three kinds of probability distribution. The first is known as a *binomial* distribution and is based on the idea that if only either of two outcomes can occur on any one occasion (for example, heads or tails if a coin is thrown), then we can work out the theoretical distribution of the different combinations of outcomes which could occur if we knew the number of occasions that had taken place. One characteristic of this distribution is that it consists of a limited or finite number of events. If, however, we threw an infinite number of coins an infinite number of times, then we would have a distribution which would consist of an infinite possibility of events. This distribution is known variously as the DeMoivre's, Gaussian, normal, standard normal, or *z*

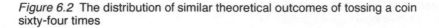

Figure 6.2 The distribution of similar theoretical outcomes of tossing a coin sixty-four times

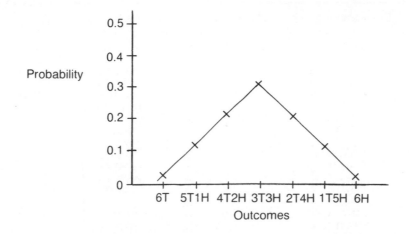

curve or distribution. (A Poisson distribution, on the other hand, is positively skewed.) If random samples of these probabilities are taken and plotted, then the shape of those distributions will depend on the size of the samples. Smaller samples will produce flatter distributions with thicker tails than the normal distribution, while larger ones will be very similar to it. These distributions are known as *t* distributions. What this means is that when we want to know the likelihood that a particular series of events could have occurred by chance, we need to take into account the size of the sample on which those events are based.

So far, in order to convey the idea that certain events may occur just by chance, we have used the example of tossing a coin. Although this may seem a bit remote from the kinds of data we collect in the social sciences, we use this underlying principle to determine issues such as whether a sample is representative of its population and whether two or more samples or treatments differ from each other. Suppose we drew a small sample of six people and wanted to determine if the proportion of males to females in it were similar to that of the population in which men and women are in equal number. Each person can only be male or female. Since there are six people, there are sixty-four possible outcomes (i.e. $2 \times 2 \times 2 \times 2 \times 2 \times 2$). These, of course, are the same as those displayed in Table 6.3 except that we now substitute males for tails and females for heads. The joint probability of all six people being either male or female would be about 0.03 (i.e. $0.016 + 0.016$), so that if this were the result we would reject the notion that the sample was representative of the population. However, if one were male and the other five female, or there were one female and five males, then the probability of this occurring by chance would be about 0.2 (i.e.

0.096 + 0.096). This would mean that at the 0.05 significance level we would accept either of these two outcomes or samples as being typical of the population because the probability of obtaining these outcomes is greater than the 0.05 level. This shows that sample values can diverge quite widely from those of their populations and still be drawn from them, although it should be emphasized that this outcome would be less frequent the larger the sample. Statistical tests which compare a sample with a population are known as *one-sample tests* and can be found in the next chapter.

The same principle underlies tests which have been developed to find out if two or more samples or treatments come from the same population or different ones, although this is a little more difficult to grasp. We may for example, be interested in finding out whether women are more perceptive than men, or whether alcohol impairs performance. In the first case, the two samples are women and men while in the second they are alcohol and no alcohol. Once again, in order to explain the idea that underlies these tests, it may be useful to think about it initially in terms of throwing a coin, except that this time we throw two coins. The two coins represent the two samples. We want to know whether the two coins differ in their tendency to be unbiased. If the two coins were unbiased and if we were to throw them six times each, then we should expect the two sets of theoretical outcomes obtained to be the same as that in Table 6.3. In other words, the two distributions should overlap each other exactly.

Now if we were to throw the two coins six times each, it is unlikely that the empirical outcomes would be precisely the same, even if the coins were unbiased. In fact, we can work out the theoretical probability of the two distributions being different in the same way as we did earlier for the coin turning up heads or tails. It may be easier in the first instance if we begin by comparing the outcomes of tossing two coins just once. If we do this, there are four possible outcomes: (1) two tails; (2) two heads; (3) one tail and one head; and (4) one head and one tail. If we look at these outcomes in terms of whether they are the same or different, then two of them are the same (two tails and two heads) while two of them are different (one tail and one head, and vice versa). In other words, the probability of finding a difference is two out of four or 0.5, which is the same as that for discovering no difference. We stand an equal chance of finding no difference as we do of a difference if we throw two unbiased coins once.

Thinking solely in terms of the outcomes of the two coins being the same or different, if we threw the two coins twice, then there would be four possible outcomes: (1) two the same; (2) two different; (3) the first the same and the second different; and (4) the first different and the second the same. In other words, the probability of obtaining the same outcome when two unbiased coins are thrown twice is 0.25. The probability of the outcomes being mixed is greater with the value being 0.5. The probability of the outcomes being the same on all six throws would be about 0.016 (0.5 × 0.5 × 0.5 × 0.5 × 0.5 × 0.5 = 0.016). Hence, if the two coins were unbiased, we would not expect them to give the same outcome on each occasion they were tossed. The distribution of the outcomes of the two coins represents, in effect, what we would expect to happen if the differences between two samples or two treatments were due to chance.

Applying this idea to the kind of question that may be asked in the social sciences, we may wish to find out if women and men differ in their perceptiveness. There are three possible answers to this question: (1) women may be more perceptive than men; (2) they may be no different from them; or (3) they may be less perceptive than them. In other words, we can have three different expectations or hypotheses about what the answer might be. Not expecting any difference is known as the *null hypothesis*. Anticipating a difference but not being able to predict what it is likely to be is called a *non-directional hypothesis*. However, it is unlikely that we would ask this sort of question if we did not expect a difference of a particular nature, since there is an infinite number of such questions which can be posed. In carrying out research we are often concerned with showing that a particular relationship either holds or does not hold between two or more variables. In other words, we are examining the direction as well as the existence of a relationship. In this case, we may be testing the idea that women are more perceptive than men. This would be an example of a *directional hypothesis*. As we shall see, specifying the direction of the hypothesis means that we can adopt a slightly higher and more lenient level of significance.

Since there are three possible outcomes (i.e. a probability of 0.33 for any one outcome) for each paired comparison, if we were to test this hypothesis on a small sample of five men and five women, then the probability of all five women being more perceptive than men just by chance would be about 0.004 (i.e. 0.33 × 0.33 × 0.33 × 0.33 × 0.33). If we were to obtain this result, and adopt the usual 0.05 or 5 per cent as the significance level at or below which this finding is unlikely to be due to chance, then we would accept the hypothesis since 0.004 is less than 0.05. In other words, we would state that women are significantly more perceptive than men below the 5 per cent level – see Figure 6.3 (a). As we shall see, SPSS provides the exact level of significance for each test. It has been customary in the social sciences to provide the significance level only for results which fall at or below the 0.05 level and to do so for certain cut-off points below that such as 0.01, 0.001, and 0.0001. However, with the advent of computer programs such as SPSS which give exact significance levels, it could be argued that such a tradition does not maximize the information which could be supplied to the reader with no obvious disadvantages.

If, however, we were to find that only four of the women were more perceptive than the men, then the probability of this happening by chance

Figure 6.3 The one-tailed and two-tailed 5 per cent levels of significance

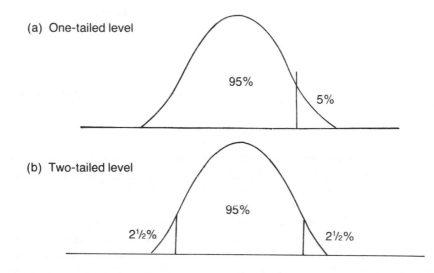

(a) One-tailed level

95%

5%

(b) Two-tailed level

95%

2½%

2½%

would be about 0.04, since there are ten ways or sequences in which this result could occur (0.004 × 10 = 0.04). This finding is still significant. However, if we had adopted a non-directional hypothesis and had simply expected a difference between men and women without specifying the direction, then this result would not be significant at the 0.05 level since this 0.05 would have to be shared between both tails of the distribution of possible outcomes, as in Figure 6.3 (b). In other words, it would become 0.025 at either end of the distribution. This result would require a probability level of 0.025 or less to be significant when stated as a non-directional hypothesis. As it is, the probability of either four women being more perceptive than men or four men being more perceptive than women is the sum of these two probabilities, namely 0.08, which is above the 0.05 level. The important point to note is that non-directional hypotheses require *two-tailed* significance levels while directional hypotheses only need *one-tailed* ones. If we find a difference between two samples or treatments we did not expect, then to test the significance of this result we need to use a two-tailed test.

It may be worth reiterating at this stage that a finding that four out of the five women being more perceptive than the five men may still be obtained by chance even at the 0.04 one-tailed level. In other words, this means that there remains a four in a hundred possibility that this result could be due to chance. In accepting this level of significance for rejecting the null hypothesis that there is no difference between men and women, we may be committing a Type I error, namely thinking that there is a difference between them when in fact there is no such difference. In other words, a

Table 6.4 Type I and Type II errors

		Reality	
		No difference	*A difference*
Interpretation of reality	*Accept no difference*	Correct	Type II error β
	Accept a difference	Type I error α	Correct (Power)

Type I error is rejecting the null hypothesis when it is true, as shown in Table 6.4. We may reduce the probability of making this kind of error by lowering the significance level from 0.05 to 0.01, but this increases the probability of committing a Type II error, which is accepting that there is no difference when there is one. A Type II error is accepting the null hypothesis when it is false. Setting the significance level at 0.01 means that the finding that four out of the five women were more perceptive than the men is assuming that this result is due to chance when it may be indicating a real difference.

The probability of correctly assuming that there is a difference when there actually is one is known as the *power* of a test. A powerful test is one that is more likely to indicate a significant difference when such a difference exists. Statistical power is inversely related to the probability of making a Type II error and is calculated by subtracting beta from one (i.e. $1 - \beta$).

Finally, it is important to realize that the level of significance has nothing to do with the size or importance of a difference. It is simply concerned with the probability of that difference arising by chance. In other words, a difference between two samples or two treatments which is significant at the 0.05 level is not necessarily bigger than one which is significant at the 0.0001 level. The latter difference is only less probable than the former one.

Exercises

1. What is the difference between a random sample and a representative sample?

2. Why might a stratified sample be superior to a simple random sample?

3. In what context might multistage cluster sampling be particularly useful?

4. If a sample of grocery shops were selected randomly from the Yellow Pages in your town, would you necessarily have a representative sample?

5. Flip a coin four times. What is the probability of finding the particular sequence of outcomes you did?

6. If the coin were unbiased, would you obtain two heads and two tails if you were to throw it four times?

7. What is the probability of obtaining any sequence of two heads and two tails?

8. You have developed a test of general knowledge, which consists of a hundred statements, half of which are false and half of which are true. Each person is given one point for a correct answer. How many points is someone who has no general knowledge most likely to achieve on this test?

9. Fifty people are tested to see if they can tell margarine from butter. Half of them are given butter and the other half are given margarine. They have to say which of these two products they were given (i.e. there were no 'don't knows'). If people cannot discriminate between them, how many people on average are likely to guess correctly?

10. If we wanted to see if women were more talkative than men, what would the null hypothesis be?

11. What would the non-directional hypothesis be?

Chapter seven

Bivariate analysis: exploring differences between scores on two variables

In this chapter we will be looking at ways of determining whether the differences between the distributions of two variables are statistically significant. Thus, for example, when analysing data we may wish to know the answers to some of the following kinds of questions: Is the proportion of black to white workers the same among men as it is among women?; Do women workers earn less than their male counterparts?; Does job satisfaction change from one month to the next?; Do the scores in one treatment group differ from those in another?

In looking at differences between two variables, the variable which we use to form our comparison groups usually has a small number of values or levels, say between two and six. We shall call this the comparison-group variable to distinguish it from the other one which we shall refer to as the criterion variable. The comparison variable is sometimes known as the independent variable, and the criterion variable as the dependent one. An example of a comparison-group variable would be gender if we wanted to compare men with women. This typically has two levels (i.e. men and women) which go to make up two comparison groups. Race or ethnic origin, on the other hand, may take on two or more levels (for example, Caucasian, Negroid, Asian, and Mongolian), thereby creating two or more comparison groups. Other examples of comparison-group variables include different experimental treatments (for example, drugs versus psychotherapy in treating depression), different points in time (for example, two consecutive months), and the categorization of subjects into various levels on some variable (such as high, intermediate, and low job satisfaction). The other variable is the one that we shall use to make our comparison (for example, income or job satisfaction).

Criteria for selecting bivariate tests of differences

There is a relatively large number of statistical tests to determine whether a difference between two or more groups is significant. In deciding which is the most appropriate statistical test to use to analyse your data, it is necessary to bear the following considerations in mind.

Categorical data

If the data are of a categorical or nominal nature, where the values refer to the number or frequency of cases that fall within particular categories such as the number of black female workers, it is only possible to use what is referred to as a *non-parametric* test (see below for an explanation). Thus, for example, in trying to determine whether there are significantly more white than black female employees, it would be necessary to use a non-parametric test.

Ordinal and interval/ratio data

If the data are of a non-categorical nature, such as the rating of how skilled workers are or how much they earn, then it is necessary to decide whether it is more appropriate to use a *parametric* or non-parametric test. Since this issue is a complex and controversial one, it will be discussed later in some detail.

Means or variances?

Most investigators who use parametric tests are primarily interested in checking for differences between means. Differences in variances are also normally carried out but only to determine the appropriateness of using such a test to check for differences in the means. *Variance* is an expression showing the spread or dispersion of data around the mean and is the square of the standard deviation. If the variances are found to differ markedly, then it may be more appropriate to use a non-parametric test. However, differences in variance (i.e. variability) may be of interest in their own right and so these tests have been listed separately. Thus, for example, it may be reasonable to suppose that the variability of job satisfaction of women will be greater than that of men, but that there will be no difference in their mean scores. In this case, it would also be necessary to pay attention to the differences between the variances to determine if this were so.

Related or unrelated comparison groups?

Which test you use also depends on whether the values that you want to compare come from different cases or from the same or similar ones. If, for example, you are comparing different groups of people such as men and women or people who have been assigned to different experimental treatments, then you are dealing with unrelated samples of subjects. It is worth noting that this kind of situation or design is also referred to in some of the following other ways: *independent* or *uncorrelated* groups or samples; and *between-subjects* design. If, on the other hand, you are comparing the way that the same people have responded on separate occasions or under different conditions, then you are dealing with *related* samples of observations. This is also true of groups of people who are or have been *matched* or *paired* on one or more important characteristics such as, for example, husbands and wives, which may also make them more similar in terms of the criterion variable under study. Once again, there is a number of other terms used to describe related scores such as the following: *dependent* or *correlated* groups or samples; *repeated measures*; and *within-subjects* design.

Two or more comparison groups?

Different tests are generally used to compare two rather than three or more comparison groups.

The tests to be used given these criteria are listed in Table 7.1. Readers may wish to use this table as a guide to the selection of tests appropriate to their needs. Page numbers are inserted in the table cells to facilitate finding the appropriate tests.

Parametric versus non-parametric tests

One of the unresolved issues in data analysis is the question of when parametric rather than non-parametric tests should be used. Some writers have argued that it is only appropriate to use parametric tests when the data fulfil the following three conditions: (1) the level or scale of measurement is of equal interval or ratio scaling, i.e. more than ordinal; (2) the distribution of the population scores is normal; and (3) the variances of both variables are equal or *homogeneous*. The term *parameter* refers to a measure which describes the distribution of the population such as the mean or variance. Since parametric tests are based on the assumption that we know certain characteristics of the population from which the sample is drawn, they are called *parametric tests*. *Non-parametric* or *distribution-free tests* are so named because they do not depend on assumptions about the precise form of the distribution of the sampled populations.

However, the need to meet these three conditions for using parametric tests has been strongly questioned. Some of the arguments will be mentioned here and these will be simply stated, with sources provided where further details can be found. As far as the first condition is concerned, level of measurement, it has been suggested that parametric tests can also be used with ordinal variables since tests apply to numbers and not to what those numbers signify (for example, Lord 1953). Thus, for

Table 7.1 Tests of differences for two variables

Nature of criterion variable	Type of test	Number of comparison groups or samples				
		Unrelated Data			Related Data	
		1	2	3+	2	3+
Categorical: nominal or frequency	Non-parametric	Binomial pp. 118–20 Chi-square pp. 120–2	Chi-square pp. 123–4	Chi-square pp. 123–4	McNemar pp. 124–6	Cochran Q pp. 126–7
Non-categorical: ordinal or ranked	Non-parametric	Kolmogorov–Smirnov pp. 126–8	Kolmogorov–Smirnov pp. 127–8 Median pp. 128–9 Mann–Whitney U pp. 129–30	Median pp. 128–9 Kruskal–Wallis H pp. 130–1	Sign pp. 131–2 Wilcoxon pp. 132–3	Friedman pp. 132–3
Non-categorical: interval or ratio	Parametric: means	t pp. 133–5	t pp. 135–6	One-way analysis of variance pp. 137–42	t pp. 143–5	Repeated measures (multivariate analysis of variance) pp. 145–8
	Variances		F p. 137	Cochran's C Hartley's F_{max} Bartlett-Box F pp. 142–3	t pp. 144–5	

example, we apply these tests to determine if two scores differ. We know what these scores indicate, but the test obviously does not. Therefore, the data are treated as if they are of interval or ratio scaling. Furthermore, it can be argued that since many psychological and sociological variables such as attitudes are basically ordinal in nature (see p. 65), parametric tests should not be used to analyse them if this first condition is valid. However, it should be noted that parametric tests are routinely applied to such variables.

With respect to the second and third conditions, the populations being normally distributed and of equal variances, a number of studies have been carried out (for example, Boneau 1960; Games and Lucas, 1966) where the values of the statistics used to analyse samples drawn from populations which have been artificially set up to violate these conditions have been found not to differ greatly from those for samples which have been drawn from populations which do not violate these conditions. Tests which are able to withstand such violations are described as being *robust*. The one situation in which tests were not found to be robust was where the samples were of different sizes *and* the variances were unequal or *heterogeneous*. In such cases, therefore, it is necessary to use a nonparametric test. It may also be more desirable to use them when the size of the samples is small, say under 15, since under these circumstances it is more difficult to determine the extent to which these conditions have been met. A fuller description of nonparametric tests may be found in Siegel (1956) or Conover (1980).

Categorical variables and non-parametric tests

Binomial test for one dichotomous variable

The binomial test is used to compare the frequency of cases actually found in the two categories of a dichotomous variable with those which are expected on some basis. Suppose, for example, that we wanted to find out whether the ratio of female to male workers in the industry covered by our Job Survey was the same as that in the industry in general, which we knew to be 1:3. We could do this by carrying out a binomial test in which the proportion of women in our survey was compared with that of an expected proportion of 1:4 or one out of every four workers.

To do this on SPSS, we would use the following command:

npar tests binomial (.75)=gender(1,2).

The proportion of cases expected to fall in the first category is placed in brackets after the keyword **binomial**. The full stop at the end of the command is only required for SPSS/PC+. Omit it if you are using SPSS-X. This point holds throughout this chapter. Since males have been coded as 1, they form the first category and the proportion of them becomes 3:4 or

0.75. If no value is placed after **binomial**, the value 0.5 will be used by default. If the proportion is 0.5, a two-tailed significance or *p* test will be calculated. If it is either greater or less than this, a one-tailed *p* test is computed. The numbers placed after the variable name correspond to the two categories being compared. If, for example, we wanted to find out if there were equal numbers of Asian and West Indian workers, we would do this by listing their two codes (2 and 3) after the variable name as follows:

npar tests binomial=ethnicgp(2,3).

If, however, we wished to determine if there were equal numbers of black and white workers, we could do this by placing 1 after the variable name:

npar tests binomial=ethnicgp(1).

In other words, a single value put in parentheses after the variable name acts as a cut-off point. All cases equal to or less than this point form the first category, while all the others form the second category.

The output for the first command is displayed in Table 7.2. (It should be noted that there are no zeros before the decimal points; this reflects a general tendency in SPSS that where the maximum value is one, there is no zero before the decimal point.) As we can see, the number of males (thirty-nine) is only slightly greater than that of females (thirty-one) and so it would appear from an inspection of these figures that the ratio of males to females is nearer 1:1 than 3:1. The hypothesis that the proportion of males to females is 0.75 is rejected since the probability of obtaining this result by chance is highly unlikely with *p* equal to 0.0003. In other words, the likelihood of this result happening by chance is 3 out of 10,000 times. Consequently, the difference between the obtained and hypothesized outcome is interpreted as being statistically different. Therefore, we would conclude that the ratio of male to female workers is not 3:1.

The output for the third command is shown in Table 7.3. The number of white workers (thirty-six) is almost the same as that of non-white ones

Table 7.2 Binomial test comparing proportion of men and women (Job-Survey SPSS/PC+ output)

————— Binomial Test		
GENDER	gender	
Cases		
		Test Prop. = .7500
39	=1	Obs. Prop. = .5571
31	=2	
——		Z Approximation
70	Total	2-tailed P = .0003

Table 7.3 Binomial test comparing proportion of whites and non-whites (Job-Survey SPSS/PC+ output)

— — — — — Binomial Test		
ETHNICGP	ethnic group	
Cases		
		Test Prop. = .5000
36	Le 1	Obs. Prop. = .5143
34	Gt 1	
--		Z Approximation
70	Total	2-tailed P = .9049

(thirty-four), so the ratio is close to 1:1. The hypothesis that there are equal numbers of white and non-white workers is accepted since the probability of obtaining this result by chance is high (i.e. *p*=0.90). In other words, since there is no significant difference between the obtained and the hypothesized result, we would conclude that there are equal numbers of white and non-white workers.

Incidentally, the similarity of these examples to those used to illustrate the notion of significance testing in the previous chapter should be noted, except that there we were comparing the frequency of finding one tail (or one male) to every five heads (or five females) against an expected frequency or probability of 0.05. To work this out using SPSS, we would have to create a data file which consisted of one sequence of such a frequency and a command file to carry out a binomial test on it.

Chi-square test for one sample

If we want to compare the observed frequencies of cases with those expected in a variable which has more than two categories, then we use a chi-square or x^2 (pronounced 'kye-square') rather than a binomial test. If, for instance, we wished to know whether there were equal numbers of workers from the four different ethnic groups coded in our Job-Survey data, then we would use a chi-square test for one sample. The SPSS command for doing this takes the following form:

npar tests chisquare=ethnicgp(1,4).

The range of categories to be examined needs to be specified in parentheses after the variable name if not all of them are to be included. In this example, we have chosen to exclude the 'other' category by listing categories one to four. This fifth category would have been included in this analysis by default if we had not specifically excluded it.

The expected frequencies are assumed to be equal, unless explicitly specified otherwise. In other words, in this case we are testing the hypothesis that the four categories will contain the same number of workers, or one in four. Should we have expected them to be different, then we need to list these expected frequencies. If, for example, we knew that in the industry covered by our Job Survey the ratio of workers in these four categories was 95:2:2:1 and we wished to find out if our sample was similar to the population in this respect, we would do this by specifying these expected frequencies as follows:

npar tests chisquare=ethnicgp(1,4)/expected=95 2 2 1.

Expected frequencies need to be greater than zero and are specified as a proportion of those listed. In this case, 95 out of 100 are expected to be white since the total adds up to 100 (95+2+2+1).

The output for the first command is shown in Table 7.4. Note that for this test, the display includes the numbers of the categories, the number of cases observed and expected in each of these categories, the residual or difference between the observed and the expected frequencies, the chi-square statistic, the degrees of freedom, and the level of significance.

The term *degrees of freedom* (*d.f.*), associated with any statistic, refers to the number of components which are free to vary. It is a difficult concept which is well explained elsewhere (Walker 1940). In this case, they are calculated by subtracting 1 from the number of categories. Since there are four categories, there are three degrees of freedom (i.e. 4−1). What this means essentially is that if we know the number of subjects in the sample and if we know the observed frequencies in three of the four categories, then we can work out from this the observed frequencies in the remaining category. In other words, if we know one of the values, the other three are free to vary.

Table 7.4 One-sample chi-square test comparing number of people in ethnic groups (Job-Survey SPSS/PC+ output)

—————— Chi-square Test

ETHNICGP   ethnic group

		Cases		
	Category	Observed	Expected	Residual
white	1	36	17.50	18.50
asian	2	18	17.50	.50
west indian	3	14	17.50	−3.50
african	4	2	17.50	−15.50
	Total	70		

Chi-Square	D.F.	Significance
34.000	3	.000

As we can see, the observed frequencies are significantly different ($p < 0.0005$) from the expected ones of there being an equal number of subjects in each of the four categories. In other words, since the probability of obtaining this result is very low (5 out of 10,000 times), we would conclude that the number of workers in each ethnic group is not equal.

There is a restriction on using chi-square when the expected frequencies are small. With only two categories (or one degree of freedom), the number of cases expected to fall in these categories should be at least 5 before this test can be applied. If the expected frequencies are less than 5, then the binomial test should be used instead. With three or more categories (or more than one degree of freedom), chi-square should not be used when any expected frequency is smaller than 1 or when more than 20 per cent of the expected frequencies are smaller than 5. In these situations, it may be possible to increase the expected frequencies in a category by combining it with those of another.

An example of the latter case is the second statistical analysis we asked for, the output of which is presented in Table 7.5. Here, three of the expected frequencies fall below 2, one of which is below 1. We would need a much larger sample of subjects to use a chi-square test on these data. If we had only two categories, whites and non-whites, we would require a minimum sample of 100 in order to have an expected frequency of 5 in the non-white category. Consequently, it would be necessary to use a binomial test to determine if the frequency of non-whites in the Job Survey is different from a hypothesized one of 5 per cent.

Table 7.5 Chi-square test with insufficient cases (Job-Survey SPSS/PC+ output)

— — — — — Chi-square Test

ETHNICGP   ethnic group

	Category	Cases Observed	Expected	Residual
white	1	36	66.50	−30.50
asian	2	18	1.40	16.60
west indian	3	14	1.40	12.60
african	4	2	.70	1.30
Total		70		

WARNING–Chi-Square statistic is questionable here.
3 Cells have expected frequencies less than 5.
Minimum expected cell frequency is .7

Chi-Square	D.F.	Significance
34.000	3	.000

Chi-square test for two or more unrelated samples

If we wanted to compare the frequency of cases found in one variable in two or more unrelated samples or categories of another variable, we would also use the chi-square test. We will illustrate this test with the relatively simple example in which we have two dichotomous variables, gender (male and female) and ethnic group (white and non-white), although it can also be applied to two variables which have three or more categories. Suppose, for instance, we wished to find out whether the proportion of male to female workers was the same in both white and black workers. We could do this by using the following commands:

```
recode ethnicgp (3 thru 5=2).
value labels ethnicgp 1 'white' 2 'nonwhite'.
crosstabs tables=gender by ethnicgp
  /option 14
  /statistic 1.
```

First of all, we have to recode the category of ethnic group, so that all the non-whites are coded as 2. If we wanted to assign value labels, we would have to provide new ones for the two groups. Second, because the chi-square test for two or more unrelated samples is only available as part of the SPSS procedure for generating tables which show the distribution of two or more variables, we have to use the relevant commands in this **crosstabs** procedure. Further details on it can be found in the next chapter, where its operation is described more fully. In order not to replicate this information, only the commands for generating chi-square will be outlined here.

The **table** command specifies the nature of the table to be produced. The variable listed first will form the rows of the table while that listed second will form the columns. If no options are asked for, **crosstabs** will only give the number of cases in each cell. Since chi-square is based on comparing the expected with the observed frequency in each cell, it is useful to have a display of the expected frequencies which is available by including **option 14**. Finally, chi-square is produced by asking for **statistic 1**. In SPSS-X, the **options** subcommand can be replaced with /**cells expected**, while on the **statistic** subcommand **1** can be substituted with **chisq**.

The output from these commands is shown in Table 7.6 which includes a table of the expected and observed frequencies in each cell, the chi-square statistic, the degrees of freedom, the significance level, the smallest expected frequency (**MIN E.F.**) and the number of cells with an expected frequency of less than 5 (**CELLS WITH E.F. < 5**). These last two values are useful when the degrees of freedom are larger than one, because as in the case of a one-sample chi-square, this test should not be used if any cell has an expected frequency of less than 1 or if 20 per cent or more of the cells

Table 7.6 Chi-square test produced by **crosstabs** comparing number of white and non-white men and women (Job-Survey SPSS/PC+ output)

Crosstabulation:		GENDER By ETHNICGP	gender ethnic group	

Count ETHNICGP —>Exp Val		white 1	non-white 2	Row Total
GENDER male	1	22 20.1	17 18.9	39 55.7%
female	2	14 15.9	17 15.1	31 44.3%
Column Total		36 51.4%	34 48.6%	70 100.0%

CHI-SQUARE	D.F.	SIGNIFICANCE	MIN E.F.	CELLS WITH E.F.<5
.48254	1	.4873	15.057	None
.87492	1	.3496	(Before Yates Correction)	

Number of Missing Observations = 0

have an expected frequency of less than 5. As the minimum expected frequency in any one cell is 15.1 (for non-white females) and there are no cells with an expected frequency of less than 5, it is appropriate to use this test. The degrees of freedom are calculated by subtracting 1 from the number of categories in each of the two variables and multiplying the remaining values (i.e. $(2-1)(2-1)=1$). The observed frequencies are displayed above the expected ones in each of the cells. Thus, the observed frequency of white males is 22, while the expected one is 20.1. Two chi-squares are given. The second is the uncorrected value while the first incorporates Yates's correction which assumes that the frequencies can be non-integral (i.e. consist of whole numbers and fractions or decimals). Since the value of chi-square is not significant, this means that the proportion of male to female workers is the same for both whites and non-whites.

McNemar test for two related samples

This test is used to compare the frequencies of a dichotomous variable from the same cases at two points in time, in two treatments, or from two samples which have been matched to be similar in certain respects such as having the same distributions of age, gender, and socio-economic status. Suppose, for example, we wanted to find out if there had been any changes in the attendance of workers at a firm's monthly meetings in two consecutive months (**attend1** and **attend2**). To do this, we would conduct a McNemar test using the following SPSS command:

npar tests mcnemar=attend1 attend2.

The use of tests to analyse information from two or more related samples will be illustrated with the small set of data in Table 7.7. This consists of one example of the three kinds of variables (categorical, ordinal, and interval/ratio) measured at three consecutive monthly intervals on twelve workers. The categorical variable is their attendance at the firm's monthly meeting (**attend1** to **attend3**), the ordinal one is the quality of their work as rated by their supervisor (**qual1** to **qual3**), while the interval/ratio one is their self-expressed job satisfaction (**satis1** to **satis3**). A study in which data are collected from the same individuals at two or more points is known as a *prospective, longitudinal,* or *panel* design. Consequently, this example will be referred to as the Panel Study.

The output presented in Table 7.8 resulted from using the foregoing command on the Panel-Study data. The table shows the number of people whose attendance changed or remained the same from the first to the second month. Since attendance is coded as 1 and non-attendance as 2, we can see that six workers attended the first but not the second meeting and that two attended the second but not the first one. If fewer than ten cases change from one sample to another as they did here, the binomial test is computed. Otherwise, the one-sample chi-square test is used. As the two-tailed level of probability is greater than 0.05, this means that there was no significant change in attendance between the first and second meeting. In other words, we would conclude that a similar number of people attended the first and the second meeting.

Table 7.7 The Panel-Study data

id	attend1	qual1	satis1	attend2	qual2	satis2	attend3	qual3	satis3
01	1	5	17	1	4	18	1	5	16
02	1	4	12	2	3	9	2	2	7
03	2	3	13	1	4	15	2	3	14
04	2	4	11	2	5	14	2	3	8
05	2	2	7	2	3	10	1	3	9
06	1	4	14	1	4	15	2	3	10
07	1	3	15	2	1	6	1	4	12
08	2	4	12	1	3	9	1	4	13
09	1	4	13	2	5	14	1	3	15
10	1	1	5	2	2	4	2	3	9
11	1	3	8	2	3	7	1	3	6
12	1	4	11	2	4	13	1	3	10

Table 7.8 McNemar test comparing attendance across two months (Panel-Study SPSS/PC+ output)

```
————— McNemar Test
    ATTEND1
with ATTEND2
```

		ATTEND2				
		2	1		Cases	12
ATTEND1	1	6	2			
	2	2	2		(Binomial) 2-tailed P	.2891

Cochran Q test for three or more related samples

To compare the distribution of a dichotomous variable across three or more related samples, the Cochran *Q* test is applied. Thus, we would use the following command to compute this test if we wanted to examine attendance at the firm's meeting over the three-month period in the Panel Study:

npar tests cochran=attend1 attend2 attend3.

This command produced the output in Table 7.9. This shows the number of people who did and did not attend the three meetings. Once again, as the probability level is above 0.05, this indicates there is no significant difference in attendance over the three meetings.

Non-categorical variables and non-parametric tests

Kolmogorov-Smirnov test for one sample

This test is used to compare the observed frequencies of the values of an ordinal variable, such as rated quality of work, against some specified theoretical distribution. It determines the statistical significance of the largest difference between them. In SPSS, the theoretical distribution can be **uniform**, **normal**, or **Poisson**. These are the keywords which must be used to specify which one of these three options is to be selected. Thus, for example, if we expected the five degrees of rated quality of work (i.e. very poor, poor, average, good, and very good) in the Job Survey to appear equally often (i.e. as a uniform distribution), we would use the following command:

npar test k-s(uniform,1,5)=qual.

If the minimum (1) and maximum (5) values are not specified (and in that order), then the lowest and the highest values in the sample data will be

Table 7.9 Cochran *Q* test comparing attendance across three months (Panel-Study SPSS/PC+ output)

```
— — — — — Cochran Q Test

Cases

= 1  = 2   Variable
  8    4   ATTEND1
  4    8   ATTEND2
  7    5   ATTEND3
```

Cases	Cochran Q	D.F.	Significance
12	2.6000	2	.2725

used. In other words, if the lowest rating was 2 and the highest 4, then SPSS will compare the distribution of this range of values. If the mean and standard deviation (in that order) are not specified for the normal distribution, then this test will use the sample mean and standard deviation, while if the mean of the Poisson distribution is not given, it will use the sample mean.

The output from this command is displayed in Table 7.10. The largest absolute, positive, and negative differences between the observed and theoretical distributions are printed, together with the Kolmogorov–Smirnov Z statistic and its probability value. The largest absolute difference is simply the largest difference, regardless of its direction. Since p is well below the two-tailed 0.05 level, the difference is significant. This means the number of cases at each of the five levels is not equal.

Kolmogorov–Smirnov test for two unrelated samples

This test is also used to compare the distribution of values in two groups. Thus, for example, the following command is used to see if the distribution of the ratings of quality of work among men is different from that among women:

npar tests k—s=qual by gender(1,2).

The variable to be compared (**qual**) is listed first, followed by the name of the two groups (**gender**) and their codes (**1,2**). This command produced the output in Table 7.11.

Once again, the largest absolute, positive, and negative differences are shown, together with the Z statistic. The number of cases or subjects in each of the two groups being compared is also shown. As the warning partly indicates, when the number of subjects in both groups is not equal and below forty, the chi-square probability tables should be consulted. The degrees of freedom in these circumstances are always 2. The chi-square

Table 7.10 One-sample Kolmogorov–Smirnov test comparing distribution of quality (Job-Survey SPSS/PC+ output)

- - - - - Kolmogorov – Smirnov Goodness of Fit Test

    QUAL   rated quality

Test Distribution – Uniform   Range: 1 To 5
             Cases: 70

	Most Extreme Differences			
Absolute	Positive	Negative	K-S Z	2-tailed P
.20714	.12857	−.20714	1.733	.005

Table 7.11 Two-sample Kolmogorov–Smirnov test comparing distribution of quality in men and women (Job-Survey SPSS/PC+ output)

- - - - - Kolmogorov – Smirnov 2-Sample Test

  QUAL   rated quality
by GENDER   gender

    Cases

      39 GENDER = 1 male
      31 GENDER = 2 female
      --
      70 Total

WARNING – Due to small sample size, probability tables should be consulted.

	Most Extreme Differences			
Absolute	Positive	Negative	K-S Z	2-tailed P
.12572	.01737	−.12572	.522	.948

value for two degrees of freedom confirms that this difference is non-significant. In other words, there is no difference in the distribution of quality-of-work ratings for men and women.

Median test for two or more unrelated samples

The median test is used to determine if the median differs for two or more unrelated samples. If we wanted to determine if the median of rated quality of work was similar for men and women, we would use the following command:

npar tests median=qual by gender(1,2).

This command gave the output in Table 7.12. It has a 2 × 2 table showing the number of cases above the median and less than or equal to it for males

Table 7.12 Median test comparing quality in men and women (Job-Survey SPSS/PC+ output)

- - - - - Median Test

QUAL   rated quality
by GENDER   gender

		GENDER	
		1	2
QUAL	Gt Median	20	12
	Le Median	19	19

Cases	Median	Chi-Square	Significance
70	3.0	.6518	.4195

and females. Since males are coded 1, we can see that there are twenty men above the median and nineteen below or equal to it. Also given is the median value, which is 3, and the chi-square statistic and its significance. Because *p* is greater than 0.05 and therefore not significant, the median rating of work quality does not differ for men and women.

To compare the median rating for the four ethnic groups, we would give the following command:

npar tests median=qual by ethnicgp(1,4).

If we are only comparing two groups, the order in which we list their two codes does not matter. However, if we are comparing more than two groups, we have to place the smallest value first, followed by the largest one as in the command above. If we had reversed this order, then a two-sample median test would have been conducted in which white workers (coded 1) would have been compared with those of African ethnic origin (coded 4).

Mann–Whitney U *test for two unrelated samples*

The Mann–Whitney test is more powerful than the median test because it compares the number of times a score from one of the samples is ranked higher than a score from the other sample rather than the number of scores which are above the median. If the two groups are similar, then the number of times this happens should also be similar for the two groups. The command for comparing the rated quality of work for men and women is:

npar tests m-w=qual by gender(1,2).

The SPSS/PC+ output produced by this command is shown in Table

Table 7.13 Mann-Whitney test comparing quality in men and women (Job-Survey SPSS/PC+ output)

- - - - - Mann-Whitney U – Wilcoxon Rank Sum W Test

QUAL   rated quality
by GENDER   gender

Mean Rank	Cases		
36.94	39	GENDER = 1	male
33.69	31	GENDER = 2	female
	--		
	70	Total	

			Corrected for Ties	
U	W	Z		2-tailed P
548.5	1044.5	−.6801		.4964

7.13. It gives the mean rank of the ratings for men and women, the number of cases on which these are based, the Mann–Whitney U statistic (with its significance level in SPSS-X), and the Wilcoxon W (which is the sum of the ranks of the smaller group and which we can ignore). Since it is necessary to correct for the number of scores which receive or tie for the same rank, it does this by giving the Z statistic and its significance level. Although the significance of U is not shown here, correcting for ties increases the value of Z slightly. As the Z statistic is still not significant (i.e. p is greater than 0.05), there is no difference between men and women in the mean ranking of the rated quality of their work.

Kruskal–Wallis H *test for three or more unrelated samples*

The Kruskal–Wallis H test is similar to the Mann–Whitney U test in that the cases in the different samples are ranked together in one series. However, unlike the Mann–Whitney U test, it can be used to compare scores in more than two groups. To compare the rated quality of work for people in the four ethnic groups, we use the following command:

npar tests k-w=qual by ethnicgp(1,4).

This command displayed the output in Table 7.14. It shows the mean rank for each group, the number of cases in them, and the chi-square statistic and its significance level, both uncorrected and corrected for rank ties. Since the significance level is greater than 0.05 on both tests, this indicates that there is no difference between workers of the four ethnic groups in the mean ranking of the rated quality of their work.

Table 7.14 Kruskal–Wallis test comparing quality between ethnic groups (Job-Survey SPSS/PC+ output)

- - - - - Kruskal-Wallis 1-way ANOVA

QUAL   rated quality
by ETHNICGP ethnic group

Mean Rank	Cases		
34.99	36	ETHNICGP − 1	white
33.47	18	ETHNICGP = 2	asian
37.71	14	ETHNICGP = 3	west indian
47.50	2	ETHNICGP = 4	african
	--		
	70	Total	

			Corrected for Ties	
CASES	Chi-Square	Significance	Chi-Square	Significance
70	1.0628	.7861	1.1213	.7719

Sign test for two related samples

The sign test compares the number of positive and negative differences between two scores from the same or similar (i.e. matched) samples such as those in the Panel Study, and ignores the size of these differences. If the two samples are similar, then these differences should be normally distributed. Thus, for example, we could compare the rated quality of work at two of the times (say, **qual1** and **qual2**) in the Panel Study. If the number of positive differences (i.e. decreases in ratings) was similar to the number of negative ones (i.e. increases in ratings), this would mean that there was no change in one particular direction between the two occasions. To compute this comparison, we use the following command:

npar tests sign=qual1 with qual2.

The output in Table 7.15 was given by this command. It shows the number of negative, positive, and zero (ties) differences. There are three ties, five positive differences, and four negative ones. Since fewer than twenty-six differences were found, it gives the binomial significance level. If more than twenty-five differences had been obtained, it would have given the significance level for the Z statistic. With almost equal numbers of positive and negative differences, it is not surprising that the test is non-significant. In other words, there is no change in rated quality of work over the two months.

Table 7.15 Sign test comparing quality across two months (Panel-Study SPSS/PC+ output)

----- Sign Test			
QUAL1 with QUAL2			
Cases			
4	− Diffs (QUAL2 Lt QUAL1)		
5	+ Diffs (QUAL2 Gt QUAL1)	(Binomial)	
3	Ties	2-tailed P =	1.000
--			
12	Total		

Wilcoxon matched-pairs signed-ranks test for two related samples

This test, like the Mann–Whitney, takes account of the size of the differences between two sets of related scores by ranking and then summing those with the same sign. If there are no differences between the two samples, then the number of positive signs should be similar to that of the negative ones. This test would be used, for example, to determine if the rated quality of work in the Panel Study was the same in the first and second month (**qual1** and **qual2**). To do this we would use the following command:

npar tests wilcoxon=qual1 with qual2.

Table 7.16 contains the output for this command. It displays the mean rank for the negative and positive ranks, the number of cases on which these are based together with the number of tied ranks, and the test statistic *Z* and its significance level. We obtain the same result with this test. The mean rank of rated quality of work does not differ between the two months.

Friedman test for three or more related samples

If we wanted to compare the scores of three or more related samples, such as the rated quality of work across all three months rather than just two of them, we would use the Friedman two-way analysis-of-variance test. It ranks the scores for each of the cases and then calculates the mean score for each sample. If there are no differences between the samples, their mean ranks should be similar. We would use the following command to compare the quality of work over the three months in the Panel Study:

npar tests friedman=qual1 qual2 qual3.

The output produced by this command is shown in Table 7.17. It contains

Table 7.16 Wilcoxon matched-pairs signed-ranks test comparing quality across two months (Panel-Study SPSS/PC+ output)

- - - - - Wilcoxon Matched-pairs Signed-ranks Test

QUAL1
with QUAL2

Mean Rank	Cases	
5.63	4	− Ranks (QUAL2 Lt QUAL1)
4.50	5	+ Ranks (QUAL2 Gt QUAL1)
	3	Ties (QUAL2 Eq QUAL1)
	--	
	12	Total
Z =	.0000	2-tailed P = 1.0000

Table 7.17 Friedman test comparing quality across three months (Panel-Study SPSS/PC+ output)

- - - - - Friedman Two-way ANOVA

Mean Rank	Variable
2.04	QUAL1
2.13	QUAL2
1.83	QUAL3

Cases	Chi-Square	D.F.	Significance
12	.5417	2	.7627

the mean rank for the three samples, the number of cases in them, the chi-square statistic, its degrees of freedom (which is the number of samples minus 1), and its significance level. The non-significant chi-square means that there is no difference in the mean ranks of rated quality of work across the three months.

Non-categorical variables and parametric tests

t *test for one sample*

This test is used to determine if the mean of a sample is similar to that of the population. If, for example, we were to know what the mean score for job satisfaction was for workers in the industry covered in the Job Survey and we wanted to find out if the mean of our sample was similar to it, we would carry out a *t* test. Although SPSS does not have a command for conducting such a test, it provides the necessary information for working it out. The test itself is easily calculated. The *t* statistic is obtained by subtracting the mean of the population from that of the sample, and dividing the difference by the standard error of the sample's mean:

$$t = \frac{\text{sample mean} - \text{population mean}}{\text{standard error of the sample mean}}$$

To produce these statistics for job satisfaction, we would implement the following command:

descriptives satis
 /statistics 1 2.

In SPSS-X, the **1** and **2** on the **statistic** subcommand can be replaced with the keywords **mean** and **semean** respectively. The sample mean is found to be about 10.84 and the standard error 0.40. If the population mean is 10, then *t* is −2.1 (−0.84/0.40). To determine if this value is significant, we need to look it up (against the appropriate degrees of freedom) in a table of *t* values, which can be found in most statistics textbooks. The degrees of freedom are the number of subjects in the sample minus 1. In the present example, the number of degrees of freedom is 67 since the scores for two of the subjects are missing. In most tables, the nearest relevant *t* value is for 60 degrees of freedom. This value for a two-tailed test of significance at the 0.05 level is 2.00. The direction of the *t* value is ignored when determining its significance. Since the value in our example is greater than 2.00, this indicates that our mean is significantly different from that of the population.

Standard error of the mean

It is important to outline more fully what the *standard error of the mean* is, since this important idea also constitutes the basis of other parametric tests such as the analysis of variance. One of the assumptions of many parametric tests is that the population of the variable to be analysed should be normally distributed. The errors of most distributions are known to take this form. Thus, for example, if a large group of people were asked to guess today's temperature, the distribution of their guesses would approximate that of a normal distribution, even if the temperature did not itself represent a normal distribution. In addition, it has been observed that the distribution of certain characteristics also takes this form. If, for example, you plot the distribution of the heights of a large group of adult human beings, it will be similar to that of a normal distribution.

   If we draw samples from a population of values which is normally distributed, then the means of those samples will also be normally distributed. In other words, most of the means will be very similar to that of the population, although some of them will vary quite considerably. The standard error of the mean represents the standard deviation of the sample means. The one-sample *t* test compares the mean of a sample with that of the population in terms of how likely that difference has arisen by chance. The smaller this difference is, the more likely it is to have resulted from chance.

t *test for two unrelated means*

This test is used to determine if the means of two unrelated samples differ. It does this by comparing the difference between the two means with the standard error of the difference in the means of different samples:

$$t = \frac{\text{sample one mean} - \text{sample two mean}}{\text{standard error of the difference in means}}$$

The *standard error of the difference in means,* like the standard error of the mean, is also normally distributed. If we draw a large number of samples from a population whose values are normally distributed and plot the differences in the means of each of these samples, the shape of this distribution will be normal. Since the means of most of the samples will be close to the mean of the population and therefore similar to one another, if we subtract them from each other the differences between them will be close to zero. In other words, the nearer the difference in the means of two samples is to zero, the more likely it is that this difference is due to chance.

To compare the means of two samples, such as the mean job satisfaction of male and female workers in the Job Survey, we would use the following command:

t-test groups=gender(1,2)/variables=satis.

The two groups or samples to be compared are listed first (i.e. **gender**), followed by the variable which is to be compared (i.e. **satis**). There are three ways of defining the two groups. First, we can define them in terms of their two codes (**1** and **2**) as has been done above. Second, if the grouping variable only has two codes, as in this case, there is no need to specify them since they can only take on one of two values. Third, one of the values can be used as a cut-off point, at or above which all the values constitute one group while those below form the other group. In this instance, the cut-off point is 2, which would be placed in parentheses after gender:

t-test groups=gender(2)/variables=satis.

The output for the previous command is displayed in Table 7.18. The number of cases in the two groups, together with their means, standard deviations, and standard errors, is listed. Since we do not know what the standard error of the difference in means is of the population in question,

Table 7.18 Unrelated *t* test comparing job satisfaction in men and women (Job-Survey SPSS/PC+ output)

Independent samples of   GENDER   gender

Group 1:   GENDER   GE   2   Group 2:   GENDER   LT   2

t-test for: SATIS   job satisfaction

	Number of Cases	Mean	Standard Deviation	Standard Error
Group 1	31	10.7097	3.329	.598
Group 2	37	10.9459	3.325	.547

		Pooled Variance Estimate			Separate Variance Estimate		
F Value	2-Tail Prob.	t Value	Degrees of Freedom	2-Tail Prob.	t Value	Degrees of Freedom	2-tail Prob.
1.00	.986	−.29	66	.771	−.29	63.90	.771

we have to estimate it. How this is done depends on whether the difference in the variances of the two samples is statistically significant. This information is provided by the *F* test (see p. 137). If the *F* test is significant (i.e. has a probability of 0.05 or less), then the variances are different and so the *separate* variance estimate is used to calculate the *t* value. If the variances are not different, the *pooled* variance estimate is employed for this purpose. In Table 7.18, the variances are not statistically different since the *p* value of the *F* test is 0.986. Consequently, we look at the *t* value based on the pooled variance estimate. This is non-significant with a two-tailed *p* value of 0.771. In other words, we would conclude that there is no significant difference in mean job satisfaction between males and females. The two-tailed test of significance is provided by default. To calculate the one-tailed level of significance, divide the two-tailed one by 2 which in this case would still be non-significant at 0.386 (0.771/2).

It should be pointed out that the variance, the standard deviation, and the standard error of a sample are related. The *variance* or mean squared deviation is calculated by subtracting the mean of the sample from each of its scores (to provide a measure of their deviation from the mean), squaring them, adding them together, and dividing them by one less than the number of cases. Since the deviations would sum to zero, they are squared to make the negative deviations positive. The *standard deviation* is simply the square root of the variance. The advantage of the standard deviation over the variance is that it is expressed in the original values of the data. Thus, for example, the standard deviation of job satisfaction is described in terms of the twenty points on this scale. The *standard error* (of the mean) is the standard deviation divided by the square root of the number of cases.

The relationships between these three measures can be checked out on the statistics shown in Table 7.18.

F *test for two unrelated variances*

To determine if the variances of scores on some variable in two unrelated samples are similar, such as the variance in job satisfaction in male and female workers, we calculate an F test in which the larger variance is divided by the smaller one. As we have seen in the description of the t test above, this statistic is provided by the **t-test** command.

Unrelated t *test and ordinal data*

Some people have argued that parametric tests should only be used on interval/ratio data (for example, Stevens 1946). Others, as we have mentioned earlier, have reasoned that such a restriction is unnecessary. In view of this controversy, it may be interesting to see whether the use of an unrelated t test on an ordinal variable such as rated quality of work gives very dissimilar results to that of the Mann–Whitney previously used. According to Siegel (1956), the Mann–Whitney test is about 95 per cent as powerful as the t test. What this means is that the t test requires 5 per cent fewer subjects than the Mann–Whitney test to reject the null hypothesis when it is false. The following command was used to generate the output in Table 7.19:

npar tests m-w=qual by gender(1,2).

As can be seen, this test also indicates that there is no significant difference between men and women in the mean rank of their job satisfaction.

Oneway analysis of variance for three or more unrelated means

To compare the means of three or more unrelated samples, such as the mean job satisfaction of the four ethnic groups in the Job Survey, it is necessary to compute a one-way analysis of variance. This is essentially an F test in which an estimate of the *between-groups* variance (or *mean-square* as the estimate of the variance is referred to in analysis of variance) is compared with an estimate of the *within-groups* variance by dividing the former with the latter:

$$F = \frac{\text{between-groups estimated variance or mean-square}}{\text{within-groups estimated variance or mean-square}}$$

The total amount of variance in the dependent variable (i.e. job satisfaction) can be thought of as comprising two elements: that which is due to the independent variable (i.e. ethnic group) and that which is due to other

Table 7.19 Mann–Whitney test comparing job satisfaction in men and women (Job-Survey SPSS/PC+ output)

----- Mann-Whitney U – Wilcoxon Rank Sum W Test

| SATIS | job satisfaction |
| by GENDER | gender |

Mean Rank	Cases	
34.89	37	GENDER = 1 male
34.03	31	GENDER = 2 female
	--	
	68	Total

		Corrected for Ties	
U	W	Z	2-tailed P
559.0	1055.0	−.1794	.8576

factors. This latter component is often referred to as *error* or *residual* variance. The variance that is due to the independent variable is frequently described as *explained* variance. If the between-groups (i.e. explained) estimated variance is considerably larger than that within-groups (i.e. error or residual), then the value of the F ratio will be higher, which implies that the differences between the means are unlikely to be due to chance.

The within-groups variance or *sum-of-squares* is the sum of the variances of the groups. Its mean-square or estimated variance is its sum-of-squares divided by its degrees of freedom. These degrees of freedom are the sum of the number of cases minus one in each group (i.e. [the number of cases in group one − 1] + [the number of cases in group two − 1] and so on). The between-groups variance or sum-of-squares, on the other hand, is obtained by subtracting each group's mean from the overall (total or grand) mean, squaring them, multiplying them by the number of cases in each group, and summing the result. It can also be calculated by sub-tracting the within-groups variance from the total variance since the total variance is the sum of the between- and within-groups variance:

$$\begin{matrix} \text{total} \\ \text{variance} \end{matrix} = \begin{pmatrix} \text{between-groups} \\ \text{(i.e. explained)} \\ \text{variance} \end{pmatrix} + \begin{pmatrix} \text{within-groups} \\ \text{(i.e. error)} \\ \text{variance} \end{pmatrix}$$

The between-groups mean-square or estimated variance is its sum-of-squares divided by its degrees of freedom. These degrees of freedom are the number of groups minus 1. The degrees of freedom from the total variance are also the sum of those for the within- and between-groups variance or the total number of subjects minus 1. Although this test may sound complicated, the essential reasoning behind it is that if the groups or samples come from the same population, then the between-groups estimate of the population's variance should be similar to the within-groups variance.

To compare the mean job satisfaction of the four ethnic groups in the Job Survey, we would use the following command:

oneway satis by ethnicgp(1,4).

The variable to be compared is listed first **(satis)** followed by the grouping variable **(ethnicgp)** and the minimum and maximum codes which define the range of the groups to be analysed in parentheses **(1** and **4)**. The output for this command is displayed in Table 7.20. The F ratio, which is the between-group mean-square divided by the within-group one (2.9122/ 11.2888=0.258), is non-significant. Consequently, there is no significant difference in job satisfaction between the four ethnic groups.

The number of cases in each group, their means, standard deviations, and the other statistics shown in Table 7.21 are produced by adding the following command immediately after the **oneway** command:

/statistic 1.

In SPSS-X, the **1** can be replaced with **descriptives** to give the same statistics.

The F test or ratio only tells us whether there is a significant difference between one or more of the groups. It does not inform us where this difference lies. To determine this, we need to carry out further statistical tests. Which tests we use depends on whether or not we predicted where the differences would be. If, for example, we *predicted* that whites would

Table 7.20 A oneway analysis-of-variance table (Job-Survey SPSS/PC+ output)

----------ONEWAY----------

Variable	SATIS	job satisfaction			
By Variable	ETHNICGP	ethnic group			

Analysis of Variance

Source	D.F.	Sum of Squares	Mean Squares	F Ratio	F Prob.
Between Groups	3	8.7366	2.9122	.2580	.8554
Within Groups	64	722.4840	11.2888		
Total	67	731.2206			

Table 7.21 Descriptive group statistics with oneway analysis of variance comparing job satisfaction across ethnic groups (Job-Survey SPSS/PC+ output)

----------O N E W A Y----------

Group	Count	Mean	Standard Deviation	Standard Error	95 Pct Conf Int for Mean	
Grp 1	35	10.5429	3.2840	.5551	9.4148 To	11.6710
Grp 2	17	10.9412	3.5964	.8722	9.0921 To	12.7903
Grp 3	14	11.2857	3.2917	.8797	9.3852 To	13.1863
Grp 4	2	12.0000	2.8284	2.0000	−13.4124 To	37.4124
Total	68	10.8382	3.3036	.4006	10.0386 To	11.6379

Group	Minimum	Maximum
Grp 1	5.0000	19.0000
Grp 2	6.0000	16.0000
Grp 3	6.0000	15.0000
Grp 4	10.0000	14.0000
Total	5.0000	19.0000

be less satisfied than Asians and the F test had been significant, then we would carry out an unrelated t test as described above using a one-tailed level of significance. We could also do this by using the **contrast** subcommand in which we specify the groups to be compared. If, for instance, we wanted to find out if Asians were more satisfied than whites, we would use the following form of commands:

oneway satis by ethnicgp(1,4)
  /contrast=-1 1 0 0.

Although the **contrast** subcommand is more flexible than this, we can specify any two groups on a single subcommand by defining one of them (i.e. whites) as minus 1, the other one (i.e. Asians) as (plus) 1, and the remaining ones (i.e. West Indian and African) as zeroes, as above.

The output for this subcommand is shown in Table 7.22. This gives the value for the contrast, its standard error, and both the pooled and separate variance estimates. However, to determine which of these to use, we need to know whether the variances of the two groups differ. To do this, we obtain the standard deviations as reported in Table 7.21, convert them to variances by squaring them, divide the larger variance by the smaller one ($F=12.934/10.785=1.20$) and look up the result in a table of critical values for F. As this information is provided by the **t-test** command, it may be simpler to use this. Because the value of the F test is non-significant, we use the pooled variance estimate. The difference in job satisfaction between whites and those of Asian ethnic origin is non-significant.

Table 7.22 Statistic provided by a oneway contrast comparing job satisfaction in groups 1 and 2 (Job-Survey SPSS/PC+ output)

```
----------ONEWAY----------
```

Variable   SATIS   job satisfaction
By Variable ETHNICGP   ethnic group

Contrast Coefficient Matrix

	Grp 1	Grp 3		
		Grp 2	Grp 4	
Contrast 1	−1.0	1.0	.0	.0

	Value	S. Error	Pooled Variance Estimate T Value	D.F.	T Prob.
Contrast 1	.3983	.9933	.401	64.0	.690

	Value	S. Error	Separate Variance Estimate T Value	D.F.	T Prob.
Contrast 1	.3983	1.0339	.385	29.3	.703

If, however, we had not expected any differences but found that the *F* test was significant, then we would need to take into account the fact that if we carried out a large number of comparisons some of these would be significant just by chance. Indeed, at the 5 per cent level of significance, 5 per cent or one in twenty comparisons could be expected to be significant by definition. A number of tests which take account of this fact have been developed and are available on the SPSS **oneway** command. Because these tests are carried out after the data have been initially analysed, they are referred to as *post hoc* or *a posteriori* tests. One of these, the Scheffé test, will be briefly outlined. This test is the most conservative in the sense that it is least likely to find significant differences between groups – or, in other words, to make a Type I error. It is also exact for unequal numbers of subjects in the groups. To conduct a Scheffé test to compare job satisfaction between every possible pair of types of ethnic group, the following two commands would be given:

oneway satis by ethnicgp(1,4)
 /ranges=scheffe.

The output for the **ranges** subcommand is shown in Table 7.23. This shows that there were no significant differences between any of the groups, taken two at a time. If there had been some significant differences, then the means of all the groups would have been listed in ascending order together

Table 7.23 Statistics provided by a oneway Scheffé test comparing satisfaction across the ethnic groups (Job-Survey SPSS/PC+ output)

----------O N E W A Y----------

Variable	SATIS	job satisfaction
By Variable	ETHNICGP	ethnic group

Multiple Range Test

Scheffe Procedure
Ranges for the .050 level —
       4.06   4.06   4.06

The ranges above are table ranges.
The value actually compared with Mean (J)—Mean (I) is . . .
          2.3758 * Range * Sqrt(1/N(I) + 1/N(J))

No two groups are significantly different at the .050 level

---

with a matrix in which asterisks are used to indicate group means which differ significantly from one another.

F *tests for three or more unrelated variances*

If we were interested in determining whether the variances, rather than the means, of three or more unrelated samples were different, we would also use an *F* test. One reason for doing this is to find out if it is appropriate to use analysis of variance to test for mean differences in the first place since this statistic is based on the assumption that the variances of the groups do not differ too widely. In fact, if the number of subjects in each group and their variances are unequal, then it is necessary to use a non-parametric test. The **oneway** command provides three tests for homogeneity of variance. To find out if the variances of job satisfaction differ in the four ethnic groups, we would send the following commands:

oneway satis by ethnicgp(1,4)
 /statistic 3.

In SPSS-X, the **3** can be replaced with **homogeneity** to give the same statistics. This produces the output in Table 7.24.

The first test is Cochran's *C*, which compares the largest variance with the sum of all the variances:

$$C = \frac{\text{largest or maximum variance}}{\text{sum of all the variances}}$$

This test should only be used if the number of subjects in each group is equal or nearly equal. Since the numbers are not equal, only an approximate

Table 7.24 Homogeneity of variance tests given by oneway (Job-Survey SPSS/PC+ output)

Tests for Homogeneity of Variances

Cochrans C = Max. Variance/Sum(Variances) =	.3039, P = .921 (Approx.)	
Bartlett-Box F =	.074 , P = .974	
Maximum Variance/Minimum Variance	1.617	

significance level is shown. The second test is the Bartlett–Box F test, which is the most widely used. It is also the most complex and consequently will not be described. It is the most appropriate test to use when the number of subjects in each group is not equal, provided that no group has fewer than three and most have more than five. Since one of the groups contains only two subjects, this test should be rerun omitting this group since it is too small to provide an estimate of job satisfaction for this category of workers. The third test is Hartley's F_{max} which compares the largest variance with the smallest one:

$$F_{max} = \frac{\text{largest or maximum variance}}{\text{smallest or minimum variance}}$$

This test should only be used if the number of subjects in each group is equal. Because this is not the case, the significance level is not given.

t test for two related means

To compare the means of the same subjects in two conditions or at two points in time, we would use a related t test. We would also use this test to compare subjects who had been matched to be similar in certain respects. The advantage of using the same subjects or matched subjects is that the amount of error deriving from differences between subjects is reduced. The unrelated t test compares the mean difference between pairs of scores within the sample with that of the population in terms of the standard error of the difference in means:

$$t = \frac{\text{sample mean differences} - \text{population mean differences}}{\text{standard error of the difference in means}}$$

Since the population mean difference is zero, the closer the sample mean difference is to zero, the less likely it is that the two sets of scores differ significantly from one another.

The difference between a related and an unrelated t test lies essentially in the fact that two scores from the same person are likely to vary less than two scores from two different people. If, for example, we weigh the same

143

Figure 7.1 A comparison of the distribution of the standard error of the differences in means for related and unrelated samples

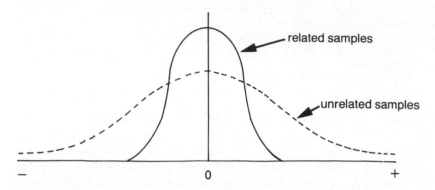

person on two occasions, the difference between those two weights is likely to be less than the weights of two separate individuals. This fact is reflected in the different way in which the standard error of the difference in means is calculated for the two tests, which we do not have time to go into here. The variability of the standard error for the related *t* test is less than that for the unrelated one, as illustrated in Figure 7.1.

In fact, the variability of the standard error of the difference in means for the related *t* test will depend on the extent to which the pairs of scores are similar or related. The more similar they are, the less the variability will be of their estimated standard error.

To compare two related sets of scores such as job satisfaction in the first two months (**satis1** and **satis2**) in the Panel Study, we would use the following command:

t-test pairs=satis1 satis2.

This command produces the output in Table 7.25. The mean, standard deviation, and standard error are given for the two sets of scores as well as for the difference between them. In addition, the extent to which pairs of scores are similar or correlated (see Chapter 8 for an exposition of correlation) is also shown. As can be seen, the correlation between the two sets of scores is significant ($p=0.029$) but the differences between their means are not significant ($p=0.742$). In other words, mean job satisfaction does not differ between the first and second month.

t test for two related variances

If we want to determine whether the variances of two related samples are significantly different from one another, we have to calculate it using the following formula (Bruning and Kintz 1977) since it is not available on SPSS:

Table 7.25 Related *t* test comparing satisfaction across months
(Panel-Study SPSS/PC+ output)

Paired samples t-test: SATIS1
SATIS2

Variable	Number of Cases	Mean	Standard Deviation	Standard Error			
SATIS1	12	11.5000	3.425	.989			
SATIS2	12	11.1667	4.282	1.236			

(Difference) Mean	Standard Deviation	Standard Error	2-Tail Corr. Prob.		t Value	Degrees of Freedom	2-Tail Prob.
.3333	3.420	.987	.626	.029	.34	11	.742

$$t = \frac{(\text{larger variance} - \text{smaller variance}) \times \sqrt{(\text{number of cases} - 2)}}{\sqrt{(1 - \text{correlation of 2 sets of scores}) \times [4 \times (\text{larger} \times \text{smaller variance})]}}$$

To apply this formula to the job satisfaction variances in the above example, we would first have to calculate their variances, which are the squares of their standard deviations (i.e. 18.34 and 11.73). Substituting the appropriate values in the above equation, we arrive at a *t* value of 0.18, which with ten degrees of freedom is not significant with a two-tailed test. To have been significant at this level, we would have needed a *t* value of 2.228 or greater.

Multivariate analysis of variance for three or more related means

The following section deals with a cluster of procedures that are highly complex and which relate to an application that many readers are unlikely to encounter in the normal course of events. Consequently, this section may either be omitted or returned to after having read Chapter 9.

To compare three or more means from the same or matched subjects, such as job satisfaction during three consecutive months, we would need to carry out a multivariate analysis of variance (MANOVA) test which has one within-subjects or *repeated-measures* variable. This variable, job satis-faction, is called a *factor* and has three *levels* since it is repeated three times. This design is referred to variously as a single-group (or factor) repeated-measures and treatments-by-subjects design. To conduct it on the present example, we would use the following commands:

```
manova satis1 satis2 satis3
 /wsfactor=month(3)
 /print=cellinfo(means) transform signif(univ averf).
```

145

Table 7.26 Repeated-measures means and standard deviations for job satisfaction (Panel-Study SPSS/PC+ output)

ANALYSIS OF VARIANCE -- DESIGN 1

Cell Means and Standard Deviations
Variable . . SATIS1

	Mean	Std. Dev.	N
For entire sample	11.500	3.425	12

Variable . . SATIS2

	Mean	Std. Dev.	N
For entire sample	11.167	4.282	12

Variable..SATIS3

	Mean	Std. Dev.	N
For entire sample	10.750	3.223	12

The three variables (**satis1**, **satis2**, and **satis3**) are listed after the **manova** command. The **wsfactor** names the within-subject (ws) factor, which has been called **month**, and specifies the number of levels it has, which is three. The **print** subcommand requests the following statistical information: **cellinfo(means)** prints the means and standard deviations of the three scores or cells of the design; **transform** produces the matrix of the transformed variables; and **signif(univ averf)** provides the separate and the averaged univariate tests.

The output giving the means and standard deviations of job satisfaction at the three times is displayed in Table 7.26, and the multivariate tests are presented in Table 7.27. Four multivariate tests are provided to assess the significance of the repeated-measures effect. These are Pillai's criterion,

Table 7.27 Repeated-measures multivariate tests (Panel-Study SPSS/PC+ output)

EFFECT . . MONTH
Multivariate Tests of Significance (S = 1, M = 0, N = 4)

Test Name	Value	Approx. F	Hypoth. DF	Error DF	Sig. of F
Pillais	.07478	.40415	2.00	10.00	.678
Hotellings	.08083	.40415	2.00	10.00	.678
Wilks	.92522	.40415	2.00	10.00	.678
Roys	.07478				

Table 7.28 Repeated-measures univariate tests of significance for transformed variables (Panel-Study SPSS/PC+ output)

EFFECT .. MONTH (CONT.)
Univariate F-tests with (1, 11) D.F.

Variable	Hypoth. SS	Error SS	Hypoth. MS	Error MS	F	Sig. of F
T2	3.37500	42.12500	3.37500	3.82955	.88131	.368
T3	.01389	81.15278	.01389	7.37753	.00188	.966

Hotelling's trace criterion, Wilks's Lambda, and Roy's *gcr* criterion. In many cases, all four tests give the same results (Stevens 1979). Provided that the number of subjects in each group is equal or almost equal, it does not matter which test is used. Where this is not the case, Pillai's criterion may be the most appropriate. The univariate tests are for the two transformed variables, T2 and T3, shown in Table 7.28.

It is important to note that T2 and T3 do not refer to the original variables having those names, but to the two transformed variables. When comparing three related scores, it is only necessary to test the statistical significance of the differences between two of them (for example, **satis1−satis2** and **satis2−satis3**) since the remaining difference (i.e. **satis1−satis3**) can be worked out if the other two differences are known (**[satis1−satis3]** = **[satis1−satis2]** + **[satis2−satis3]**). The number of unrelated comparisons is always one less than the number of variables being compared. Unless requested otherwise, SPSS automatically transforms the variables in a repeated-measures design so that the comparisons are statistically independent. The nature of these transformations can be determined by examining the transformation matrix. However, this is normally done only when the univariate tests are significant, which is not the case here. The values for both the multivariate and univariate tests are

Table 7.29 Repeated-measures averaged test of significance (Panel-Study SPSS/PC+ output)

** ANALYSIS OF VARIANCE - - DESIGN 1 **

Tests involving 'MONTH' Within-Subject Effect.

AVERAGED Tests of Signficance for SATIS using UNIQUE sums of squares

Source of Variation	SS	DF	MS	F	Sig. of F
WITHIN CELLS	123.28	22	5.60		
MONTH	3.39	2	1.69	.30	.742

not significant. In other words, there is no difference between job satisfaction over the three months.

The result of the averaged univariate test is presented in Table 7.29, which is also not significant.

As was the case for the one-way analysis of variance test, the F test only tells us whether there is a significant difference between the three related scores but does not inform us where this difference lies. If a significant overall difference had been found, we would need to carry out some supplementary analyses. If we had predicted a difference between two scores, then we could have determined if this prediction was confirmed by conducting a related t test as described above. If we had found but had not predicted a difference, then we would need to use a *post hoc* test, of which there are a number (Maxwell 1980). Since these are not available on SPSS, they have to be calculated separately. If the scores are significantly correlated, the Bonferroni inequality test is recommended, whereas if they are not, the Tukey test is advocated.

The Bonferroni test is based on the related t test but modifies the significance level to take account of the fact that more than one comparison is being made. To calculate this, work out the total number of possible comparisons between any two groups, divide the chosen significance level (which is usually 0.05) by this number, and treat the result as the appropriate significance level for comparing more than three groups. In the case of three groups, the total number of possible comparisons is three which means that the appropriate significance level is 0.017 (0.05/3).

The calculation for the Tukey test is more complicated (Stevens 1986). The difference between any two means is compared against the value calculated by multiplying the square root of the repeated-measures within-cells mean-square error term (divided by the number of cases) with the studentized range statistic, a table of which can be found in Stevens (1986). If the difference between any two means is greater than this value, then this difference is a significant one. The within-cells mean-square error term is presented in the output in Table 7.29 and is about 5.6. The square root of this divided by the number of cases is 0.68 ($\sqrt{5.6/12}$). The appropriate studentized range value with three groups and 22 degrees of freedom for the error term is 3.58. This multiplied by 0.68 gives 2.43. If any two means differed by more than this, they would be significant at the 0.05 level.

Exercises

1. Suppose you wanted to find out whether there had been a significant change in the number of books sold by a particular shop in the three months of October, November, and December. What test would you use to determine if there had been a significant change?

2. What would the null hypothesis be?

3. If the SPSS names were **booksold** for the number of books sold and **months** for the three months, what would be the command for running this test?

4. Would you use a one- or a two-tailed level of significance?

5. If the probability level of the result of this test were 0.25, what would you conclude about the number of books sold?

6. Would a finding with a probability level of 0.0001 mean that there was a greater change in the number of books sold than one with a probability level of 0.037?

7. If this test were significant, how would you determine if there had been a significant change between any two months, say October and November?

8. If October was coded as 1 and November as 2, what command would you use to run this test?

9. Would you use a one- or a two-tailed level of significance to test the expectation that more books were sold in November than in December?

10. How would you determine a one-tailed level of significance from a two-tailed one of, say, 0.084?

11. If you wanted to find out if more men than women reported having fallen in love at first sight, would it be appropriate to test for this difference using a binomial test in which the number of men and women saying that they had had this experience was compared?

12. What SPSS command would you use to run the appropriate test if the variable name for men and women was **gender** and that for having or never having fallen in love at first sight was **love**?

13. What test would you use to determine if women reported having a greater number of close friends than men?

14. When would you use the pooled rather than the separate variance estimates in interpreting the results of a t-test?

15. What test would you use if you wanted to find out if the average number of books sold by the same ten shops had changed significantly in the three months of October, November, and December?

Chapter eight

Bivariate analysis: exploring relationships

This chapter focuses on relationships between pairs of variables. Having examined the distribution of values for particular variables through the use of frequency tables, histograms, and associated statistics as discussed in Chapter 5, a major strand in the analysis of a set of data is likely to be bivariate analysis – how two variables are related to each other. The analyst is unlikely to be satisfied with the examination of single variables alone, but will probably be concerned to demonstrate whether variables are related. The investigation of relationships is an important step in explanation and consequently contributes to the building of theories about the nature of the phenomena in which we are interested. The emphasis on relationships can be contrasted with the material covered in the previous chapter, in which the ways in which cases or subjects may differ in respect to a variable were described. The topics covered in the present chapter bear some resemblance to those examined in Chapter 7, since the researcher in both contexts is interested in exploring variance and its connections with other variables. Moreover if we find that members of different ethnic groups differ in regard to a variable, such as income, this may be taken to indicate that there is a relationship between ethnic group and income. Thus, as will be seen, there is no hard-and-fast distinction between the exploration of differences and of relationships.

What does it mean to say that two variables are related? We say that there is a relationship between two variables when the distribution of values for one variable is associated with the distribution exhibited by another variable. In other words, the variation exhibited by one variable is patterned in such a way that its variance is not randomly distributed in relation to the other variable. Examples of relationships that are frequently encountered are: middle-class individuals are more likely to vote Conservative than members of the working class; infant mortality is higher among countries with a low per-capita income than those with a high per-capita income; work alienation is greater in routine, repetitive work than in varied work. In each case, a relationship between two variables is indicated: between social class and voting behaviour; between the infant mortality rate and one measure of a nation's prosperity (per-capita income); and between work alienation and job characteristics. Each of these examples implies that the variation in one variable is patterned, rather than randomly distributed, in relation to the other variable. Thus, in saying that there is a relationship between social class and voting behaviour in the above example, we are saying that people's tendency to vote Conservative is not randomly distributed across categories of social class. Middle-class individuals are more likely to vote for this party; if there were *no* relationship we would not be able to detect such a tendency since there would be no evidence that the middle and working classes differed in their propensity to vote Conservative.

Cross-tabulation

In order to put some more flesh on these ideas the idea of *cross-tabulation* will be introduced in conjunction with an example. Cross-tabulation is one of the simplest and most frequently used ways of demonstrating the presence or absence of a relationship. To illustrate its use, consider the hypothetical data on thirty individuals that are presented in Table 8.1. We have data on two variables: whether each person exhibits job satisfaction and whether they have been absent from work in the past six months. For ease of presentation, each variable can assume either of two values – yes or no. In order to examine the relationship between the two variables, individuals will be allocated to one of the four possible combinations that the two variables in conjunction can assume. Table 8.2 presents these four possible combinations, along with the frequency of their occurrence (as indicated from the data in Table 8.1). This procedure is very similar to that associated with frequency tables for one or more variables. We are trying to summarize and reduce the amount of information with which we are confronted to make it readable and analysable. Detecting a pattern in the relationship between two variables as in Table 8.1 is fairly easy when there are only thirty subjects and the variables are dichotomous; with larger data sets and more complex variables the task of seeing patterns without the employment of techniques for examining relationships would be difficult and probably lead to misleading conclusions.

The cross-tabulation of the two variables is presented in Table 8.3. This kind of table is often referred to as a *contingency table*. Since there are four possible combinations of the two variables, the table requires four *cells*, in which the frequencies listed in Table 8.2 are placed. The following additional information is also presented. First, the figures to the right of the table are called the *row marginals* and those at the bottom of the table are the *column marginals*. These two items of information help us to interpret frequencies in the cells. Also, if the frequencies for each of the two variables have not been presented previously in a report or publication, the

Table 8.1 Data for thirty individuals on job satisfaction and absenteeism

Subject	Job satisfaction	Absent
1	Yes	No
2	Yes	Yes
3	No	Yes
4	Yes	Yes
5	No	Yes
6	No	Yes
7	Yes	No
8	Yes	No
9	No	No
10	Yes	No
11	No	No
12	No	Yes
13	No	Yes
14	No	No
15	No	Yes
16	Yes	No
17	Yes	Yes
18	No	No
19	Yes	No
20	No	Yes
21	No	No
22	Yes	No
23	No	Yes
24	No	Yes
25	Yes	No
26	Yes	Yes
27	Yes	No
28	No	Yes
29	Yes	No
30	Yes	No

row and column marginals provide this information. Second, a percentage in each cell is presented. This allows any patterning to be easily detectable, a facility that becomes especially helpful and important when tables with large numbers of cells are being examined. The percentages presented in Table 8.3 are *column percentages* – that is, the frequency in each cell is treated as a percentage of the column marginal for that cell. Thus, for cell 1 the frequency is 4 and the column marginal is 14; the column percentage is $\frac{4}{14} \times 100$ i.e. 28.6 (rounded up to 29 per cent).

What then does the contingency table show? Table 8.3 suggests that there *is* a relationship between job satisfaction and absence. People who express job satisfaction tend not to have been absent from work (cell 3), since the majority (71 per cent) of the fourteen individuals who express satisfaction have not been absent; on the other hand, of the sixteen people who are not satisfied, a majority of 69 per cent have been absent from work (cell 2). Thus, a relationship is implied; satisfied individuals are considerably less likely to be absent from work than those who are not satisfied.

Table 8.2 Four possible combinations

Job satisfaction	Absenteeism	N
Yes	Yes	4
Yes	No	10
No	Yes	11
No	No	5

In saying that a relationship exists between job satisfaction and absence, we are not suggesting that the relationship is perfect; some satisfied individuals *are* absent from work (cell 1) and some who are not satisfied have not been absent (cell 4). A relationship does not imply a perfect correspondence between the two variables. Such relationships are not specific to the social sciences – everyone has heard of the relationship between lung cancer and smoking, but no one believes that it implies that everyone who smokes will contract lung cancer or that lung cancer only afflicts those who smoke. If there had been a perfect relationship between satisfaction and absence, the contingency table presented in Table 8.4a would be in evidence; if there were no relationship, the cross-tabulation in Table 8.4b would be expected. In the case of Table 8.4a, all individuals who express satisfaction would be in the 'No' category, and all who are not satisfied would be in the absence category. With Table 8.4b, those who are not satisfied are equally likely to have been absent as not absent.

Table 8.3 The relationship between job satisfaction and absenteeism

		Job satisfaction		
		Yes	No	Row marginals
Absenteeism	Yes	1 4 (7) 29%	2 11 (8) 69%	15
	No	3 10 (7) 71%	4 5 (8) 31%	15
Column marginals		14	16	30

The top figure in each cell is the frequency, i.e. the number of cases to which that cell applies. The figure in brackets is the expected frequency — that is, the frequency that would be obtained on the basis of chance alone (see discussion of χ^2). The percentages are column percentages.

Table 8.4 Two types of relationship

(a) A PERFECT RELATIONSHIP

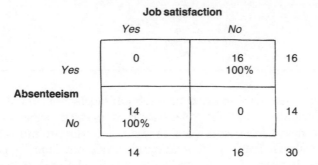

Job satisfaction

	Yes	No	
Absenteeism Yes	0	16 100%	16
No	14 100%	0	14
	14	16	30

(b) NO RELATIONSHIP

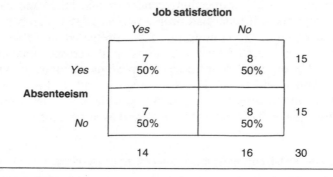

Job satisfaction

	Yes	No	
Absenteeism Yes	7 50%	8 50%	15
No	7 50%	8 50%	15
	14	16	30

As noted above, the percentages in Tables 8.2 to 8.4 are column percentages. Another kind of percentage that might have been preferred is a *row percentage*. With this calculation, the frequency in each cell is calculated in terms of the row totals, so that the percentage for cell 1 would be $\frac{4}{15} \times 100$, i.e. 27 per cent. The row percentages for cells 2, 3, and 4 would be 73, 67, and 33 per cent respectively. In taking row percentages, we would be emphasizing a different aspect of the table – for example, the percentage of those who have been absent who are satisfied (27 per cent in cell 1) and the percentage who are not satisfied with their jobs (73 per cent in cell 2). The question of whether to use row or column percentages in part depends on what aspects of the data you want to highlight. It is sometimes suggested that the decision depends on whether the independent variable is across the top or along the side: if the former, column percentages should be used; if the latter, row percentages should be employed. However, this suggestion implies that there is a straightforward means of identifying the independent and dependent variables, but this is not always the case and great caution should be exercised in making such an inference for reasons that will be explored below. It may appear that job satisfaction is the independent and absence the dependent variable, but it is hazardous to make such an attribution.

SPSS can produce tables without percentages – though such tables are unlikely to be very helpful – and can produce output with either row or column percentages or both. It can also provide *cumulative percentages*, which take the frequency in each cell as a percentage of the total number of subjects. The cumulative percentage for cell 1 in Table 8.2 would be $\frac{4}{30}$ × 100, i.e. 13 per cent. However, cumulative percentages are rarely used in data analysis and it is always advisable to emphasize row or column percentages.

Cross-tabulation with SPSS

Cross-tabulations can easily be created on SPSS. Let us turn now to the Job-Survey data. If we wanted to look at the relationship between **skill** and **gender**, the SPSS commands would be:

crosstabs tables=skill by gender
  /options 3 4.

Remember to omit the full stop after **4** if SPSS-X is being used. The commands will produce a contingency table with **gender** going across the table and **skill** down and with both row and column percentages (**options 3** and **4** respectively). If column percentages only were required, only the digit **4** need be entered as an option. Table 8.5 provides the output deriving from these instructions along with some additional features that will be explained below. In SPSS-X, the **options** subcommand may be replaced by **cells** and keywords are employed instead of numbers. Consequently, **3** and **4** can be substituted with **row** and **column** respectively. Thus, the sub-command is

  /cells row column

There is a number of important extensions to the **crosstabs** command. If, for example, we want to examine the relationship between **skill** and *both* **gender** and **ethnicgp**, the command would be

crosstabs tables=skill by gender ethnicgp.

or both **skill** and **prody** by **gender**

crosstabs tables=skill prody by gender.

or both **skill** and **prody** by both **gender** and **ethnicgp**

crosstabs tables=skill prody by gender ethnicgp.

Table 8.5 Contingency table for rated skill by gender (SPSS-X output from Job-Survey data)

		CROSSTABULATION OF		
SKILL				BY GENDER

		GENDER		
	COUNT EXP VAL ROW PCT COL PCT	male 1	female 2	ROW TOTAL
SKILL				
unskilled	1	5 7.8 35.7% 12.8%	9 6.2 64.3% 29.0%	14 20.0%
semi-skilled	2	11 10.0 61.1% 28.2%	7 8.0 38.9% 22.6%	18 25.7%
fairly skilled	3	11 11.7 52.4% 28.2%	10 9.3 47.6% 32.3%	21 30.0%
highly skilled	4	12 9.5 70.6% 30.8%	5 7.5 29.4% 16.1%	17 24.3%
COLUMN TOTAL		39 55.7%	31 44.3%	70 100.0%

CHI-SQUARE	D.F.	SIGNIFICANCE	MIN E.F.	CELLS WITH E.F. < 5
4.10100	3	0.2508	6.200	NONE

STATISTIC	VALUE	SIGNIFICANCE
CRAMER'S V	0.24204	

NUMBER OF MISSING OBSERVATIONS = 0

This last command would yield four tables: **skill** by both **gender** and **ethnicgp**; **prody** by both **gender** and **ethnicgp**. If the researcher wanted to look at **skill**, **prody**, and **qual**, rather than **tables=skill prody qual**, the command can read

crosstabs tables=skill to qual by gender ethnicgp.

This can save a great deal of time at the terminal when many variables are to be cross-tabulated and also reduces the likelihood of typing errors. In addition, as with the generation of frequencies, **all** may be used:

`crosstabs tables=all by gender ethnicgp.`

This would produce cross-tabulations for all variables by both **gender** and **ethnicgp**.

However, this command would make little sense for interval variables, such as **age** and **income**, since these would each have to be recoded into a smaller number of categories before such an analysis can be conducted. Thus, for example, there are thirty-three categories of **income** into which the seventy respondents fall. If we wanted to see whether **income** and **gender** were related using **crosstabs**, the data for **income** would have to be collapsed, i.e. recoded, into, say, three groups. The cut-off points can be established in a number of ways, one of which might be to collapse respondents into three equal groups with roughly equal numbers in each group. For example, the following command might be used:

`recode income(5900 thru 7299=1)(7300 thru 8299=2)`
` (8300 thru 10500=3).`

This command will generate three groups of respondents of roughly equal size.

Finally, if the researcher wanted to cross-tabulate **absence** by **gender** and **prody** by **ethnicgp** only (i.e. **absence** by **ethnicgp** and **prody** by **gender** are *not* required), the command would read:

`crosstabs tables=skill by gender/prody by ethnicgp.`

In other words, separate groups of cross-tabulations must be separated by a slash /.

Cross-tabulation and significance: the chi-square (x^2) test

As the discussion of statistical significance in Chapter 6 implies, a problem that is likely to be of considerable concern is the question of whether there really is a relationship between the two variables or whether the relationship has arisen by chance, for example as a result of sampling error having engendered an idiosyncratic sample. If the latter were the case, concluding that there is a relationship would entail an erroneous inference being made: if we find a relationship between two variables from an idiosyncratic sample, we would infer a relationship even though the two variables are *independent* (i.e. not related) in the population from which the sample were taken. What we need to know is the probability that there is a relationship between the two variables in the population from which the sample was derived. In order to establish this probability, the chi-square (x^2) test is widely used in conjunction with contingency tables. This is a test of statistical significance, meaning that it allows the researcher to ascertain the probability that the observed relationship between two variables may have arisen by chance. In the case of Table 8.3, this would imply that there is no relationship between job satisfaction and absence in the company as a whole, and that the relationship observed in our sample is a product of sampling error (i.e. the sample is in fact unrepresentative).

The starting-point for the administration of a chi-square test, as with tests of statistical significance in general, is a *null hypothesis* of no relationship between the two variables being examined. In seeking to discern whether a relationship exists between two variables in the population from which a sample was selected, the procedure entails needing to reject the null hypothesis. If the null hypothesis is confirmed, the proposition that there is a relationship must be rejected. The chi-square statistic is then calculated. This statistic is calculated by comparing the observed frequencies in each cell in a contingency table with those that would occur if there were no relationship between the two variables. These are the frequencies that would occur if the values associated with each of the two variables were randomly distributed in relation to each other. In other words, the chi-square test entails a comparison of actual frequencies with those which would be expected to occur on the basis of chance alone (often referred to as the *expected frequencies*). The greater the difference between the observed and the expected frequencies, the larger the ensuing chi-square value will be; if the observed frequencies are very close to the expected frequencies, a small value is likely to occur.

The next step is for the researcher to decide what *significance level* to employ. This means that the researcher must decide what is an acceptable risk that the null hypothesis may be incorrectly rejected (i.e. a Type I error). The null hypothesis would be incorrectly rejected if, for example, there were in fact no relationship between job satisfaction and absence in the population, but our sample data (see Table 8.3) suggested that there was such a relationship. The significance level relates to the probability that we might be making such a false inference. If we say that the computed chi-square value is significant at the 0.05 level of statistical significance, we are saying that we would expect that a maximum of five in every hundred possible samples that could be drawn from a population might appear to yield a relationship between two variables when in fact there is no relationship between them in that population. In other words, there is a one in twenty chance that we are rejecting the null hypothesis when we should in fact be confirming it. If we set a more stringent qualification for rejection, the 0.01 level of significance, we are saying that we are only prepared to accept a chi-square value that implies a maximum of one sample in every hundred showing a relationship where none exists in the population. The probability estimate here is important – the probability of your having a deviant sample (i.e. one suggesting a relationship where none exists in the population) is greater if the 0.05 level is preferred to the 0.01 level. With the former, there is a one in twenty chance, but with the latter a one in a hundred chance, that the null hypothesis will be erroneously rejected. An even more stringent test is to take the 0.001 level, which implies that a maximum of one in a thousand samples might constitute a deviant sample. These three significant levels – 0.05, 0.01, 0.001 – are the ones most frequently encountered in reports of research results.

The calculated chi-square value must therefore be related to a significance level, but how is this done? It is *not* the case that a larger value implies a higher significance level. For one thing, the larger a table is, i.e. the more cells it has, the larger the chi-square value is likely to be. This is because the value is computed by taking the difference between the observed and the expected frequencies for each cell in a contingency table and then adding all the differences. It would hardly be surprising if a contingency table comprising four cells exhibited a lower chi-square value than one with twenty cells. This would be a ridiculous state of affairs, since larger tables would always be more likely to yield statistically significant results than smaller ones. In order to relate the chi-square value to the significance level it is necessary to establish the number of *degrees of freedom* associated with a cross-tabulation. This is calculated as follows:

(number of columns − 1) (number of rows − 1)

In Table 8.3, there are two columns and two rows (excluding the column and row marginals which are of no importance in calculating the degrees of freedom), implying that there is one degree of freedom, i.e. (2−1) (2−1). In addition to calculating the chi-square value, SPSS will calculate the degrees of freedom associated with each cross-tabulation and the significance level that is attained (see Table 8.5). In order to generate such output, the following instruction should be inserted underneath the **options** line (or **cells** for SPSS-X) which is under the **crosstabs** command

/statistics 1.

With SPSS-X a keyword approach may be employed and the command would read

/statistics chisq

Chi-square will then be calculated for each of the contingency tables contained within the **crosstabs** command. Table 8.5 presents the SPSS-X output for **skill** by **gender**. The chi-square value is 4.101 with three degrees of freedom and the significance level is 0.25. This last figure suggests that there is unlikely to be a relationship between the two variables: although, for example, men (1) are more likely than women (2) to work on higher skill jobs (4), the respective column percentages being 30.8 per cent and

16.1 per cent, the chi-square value is not sufficiently large for us to be confident that the relationship could not have arisen by chance since as many as 25 per cent of samples could fail to yield a relationship. In other words, the null hypothesis of independence between the two variables is confirmed. By contrast, the contingency table presented in Table 8.3 generates a chi-square value of 4.82, which is significant at the 0.05 level, implying that we could have confidence in a relationship between the two variables in the population.

If desired, SPSS can also provide the expected values upon which the calculation of chi-square depends. These are presented in Table 8.5 beneath the frequency **counts**. This enhancement can be of interest in order to provide a stronger 'feel' for the degree to which the observed frequencies differ from the distribution that would occur if chance alone were operating. This additional information can aid the understanding and interpretation of a relationship, but is rarely provided in tables when they are presented to the reader. Expected frequencies can be obtained by inserting a **14** into the existing options command, or by inserting **options 14** after the **crosstabs** command. The commands should read:

```
crosstabs tables=skill by gender
 /options 3 4 14
 /statistics 1.
```

This will provide the contingency table, row and column percentages, chi-square, and expected values. The **options** subcommand can be replaced by **cells count row column expected** in SPSS-X. In each cell, underneath the expected values are the row percentages and underneath these are the column percentages.

When presenting a contingency table and its associated chi-square test for a report or publication, some attention is needed to its appearance and to what is conveyed. Table 8.6 presents a 'cleaned' table of the output

Table 8.6 Rated skill by gender (Job-Survey data)

		Gender	
		Male (%)	*Female (%)*
Rated skill	*Unskilled*	13	29
	Semi-skilled	28	23
	Fairly skilled	28	32
	Skilled	31	16
	Total	N = 39	N = 31

$\chi^2 = 4.10$ NS, p > .05

provided in Table 8.5. A number of points should be noted. First, only column marginals have been presented. Second, observed and expected frequencies are not included. Some writers prefer to include observed frequencies, but if as in Table 8.6 the column marginals are included, they need not be included. Percentages have been rounded up or down. Strictly speaking, this should only be done for large samples (for example, in excess of 200), but rounding is often undertaken on smaller samples since it simplifies the understanding of relationships. The chi-square value is inserted at the bottom with the associated level of significance. In this case, the value is not significant at the 0.05 level, the usual minimum level for rejecting the null hypothesis. This is often indicated by NS (i.e. *non-significant*) and an indication of the significance level employed. Thus, $p > 0.05$ means that the chi-square value is below that necessary for achieving the 0.05 level, meaning that there is more than a 5 per cent chance that there is no relationship in the population. If the chi-square value exceeds that necessary for achieving the 0.05 level, one would write $p < 0.05$. Another point to bear in mind is how to deal with missing values. SPSS assumes that cases with missing values should be ignored for each table unless an alternative indication is given. **Option 7** allows missing values to be included in the table but excluded from the calculation of column and row percentages and of statistical tests. This option is not available with SPSS/PC+. With SPSS-X, the subcommand **missing=report** can be used instead. However, for most purposes the default mechanism within SPSS will suffice.

A number of points about chi-square should be registered in order to facilitate an understanding of its strengths and limitations, as well as some further points about its operation. First, chi-square is not a strong statistic in that it does not convey information about the *strength* of a relationship. This notion of strength will be examined in greater detail below when correlation is examined. By strength is meant that a large chi-square value and a correspondingly strong significance level (for example $p < 0.001$) cannot be taken to mean a closer relationship between two variables than when chi-square is considerably smaller but moderately significant (for example, $p < 0.05$). What it is telling us is how confident we can be that there is a relationship between two variables. Second, the combination of a contingency table and chi-square is most likely to occur when *either* both variables are nominal (categorical) *or* when one is nominal and the other is ordinal. When both variables are ordinal or interval other approaches to the elucidation of relationships, such as correlation which allows strength of relationships to be examined and which therefore conveys more information, are likely to be preferred. When one variable is nominal and the other interval, such as the relationship between voting preference and age, the latter variable will need to be 'collapsed' into ordinal groupings (i.e. 20–29, 30–39, 40–49, and so on) in order to allow a contingency table and its associated chi-square value to be provided.

Third, chi-square has to be adapted for use in relation to a 2 × 2 table, such as Table 8.3. A different formula is employed, using what is called 'Yates's Correction for Continuity'. It is not necessary to go into the technical reasons for this correction, save to say that some writers take the view that the conventional formula results in an overestimate of the chi-square value when applied to a 2 × 2 table. When SPSS is used to calculate chi-square for such a table, two sets of computations are provided – one with and one before Yates's correction. Normally, the results of the former should be used. If Yates's correction has been used in the computation of the chi-square statistic, this should be clearly stated when the data are presented for publication.

Some writers suggest that the phi (ϕ) coefficient can be preferable as a test of association between two dichotomous variables. This statistic, which is similar to the correlation coefficient (see below) in that it varies between 0 and 1 to provide an indication of the strength of a relationship, can be generated by the instruction

/statistics 2.

If SPSS-X is being used, this subcommand can be **statistics phi**. However, SPSS does not provide a significance test for this statistic though such a test can be contrived. Cohen and Holliday (1982) observe that chi-square equals n (number of cases) multiplied by phi squared. Thus, if phi equals -0.6 and there are eighty cases, chi-square is equal to $(80)(-0.6)^2$, i.e. 28.8. The significance of phi can then be examined by checking the chi-square values for one degree of freedom (since a 2 × 2 table will always yield one degree of freedom) in a table of chi-square values. For $p < 0.05$ the chi-square value will need to be at or equal to 3.8414; at $p < 0.01$ the relevant value is 6.6349; and for $p < 0.001$ it is 10.828. Thus, in our example, the phi value of -0.6 with eighty cases would imply that there is very likely to be a relationship in the population. Tables of chi-square values can be found in many statistics textbooks (for example, Cohen and Holliday 1982). The phi coefficient will be returned to in a later section in this chapter.

Fourth, chi-square can be unreliable if expected cell frequencies are less than five, although like Yates's correction for 2 × 2 tables, this is a source of some controversy. SPSS prints the number and percentage of such cells for each table for which chi-square is requested.

Correlation

The idea of correlation is one of the most important and basic in the elaboration of bivariate relationships. Unlike chi-square, measures of correlation indicate both the strength and the direction of the relationship between a pair of variables. Two types of measure can be distinguished: measures of linear correlation using interval variables and measures of rank correlation using ordinal variables. While these two types of measure of correlation share some common properties, they also differ in some important respects which will be examined after the elucidation of measures of linear correlation.

Linear correlation: relationships between interval variables

Correlation entails the provision of a yardstick whereby the intensity or strength of a relationship can be gauged. To provide such estimates, *correlation coefficients* are calculated. These provide succinct assessments of the closeness of a relationship among pairs of variables. Their widespread use in the social sciences has meant that the results of tests of correlation have become easy to recognize and interpret. When variables are interval, by far the most common measure of correlation is *Pearson's Product Moment Correlation Coefficient*, often referred to as Pearson's *r*. This measure of correlation presumes that interval variables are being used, so that even ordinal variables are not supposed to be employed, although this is a matter of some debate (for example, O'Brien 1979).

In order to illustrate some of the fundamental features of correlation, *scatter diagrams* (often called 'scattergrams') will be employed. A scatter diagram plots each individual case on a graph, thereby representing for

Table 8.7 Data on age, income, and political liberalism

Case no.	Income	Age	Political– liberalism score
1	9,000	23	18
2	11,000	33	11
3	7,000	21	23
4	12,500	39	13
5	10,000	27	17
6	11,500	43	19
7	8,500	21	22
8	8,500	27	20
9	15,000	43	9
10	13,000	38	14
11	7,500	30	21
12	14,500	54	11
13	16,000	63	8
14	15,500	58	10
15	8,000	25	22
16	10,500	51	12
17	10,000	36	15
18	12,000	34	16

each case the points at which the two variables intersect. Thus, if we are examining the relationship between income and political liberalism in the imaginary data presented in Table 8.7, each point on the scatter diagram represents each respondent's position in relation to each of these two variables. Let us say that political liberalism is measured by a scale of five statements to which individuals have to indicate their degree of agreement on a five-point array ('Strongly Agree' to 'Strongly Disagree'). The maximum score is 25, the minimum 5. Table 8.7 presents data on eighteen individuals for each of the two variables. The term 'cases' is employed in the table, rather than subjects, as a reminder that the objects to which data may refer can be entities such as firms, schools, cities, and the like. In Figure 8.1, the data on income and political liberalism from Table 8.7 are plotted (using SPSS/PC+) to form a scatter diagram. Each asterisk represents one case. Thus, case number 1, which has an income of £9,000 and a liberalism score of 18, is positioned at the intersection of these two values on the graph. This case has been encircled to allow it to stand out.

Figure 8.1 Scatter diagram: political liberalism by income (SPSS/PC+ **plot**)

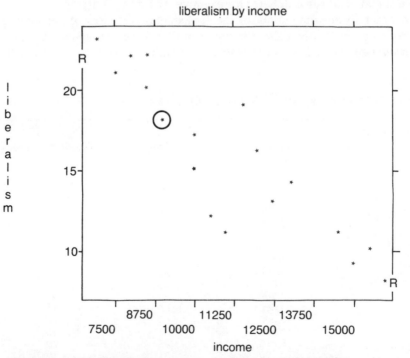

18 cases plotted. Regression statistics of LIBERAL on INCOME:
Correlation −.89194 R Squared .79556 S.E. of Est   2.26717 Sig.   .0000
Intercept(S.E.)   32.60723(2.21924)   Slope(S.E.)   −.00153(.00019)

Initially, the nature of the relationship between two variables will be focused upon. It should be apparent that the pattern of the dots moves downwards from left to right. This pattern implies a *negative relationship*, meaning that as one variable increases the other decreases: higher incomes are associated with *lower* levels of political liberalism; lower incomes with *higher* levels of liberalism. In Figure 8.2 a different kind of relationship between two variables is exhibited. Each 1 represents one case and is an alternative to an asterisk as a means of representing one case in SPSS. Here, there is a *positive relationship*, with higher values on one variable (income) being associated with higher values on the other (age). These data derive from Table 8.7. In Figure 8.2, case number 1 is again circled. Notice how in neither case is the relationship between the two variables a perfect one. If there were a perfect linear relationship, all of the points in the scatter diagram would be on a straight line (see Figure 8.3), a situation which almost never occurs in the social sciences. Instead, we tend to have,

Figure 8.2 Scatter diagram: income by age (SPSS/PC+ **plot**)

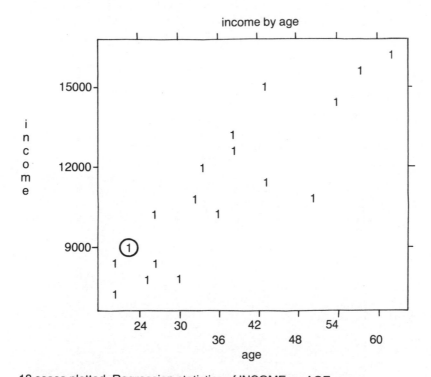

18 cases plotted. Regression statistics of INCOME on AGE:
Correlation   .86277 R Squared   .74438   S.E. of Est 1478.25316
Sig.   .0000
Intercept(S.E.) 4063.17811(1089.7430)   Slope(S.E.)   190.48468(27.90648)

Figure 8.3 A perfect relationship

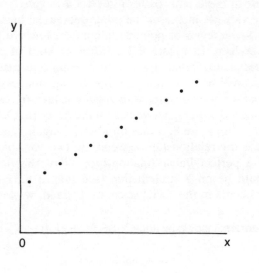

Figure 8.4 No relationship (or virtually no relationship)

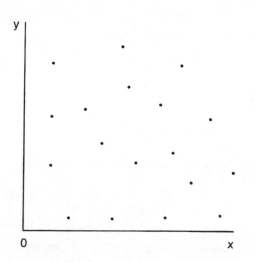

as in Figures 8.1 and 8.2, a certain amount of scatter, though a pattern is often visible, such as the negative and positive relationships each figure respectively exhibits. If there is a large amount of scatter, so that no patterning is visible, we can say that there is no or virtually no relationship between two variables (see Figure 8.4).

In addition to positive and negative relationships we sometimes find *curvilinear relationships*, in which the shape of the relationship between two variables is not straight, but curves at one or more points. Figure 8.5 provides three different types of curvilinear relationship. The relationship between organizational size and organizational properties, like the amount of specialization, often takes a form similar to diagram (c) in Figure 8.5 (Child 1973). When patterns similar to those exhibited in Figure 8.5 are found, the relationship is *non-linear*, that is it is not straight, and it is not appropriate to employ a measure of linear correlation like Pearson's *r*. When scatter diagrams are similar to the patterns depicted in Figure 8.5b and 8.5c, researchers often transform the independent variable into a logarithmic scale, which will usually engender a linear relationship and hence will allow the employment of Pearson's *r* (see Chapter 9 for further discussion of transformation). Here we see an important reason for investigating scatter diagrams before computing *r* – if there is a non-linear relationship the computed estimate of correlation will be meaningless, but unless a scatter diagram is checked it is not possible to determine whether the relationship is not linear.

Scatter diagrams allow three aspects of a relationship to be discerned: whether it is linear; the direction of the relationship (i.e. whether positive or negative); and the strength of the relationship. The amount of scatter is indicative of the strength of the relationship. Compare the pairs of positive and negative relationships in Figures 8.6 and 8.7 respectively. In each case the right-hand diagram exhibits more scatter than the left-hand diagram, with the points on the graph departing more and more from the straight line that was depicted in Figure 8.4. In each case, therefore, the left-hand

Figure 8.5 Three curvilinear relationships

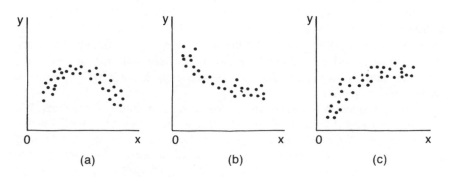

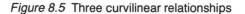

Figure 8.6 Two positive relationships

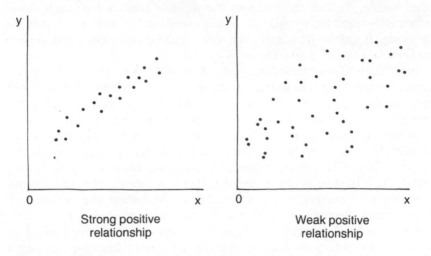

Strong positive
relationship

Weak positive
relationship

diagram represents a stronger relationship since the points are less scattered.

Scatter diagrams are useful aids to the understanding of correlation. Pearson's *r* allows the strength and direction of linear relationships between variables to be gauged. Pearson's *r* varies between −1 and +1. A relationship of −1 or +1 would indicate a perfect relationship, negative or positive respectively, between two variables. Thus, Figure 8.4 would denote a perfect positive relationship of +1. The complete absence of a relationship would engender a computed *r* of zero. The closer *r* is to 1 (whether positive or negative), the stronger the relationship between two variables. The nearer *r* is to zero (and hence the further it is from + or −1), the weaker the relationship. These ideas are expressed in Figure 8.8. If *r* is 0.82, this would indicate a strong positive relationship between two variables, whereas 0.24 would denote a weak relationship. Similarly, −0.79 and −0.31 would be indicative of strong and weak negative relationships respectively. In Figures 8.6 and 8.7, the left-hand diagrams would be indicative of larger computed *r* values than those on the right.

What is a large correlation? Cohen and Holliday (1982) suggest the following: below 0.19 is very low; 0.20 to 0.39 is low; 0.40 to 0.69 is modest; 0.70 to 0.89 is high; and 0.90 to 1 is very high. However, these are rules of thumb and should not be regarded as definitive indications, since there are hardly any guidelines for interpretation over which there is substantial consensus.

Further, caution is required when comparing computed coefficients. We can certainly say that an *r* of −0.60 is larger than one of −0.30, but we cannot say that the relationship is twice as strong. In order to see why not, a useful aid to the interpretation of *r* will be introduced – the *coefficient of*

Figure 8.7 Two negative relationships

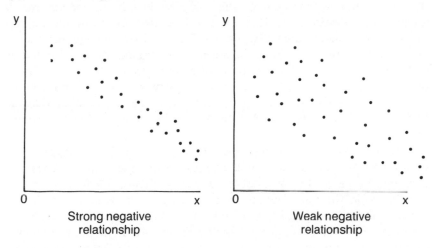

Strong negative
relationship

Weak negative
relationship

determination (r^2). This is simply the square of *r* multiplied by 100. It provides us with an indication of how far variation in one variable is accounted for by the other. Thus, if $r = -0.6$, then $r^2 = 36$ per cent. This means that 36 per cent of the variance in one variable is due to the other. When r = −0.3, then r^2 will be 9 per cent. Thus, although an *r* of −0.6 is twice as large as one of −0.3, it cannot indicate that the former is twice as strong as the latter, because *four* times more variance is being accounted for by an *r* of −0.6 than one of −0.3. Thinking about the coefficient of determination can have a salutory effect on one's interpretation of *r*. Thus, for example, when correlating two variables, x and y, an *r* of 0.7 sounds quite high, but it would mean that less than half of the variance in y can be attributed to x (i.e. 49 per cent). In other words, 51 per cent of the variance in y is due to variables other than x.

A word of caution is relevant at this point. In saying that 49 per cent of the variation in y is attributable to x, we must recognize that this also means that 49 per cent of the variation in x is due to y. Correlation is not the same as cause. We cannot determine from an estimate of correlation that one variable causes the other, since correlation provides estimates of co-variance, i.e. that two variables are related. We may find a large correlation

Figure 8.8 The strength and direction of correlation coefficients

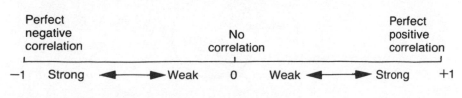

169

of 0.8 between job satisfaction and organizational commitment, but does this mean that 64 per cent of the variation in job satisfaction can be attributed to commitment? This would suggest that organizational commitment is substantially caused by job satisfaction. However, the reverse can also hold true: 64 per cent of the variation in organizational commitment may be due to job satisfaction. It is not possible from a simple correlation between these two variables to arbitrate between the two possibilities. Indeed, as Chapter 10 will reveal, there may be reasons other than not knowing which causes which for needing to be cautious about presuming causality.

Another way of expressing these ideas is through Venn diagrams (see Figure 8.9). If we treat each circle as representing the amount of variance exhibited by each of two variables, x and y, Figure 8.9 illustrates three conditions: in the top diagram we have independence in which the two variables do not overlap, i.e. a correlation of zero as represented by Figure 8.4 or in terms of a contingency table by Table 8.4b; in the middle diagram there is a perfect relationship in which the variance of x and y coincides perfectly, i.e. a correlation of 1 as represented by Figure 8.3 or the contingency

Figure 8.9 Types of relationship

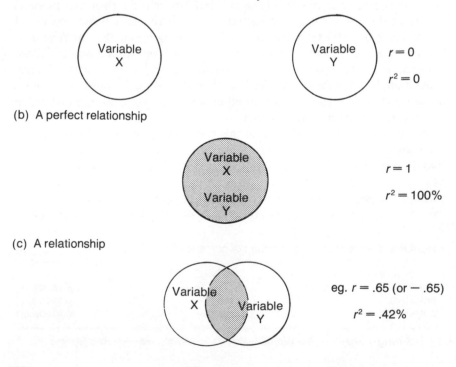

(a) Independence: the two variables are totally unrelated

Variable X   Variable Y $r = 0$

$r^2 = 0$

(b) A perfect relationship

Variable X $r = 1$

Variable Y $r^2 = 100\%$

(c) A relationship

Variable X   Variable Y   eg. $r = .65$ (or $- .65$)

$r^2 = .42\%$

table in Table 8.4a; and the bottom diagram which points to a less than perfect, though strong, relationship between x and y, i.e. as represented by the left-hand diagrams in Figures 8.6 and 8.7. Here only part of the two circles intersects, i.e. the shaded area, which represents just over 42 per cent of the variance shared by the two variables; the unshaded area of each circle denotes a sphere of variance for each variable that is unrelated to the other variable.

It is possible to provide an indication of the statistical significance of r. The way in which its significance is calculated is strongly affected by the number of cases for which there are pairs of data. If, for example, you have approximately 500 cases, r only needs to be 0.088 or 0.115 to be significant at the 0.05 and 0.01 levels respectively with a one-tailed test. If you have just eighteen cases (as in Table 8.6), the r values will need to be at least 0.468 or 0.590 respectively. Some investigators only provide information about the significance of relationships. However, this is a grave error since what is and what is not significant is profoundly affected by the number of cases. What statistical significance does tell us is the likelihood that a relationship of at least this size could have arisen by chance. It is necessary to interpret both r and the significance level when computing correlation coefficients. Thus, for example, a correlation of 0.17 in connection with a random sample of 1,000 individuals would be significant at the 0.001 level, but would indicate that this weak relationship was unlikely to have arisen by chance and that we can be confident that a relationship of at least this size holds in the population. Consider an alternative scenario of a correlation of 0.43 based on a sample of 42. The significance level would be 0.01, but it would be absurd to say that the former correlation was more important than the latter simply because the correlation of 0.17 is more significant. The second coefficient is larger, though we have to be somewhat more circumspect in this second case than in the first in inferring that the relationship could not have arisen by chance. Thus, the size of r and the significance level must be considered in tandem.

Generating scatter diagrams and computing r with SPSS

The command for generating scatter diagrams with SPSS is **plot**. Taking the Job-Survey data, if you wanted to plot **satis** and **routine**, the commands would be:

```
plot format=regression
  /title='plot of job routine on job satisfaction'
  /vertical='job satisfaction'
  /horizontal='job routine'
  /plot=satis with routine.
```

This list of commands will provide a scatter diagram with **routine** on the horizontal axis. Also, a title for the plot is provided and the variables on

Table 8.8 Matrix of Pearson product moment correlation coefficients
(SPSS-X output from Job-Survey data)

	PEARSON		
	SATIS	AUTONOM	ROUTINE
SATIS	1.0000 (0) P=*****	0.7333 (68) P=0.000	−0.5801 (68) P=0.000
AUTONOM	0.7333 (68) P=0.000	1.0000 (0) P=*****	−0.4872 (70) P=0.000
ROUTINE	−0.5801 (68) P=0.000	−0.4872 (70) P=0.000	1.0000 (0) P=*****

(COEFFICIENT / (CASES) / SIGNIFICANCE)

each axis are fully labelled. The **format=regression** subcommand will mean that a number of statistics relevant to correlation and regression will be provided (including Pearson's r, r^2, and the significance of r). Examples of output from **plot** are provided in Figures 8.1 and 8.2. SPSS will indicate each point on a scatter diagram with a 1, as in Figure 8.2. When there are two cases at that point, a 2 is produced. If asterisks are preferred (as in Figure 8.1), **/symbols='*'** should be inserted at the end of the **/format=regression** line.

In addition to being computed through the regression format with **plot**, Pearson's r can be calculated by the **correlations** command. The command

correlations variables=satis with autonom routine.

will correlate **satis** with both **autonom** and **routine**. A common procedure is to request a matrix of coefficients, such as that provided in Table 8.8, with the command

correlations variables=satis routine autonom.

With this command, each variable is correlated with each other variable in the list. If separate groups of variables are to be correlated, the following format should be used

correlations variables=satis with autonom/income with absence.

which will correlate **satis** with **autonom** and **income** with **absence**.

The output (see Table 8.8) will contain both significance levels and number of cases for each pair. The latter will vary since missing values for particular variables will reduce the number of cases in some pairs (often referred to as *pairwise* deletion of cases with missing values). However, SPSS/PC+ excludes cases with missing values on a *listwise* basis, whereby all cases with a missing value on any of the variables listed will be excluded from all analyses. If pairwise deletion is preferred when using SPSS/PC+, the subcommand **/options 2** should be included.

The significance tests are one-tailed. If two-tailed tests are required, the procedure for generating such tests for SPSS-X is the subcommand **/print=twotail** which should follow the **correlations** command; with SPSS/PC+, **/options 3.** should be inserted after the **correlations** command. It should also be noted that the presentation of significance levels in SPSS output for Pearson's *r* varies according to whether SPSS-X or SPSS/PC+ is being used. With SPSS-X output exact statistical significance levels are provided by default, whereas with SPSS/PC+ these are obtained by including **/options 5.** after the **correlations** command.

Means, standard deviations, and number of cases of each variable specified can be provided in SPSS by the subcommand **/statistics 1**. In SPSS-X, the **1** can be substituted by **descriptives**.

Rank correlation: relationships between ordinal variables

In order to employ Pearson's *r*, variables must be interval and the relationship must be linear. When variables are at the ordinal level, an alternative measure of correlation can be used called *rank correlation*. Two prominent methods are available – Spearman's rho (ρ) and Kendall's tau (τ) – the former probably being more common in reports of research findings. The interpretation of the results of either of these methods is identical to Pearson's *r*, in that the computed coefficient will vary between -1 and $+1$. Thus, both methods provide information on the strength and direction of relationships. Moreover, unlike Pearson's *r*, rho and tau are non-parametric methods, which means that they can be used in a wide variety of contexts since they make fewer assumptions about variables. Obviously, the formulae for the two measures differ, but the areas of divergence need not concern us here. Kendall's tau usually produces slightly lower correlation coefficients, but since rho is more commonly used by researchers, it is probably preferable to report this statistic unless there are obvious reasons for thinking otherwise. One possible reason that is sometimes suggested for preferring tau is that it deals better with tied ranks – for example, when two or more people are at the same rank for both variables. Thus, if there seems to be quite a large proportion of tied ranks, such as many individuals having the same values on one or both variables when there are only twenty subjects, tau may be preferable.

Let us say that we want to correlate **skill**, **prody**, and **qual**, each of which is an ordinal measure. SPSS-X allows both tau and rho to be computed, but with SPSS/PC+ only tau can be generated. If SPSS/PC+ is being used, tau can be provided through **crosstabs** by inserting **/statistics 6** after the **crosstabs** command. If SPSS-X is being used, to provide a matrix of correlations, using both rho and tau, the following format should be used:

nonpar corr variables=skill prody qual
 /print=both

The resulting output is provided in Table 8.9. If only tau is required, **Kendall** should be inserted after **print=**; if only rho is required, **Spearman** should be inserted. If two-tailed tests of significance are required, **/print=twotail** should be selected. All of the correlations reported in Table 8.9 are low, the largest being the correlation between **prody** and **skill** (0.24 rounded up) for rho. Only the correlations between **prody** and **skill** achieve statistical significance at $p < 0.05$. Thus, there is a tendency for better skilled workers to be more productive.

Although rank correlation methods are more adaptable than Pearson's *r*, the latter tends to be preferred because interval variables comprise more information than ordinal ones. One of the reasons for the widespread use in the social sciences of questionnaire items which are built up into scales

Table 8.9 Matrix of Spearman's rho and Kendall's tau correlation coefficients (SPSS-X output from Job-Survey data)

```
                          SPEARMAN

PRODY          .2389
               N(  69)
               SIG .024

QUAL           .0133          .1710
               N(  70)        N(  69)
               SIG .457       SIG .080

               SKILL          PRODY
          "." IS PRINTED IF A COEFFICIENT CANNOT BE COMPUTED.
```

```
                          KENDALL

PRODY          .1944
               N(  69)
               SIG .026

QUAL           .0171          .1484
               N(  70)        N(  69)
               SIG .431       SIG .066

               SKILL          PRODY
          "." IS PRINTED IF A COEFFICIENT CANNOT BE COMPUTED.
```

or indices (and which are then treated as interval variables) is probably that stronger approaches to the investigation of relationships like Pearson's *r* (and regression – see below) can be employed.

Other approaches to bivariate relationships

Up to now, the approach to the examination of relationships has been undertaken within a framework within which the nature of the variables has been the most important factor: cross-tabulation and chi-square are most likely to occur in conjunction with nominal variables; Pearson's *r* presumes the use of interval variables; and when examining pairs of ordinal variables, rho or tau should be employed. However, what if, as can easily occur in the social sciences, pairs of variables are of different types, for example, nominal plus ordinal or ordinal plus interval? There are methods for the elucidation of relationships which can deal with such eventualities. Freeman (1965), for example, catalogues a vast array of methods that can be used in such circumstances. There are problems with many of these methods. First, they are unfamiliar to most readers who would therefore experience great difficulty in understanding and interpreting the results of calculations. Second, while particular statistical methods should not be followed fetishistically, the notion of learning a new statistical method each time a particular combination of circumstances arises is also not ideal. Third, for many unusual methods, software is not available, even within a wide-ranging package like SPSS.

One rule of thumb that can be recommended is to move downwards in measurement level when confronted with a pair of different variables. Thus, if you have an ordinal and an interval variable, a method of rank correlation could be used. If you have an ordinal and a nominal variable, you should use cross-tabulation and chi-square. This may mean collapsing ranks into groups (for example, 1–5, 6–10, 11–15, and so on) and assigning ranks to the groupings (for example, 1–5 = 1, 6–10 = 2, 11–15 = 3, and so on), using the **recode** command within SPSS. If you have a nominal and an interval variable, again the combination of a contingency table and chi-square is likely to be used. As suggested in the discussion of cross-tabulation, the interval variable will need to be collapsed into groups. The chief source of concern with collapsing values of an ordinal or interval variable is that the choice of cut-off points is bound to be arbitrary and will have a direct impact on the results obtained. Accordingly, it may be better to use more than one method of grouping or to employ a fairly systematic procedure like quartiles as a means of collapsing cases into four groups.

When pairs of variables are dichotomous, the phi coefficient should be given serious consideration. Its interpretation is the same as Pearson's *r*, in that it varies between 0 and +1. A description of a test of statistical significance for phi was provided in the section on cross-tabulation. Phi represents something of a puzzle. Many textbooks indicate that phi can take a positive or negative value, which means that it can measure both the strength and direction of relationships among dichotomous variables. However, the phi coefficient that is generated by SPSS can only assume a positive value. The reason for this apparent inconsistency lies in the different formulae that are employed.

Statistics textbooks often present a host of methods for examining relationships which are rarely seen in reports of research. It is not proposed to provide such a catalogue here, but two methods are particularly worthy of attention. First, in order to provide a measure of the strength of the relationship between two variables from a contingency table, Cramer's V can be recommended. This test, whose calculation in large part derives from chi-square, provides results which vary between 0 and +1. Moreover, in a 2 $\times$ 2 table, phi and Cramer's V will yield the same result. Table 8.5 provides the result of computing Cramer's V for **skill** by **gender**. The coefficient is 0.24 (rounded down), suggesting a weak relationship. There is no significance test, but the use of Cramer's V in conjunction with chi-square can provide information that approximates to a direct significance test. The following instruction (following the **options** subcommand which comes after the **crosstabs** command) will provide both chi-square and Cramer's V with SPSS-X:

/statistics chisq phi

The **phi** in this command will provide phi for 2 $\times$ 2 tables and Cramer's V for larger tables. With SPSS/PC+ the subcommand would be **/statistics 1 2.** for chi-square and V respectively.

Second, when the researcher is confronted with an interval dependent variable and an independent variable that is either nominal or ordinal, the eta coefficient warrants consideration. Like Cramer's V, it can only vary between 0 and +1. It can be computed as a command within the **crosstabs** routine. Thus, for SPSS-X

/statistics eta

after a **crosstabs** command will produce eta. For SPSS/PC+, **eta** should be substituted with **10**. A common derivation of eta is eta-squared, which is similar to r^2 in its underlying interpretation. Thus, eta-squared refers to the amount of variation in the dependent (i.e. interval) variable that is accounted for by the independent (i.e. nominal or ordinal) variable. Both eta and eta-squared are also produced by SPSS when an analysis of variance is requested in association with the **means** routine (**statistics 1** produces both the analysis of variance and eta). Eta can be regarded as a useful test which provides a measure of strength of relationship in the contexts cited above. However, because it forces the researcher to commit him- or himself to which variable is independent, eta may be sensible to avoid when such decisions are particularly difficult.

The SPSS **means** procedure provides an interesting way of analysing pairs of variables when the dependent variable is interval and the independent variable is either nominal, ordinal, or dichotomous. This procedure is very similar to **crosstabs**, except that with **means** the dependent variable is broken down in terms of the independent variable and the mean and standard deviation of the dependent variable for each subgroup of the independent variable is computed. Thus, if we knew the incomes and ethnic group membership of a sample of individuals, we could examine the mean income of each of the ethnic groups identified, as well as the standard deviations for each subgroup mean. This allows the impact of the independent variable on the dependent variable to be examined. Earlier it was suggested that if we have an interval and an ordinal variable, we should examine the relationship between them using rank correlation. However, if the ordinal variable has relatively few categories and the interval variable has many values, it is likely to be more appropriate to use **means**. If rank correlation is used in such a context, the contrast between the two variables is considerable and makes the ensuing statistic difficult to interpret.

Let us say that we wish to look at the relationship between **satis** and **skill** (which only has four categories) in the Job-Survey data. The command is

means tables=satis by skill.

In addition, if this command is followed by /**statistics all** an analysis of variance table will be produced, the *F* ratio (which provides a test of statistical significance), and eta and eta-squared. Table 8.10 provides SPSS-X output from this set of commands. As this output shows, job satisfaction varies by skill (with lower **satis** means for lower **skill** levels) and the *F* ratio of 19.844 is significant at the 0.0005 level, suggesting a strong probability of a relationship in the population. The eta-squared suggests that about one-quarter of the variance in **satis** can be attributed to **skill**. Thus, **means** can be considered a useful tool for examining relationships when there is an interval dependent variable and a nominal, dichotomous, or short ordinal variable. However, it only makes sense if the interval variable can be unambiguously recognized as the dependent variable.

Regression

Regression has become one of the most widely used techniques in the analysis of data in the social sciences. It is closely connected to Pearson's *r*, as will become apparent at a number of points. Indeed, it shares many of the same assumptions as *r*, such as that relationships between variables are linear and that variables are interval. In this section, the use of regression to explore relationships between pairs of variables will be examined. It should become apparent that regression is a powerful tool for summarizing the

Table 8.10 Sample **means** SPSS-X output (Job-Survey data)

CRITERION VARIABLE SATIS

VARIABLE	CODE	VALUE LABEL	SUM	MEAN	STD DEV	SUM OF SQ	N
				— A N A L Y S I S O F V A R I A N C E —			
SKILL	1.	unskilled	121.0000	8.6429	2.4995	81.2143	(14)
SKILL	2.	semi-skilled	174.0000	9.6667	2.4010	98.0000	(18)
SKILL	3.	fairly skilled	224.0000	11.7895	3.3760	205.1579	(19)
SKILL	4.	highly skilled	218.0000	12.8235	3.2641	170.4706	(17)
WITHIN GROUPS TOTAL			737.0000	10.8382	2.9444	554.8428	(68)

ANALYSIS OF VARIANCE

SOURCE	SUM OF SQUARES	D.F.	MEAN SQUARE	F	SIG.
BETWEEN GROUPS	176.378	3	58.793	6.782	0.0005
LINEARITY	172.038	1	172.038	19.844	0.0000
DEV. FROM LINEARITY	4.340	2	2.170	0.250	0.7793
	$R = 0.4851$	R SQUARED $= 0.2353$			
WITHIN GROUPS	554.843	64	8.669		
	ETA $= 0.4911$	ETA SQUARED $= 0.2412$			

nature of the relationship between variables and for making predictions of likely values of the dependent variable.

At this point, it is worth returning to the scatter diagrams encountered in Figures 8.1 and 8.2. Each departs a good deal from Figure 8.3 in which all of the points are on a straight line, since the points in Figures 8.1 and 8.2 are more scattered. The idea of regression is to summarize the relationship between two variables by producing a line which fits the data closely. This line is called the *line of best fit*. Only one line will minimize the deviations of all of the dots in a scatter diagram from the line. Some points will appear above the line, some below it, and a small proportion may actually be on the line. Because only one line can meet the criterion of line of best fit, it is unlikely that it can be drawn accurately by hand. This is where regression comes in. Regression procedures allow the precise line of best fit to be computed. Once we know the line of best fit, we can make predictions about likely values of the dependent variable, for particular values of the independent variable.

In order to understand how the line of best fit operates, it is necessary to get to grips with the simple equation that governs its operation and how we make predictions from it. The equation is

$$y = a + bx + e$$

In this equation, y and x are the dependent and independent variables respectively. The two elements, a and b, refer to aspects of the line itself. First, element a is known as the intercept, which is the point at which the line cuts the vertical axis. Second, element b is the slope of the line of best fit and is usually referred to as the regression coefficient. By the 'slope' is meant the rate at which changes in values of the independent variable (x) affect values of the dependent variable (y). In order to predict y for a given value of x, it is necessary to

(1) multiply the value of x by the regression coefficient, b; and
(2) add this calculation to the intercept, a.

Finally, e is referred to as an *error term*, which points to the fact that a proportion of the variance in the dependent variable, y, is unexplained by the regression equation. For the purposes of making predictions the error term is ignored and so will not be referred to below.

Consider the following example. A researcher may want to know whether managers who put in extra hours after the normal working day tend to get on better in the organization than others. The researcher finds out the average amount of time a group of twenty new managers in a firm spend working on problems after normal working hours. Two years later the managers are re-examined to find out their annual salaries. Individuals' salaries are employed as an indicator of progress, since incomes often reflect how well a person is getting on in a firm. Moreover, for these

Figure 8.10 A line of best fit

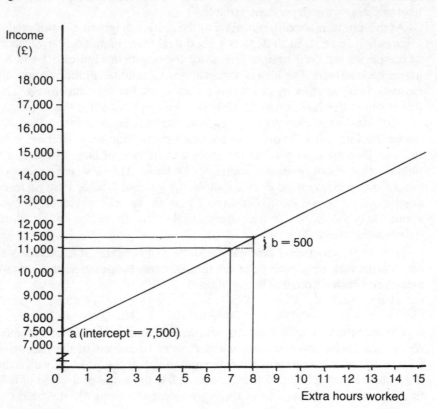

managers, extra hours of work are not rewarded by overtime payments, so salaries are a real indication of progress.

Let us say that the regression equation which is derived from the analysis is

$y = 7500 + 500x$

The line of best fit is drawn in Figure 8.10. The intercept, *a*, is 7,500, i.e. £7,500; the regression coefficient, *b*, is 500, i.e. £500. The latter means that each extra hour worked produces an extra £500 to a manager's annual salary. We can calculate the likely annual salary of someone who puts in an extra seven hours per week as follows:

$y = 7,500 + (500)(7)$
which becomes
$y = 7,500 + 3,500$
which becomes
$y = 11,000$ (i.e. £11,000).

180

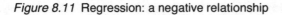

Figure 8.11 Regression: a negative relationship

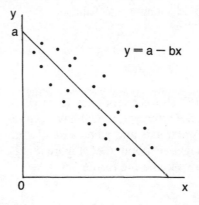

For someone who works an extra eight hours per week, the likely salary will be £11,500, i.e. 7,500+(500)(8). If a person does not put in any extra work, the salary is likely to be £7,500, i.e. 7,500+(500)(0). Thus, through regression, we are able to show how *y* changes for each additional increment of *x* (because the regression coefficient expresses how much more of *y* you get for each extra increment of *x*) and to predict the likely value of *y* for a given value of *x*. When a relationship is negative, the regression equation for the line of best fit will take the form

$y = a - bx$ (see Figure 8.11).

Figure 8.12 Regression: a negative intercept

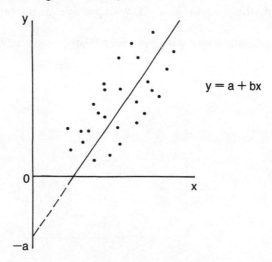

Thus, if a regression equation were $y = 50 - 2x$, each extra increment of x would produce a decrease in y. If we wanted to know the likely value of y when $x=12$, we would substitute as follows

$y = 50 - 2x$
$y = 50 - (2)(12)$
$y = 50 - 24$
$y = 26.$

When a line of best fit shows a tendency to be vertical and to intersect with the horizontal axis, the intercept, a, will have a minus value. This is because it will cut the horizontal axis and when extended to the vertical axis it will intercept it at a negative point (see Figure 8.12). In this situation, the regression equation will take the form

$y = -a + bx$

Supposing that the equation were $y = -7 + 23x$, if we wanted to know the likely value of y when $x=3$, we would substitute as follows

$y = -7 + 23x$
$y = -7 + (23)(3)$
$y = -7 + 69$
$y = 69 - 7$
$y = 62$

As suggested at the start of this section, correlation and regression are closely connected. They make identical assumptions that variables are interval and that relationships are linear. Further, r and r^2 are often employed as indications of how well the regression line fits the data. Thus, for example, if $r=1$, the line of best fit would simply be drawn straight through all of the points (see Figure 8.13). Where points are more scattered, the line of best fit will provide a poorer fit with the data.

Figure 8.13 Regression: a perfect relationship

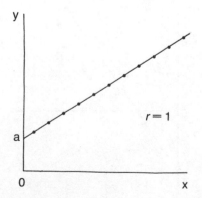

Figure 8.14 The accuracy of the line of best fit

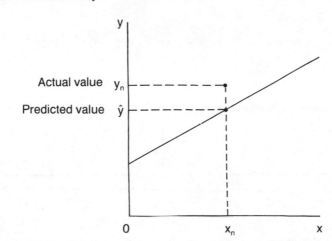

Accordingly, the more scatter there is in a scatter diagram, the less accurate the prediction of likely y values will be. Thus, the closer r is to 1, the less scatter there is and, therefore, the better the fit between the line of best fit and the data. If the two scatter diagrams in Figures 8.6 and 8.7 are examined, the line of best fit for the left-hand diagram in each case will constitute a superior fit between data and line and will permit more accurate predictions. This can be further illustrated by reference to Figure 8.14. If we take a particular value of x, i.e. x_n, then we can estimate the likely value of y ($\hat{y}_n$) from the regression line. However, the corresponding y value for a particular case may be y_n, which is different from $\hat{y}_n$. In other words, the latter provides an estimate of y, which is likely not to be totally accurate. Clearly, the further the points are from the line, the less accurate estimates are likely to be. Therefore, where r is low, scatter will be greater and the regression equation will provide a less accurate representation of the relationship between the two variables.

On the other hand, although correlation and regression are closely connected, it should be remembered that they serve different purposes. Correlation is concerned with the degrees of relationship between variables and regression with making predictions. But they can also be usefully used in conjunction, since, unlike correlation, regression can express the character of relationships. Compare the two scatter diagrams in Figure 8.15. The pattern of dots is identical and each would reveal an identical level of correlation (say 0.75), but the slope of the dots in (a) is much steeper than for (b). This difference would be revealed in a larger regression coefficient for (a) and a larger intercept for (b). Thus, the nature of the two relationships differs, even though the level of correlation is identical.

The r^2 value is often used as an indication of how well the model

Figure 8.15 Scatter diagrams for two identical levels of correlation

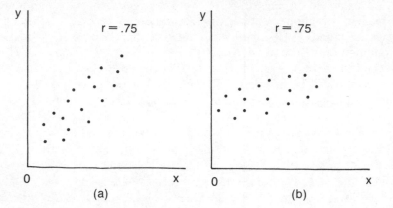

(a) (b)

implied by the regression equation fits the data. If we conceive of y, the dependent variable, as exhibiting variance which the independent variable goes some of the way towards explaining, then we can say that r^2 reflects the proportion of the variation in y explained by x. Thus, if r^2 equals 0.74, the model is providing an explanation of 74 per cent of the variance in y.

It should be noted that although we have been talking about y as the dependent and x as the independent variable, in many instances it makes just as much sense to treat x as dependent and y as independent. When this is done, the regression equation will be totally different. Three other words of caution should be registered. First, regression assumes that the dispersion of points in a scatter diagram is *homoscedastic,* or where the pattern of scatter of the points about the line shows no clear pattern. When the opposite is the case, and the pattern exhibits *heteroscedasticity,* where the amount of scatter around the line of best fit varies markedly at different

Figure 8.16 Heteroscedasticity

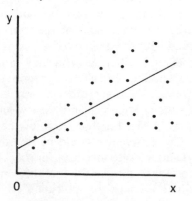

points, the use of regression is questionable. An example of heteroscedasticity is exhibited in Figure 8.16, which suggests that the amount of unexplained variation exhibited by the model is greater at the upper reaches of x and y. It should be noted that homoscedasticity is also a precondition of the use of Pearson's r.

Second, the size of a correlation coefficient and the nature of a regression equation will be affected by the amount of variance in either of the variables concerned. If, for example, one variable has a restricted range and the other a wider range, the size of the correlation coefficient may be smaller than would be the case if both were of equally wide variance.

Third, *outliers*, that is extreme values of x or y, can exert an excessive influence on the results of both correlation and regression. Consider the data in Table 8.11. We have data on twenty firms regarding their size (as measured by the number of employees) and the number of specialist functions in the organization (that is, the number of specialist areas, such as accounting, personnel, marketing, or public relations, in which at least one person spends 100 per cent of his or her time). In Table 8.11, we have an

Table 8.11 The impact of outliers: the relationship between size of firm and number of specialist functions (imaginary data)

Case no.	Size of firm (number of employees)	Number of specialist functions
1	110	3
2	150	2
3	190	5
4	230	8
5	270	5
6	280	6
7	320	7
8	350	5
9	370	8
10	390	6
11	420	9
12	430	7
13	460	3
14	470	9
15	500	12
16	540	9
17	550	13
18	600	14
19	640	11
20	2,700	16

When case 20 is included Pearson's $r = 0.67$ and the regression equation is specialization $= 5.55 + 0.00472$ size.

When case 20 is excluded Pearson's $r = 0.78$ and the regression equation is specialization $= 0.78 + 0.0175$ size.

outlier – case number 20 – which is much larger than all of the other firms in the sample. It is also somewhat higher in terms of the number of specialist functions than the other firms. In spite of the fact that this is only one case, its impact on estimates of both correlation and regression is quite pronounced. The Pearson's r is 0.67 and the regression equation is $y = 5.55 + 0.00472$ size. If the outlier is excluded, the magnitude of r rises to 0.78 and the regression equation is $y = 0.78 + 0.0175$. Such a difference can have a dramatic effect on predictions. If we wanted to know the likely value of y (number of specialist functions) for an organization of 340 employees with all twenty cases, the prediction would be 7.15; with the outlying case omitted the prediction is 6.73. Thus, this one outlying case can have an important impact upon the predictions that are generated. When such a situation arises, serious consideration has to be given to the exclusion of such an outlying case.

The purpose of this section has been to introduce the general idea of regression. In Chapter 10, it will receive a much fuller treatment, when the use of more than one independent variable will be examined, an area in which the power of regression is especially evident. SPSS contains a sophisticated set of instructions for generating a host of information relating to regression. However, much of this information is impenetrable; only some of it will be examined in Chapter 10. It is proposed to postpone a detailed treatment of generating regression information until this later chapter. However, if a simple introduction is required at this stage, it should be noted that subcommands following **plot** will generate basic information. If we return to the earlier example on p. 171 in which a scatter diagram was to be produced with **satis** as the dependent and **routine** as the independent variable, the subcommand

   /**format=regression.**

will produce information about the intercept, the slope (regression coefficient), and the standard error of the regression coefficient (which will be examined in Chapter 10), as well as r, r^2, and the significance of r. Such information can be found in Figures 8.1 and 8.2. In the case of Figure 8.1, the regression equation is

liberalism $= 32.60723 - 0.00153$income

When such basic information on the components of a regression equation is required, the **plot** procedure, which produces much additional useful information, has much to recommend it. In addition, the scatter diagram produced with **plot** prints two Rs, which, when joined, provide the line of best fit.

Overview of types of variable and methods of examining relationships

The following rules of thumb are suggested for the various types of combination of variable that may occur.

(1) Nominal–nominal. Contingency-table analysis in conjunction with chi-square as a test of statistical significance can be recommended. To test for strength of association, Cramer's V can be used.

(2) Ordinal–ordinal. Spearman's rho or Kendall's tau and their associated significance tests.

(3) Interval–interval. Pearson's r and regression for estimates of the strength and character of relationships respectively. Each can generate tests of statistical significance, but more detail in this regard for regression is provided in Chapter 10.

(4) Dichotomous–dichotomous. Same as under 1 for nominal–nominal, except that phi should be used instead of Cramer's V (and will be generated by SPSS instead of V).

(5) Interval–ordinal. If the ordinal variable assumes quite a large number of categories, it will probably be best to use rho or tau. Contingency-table analysis may be used if there are few categories in both the ordinal and interval variables (or if categories can be 'collapsed'). If the interval variable can be relatively unambiguously identified as the dependent variable and if the ordinal variable has few categories, another approach may be to use the **means** routine and to request an analysis of variance which will in turn allow an F ratio to be computed. In this way, a test of statistical significance can be provided, along with eta-squared.

(6) Interval–nominal or dichotomous. Contingency-table analysis plus the use of chi-square may be employed if the interval variable can be sensibly 'collapsed' into categories. This approach is appropriate if it is not meaningful to talk about which is the independent and which is the dependent variable. If the interval variable can be identified as a dependent variable, the **means** procedure and its associated statistics should be considered.

(7) Nominal–ordinal. Same as 1.

Exercises

1. (a) What SPSS commands would you need to create a contingency table for the relationship between **gender** and **prody**, with the former variable going across, along with column percentages (Job-Survey data)?
   (b) How would you assess the statistical significance of the relationship using SPSS?
   (c) In your view, is the relationship statistically significant?
   (d) What is the percentage of women who are described as exhibiting 'good' productivity?

2. A researcher carries out a study of the relationship between ethnic group and voting behaviour. The relationship is examined through a contingency table, for which the researcher computes the chi-square statistic. The value of chi-square turns out to be statistically significant at $p < 0.01$. The researcher concludes that this means that the relationship between the two variables is important and strong. Assess this reasoning.

3. (a) What SPSS commands would be needed to generate a matrix of Pearson's r correlation coefficients for **income, years, satis,** and **age,** along with a two-tailed significance test for each pair of relationships and means and standard deviations for all four variables (Job-Survey data)?
   (b) Conduct an analysis using the commands from question 3(a). Which pair of variables exhibits the largest correlation?
   (c) Taking this pair of variables, how much of the variance in one variable is explained by the other?

4. A researcher wants to examine the relationship between social class and number of books read in a year. The first hundred people are interviewed as they enter a public library in the researcher's home town. On the basis of the answers given, the sample is categorized in terms of a fourfold classification of social class: upper middle class / lower middle class / upper working class / lower working class. Using Pearson's r, the level of correlation is found to be 0.73, which is significant at $p < 0.001$. The researcher concludes that the findings have considerable validity, especially since 73 per cent of the variance in number of books read is explained by social class. Assess the researcher's analysis and conclusions.

5. A researcher finds that the correlation between income and a scale measuring interest in work is 0.55 (Pearson's r), which is non-significant since p is greater than 0.05. This finding is compared to another study using the same variables and measures which found the correlation to be 0.46 and $p = < 0.001$. How could this contrast arise? In other words, how could the larger correlation be non-significant and the smaller correlation be significant?

6. (a) What statistic or statistics would you recommend to estimate the strength of the relationship between **prody** and **commit** (Job-Survey data)?
   (b) What SPSS commands would you use to generate the relevant estimates?
   (c) What is the result of using these commands?

7. The regression equation for the relationship between **age** and **autonom** (with the latter as the dependent variable) is
   autonom $= 6.96435 + 0.06230$**age** $r = 0.28$
   (a) Explain what 6.94426 means.
   (b) Explain what 0.06230 means.
   (c) How well does the regression equation fit the data?
   (d) What is the likely level of autonomy for someone age 54?
   (e) Using **plot,** what commands will be required to provide this regression information?

Chapter nine

Multivariate analysis: exploring differences among three or more variables

In most studies in the social sciences we collect information on more than just two variables. Although it would be possible and more simple to examine the relationships between these variables just two at a time, there are serious disadvantages to restricting oneself to this approach, as we shall see. It is preferable initially to explore these data with multivariate rather than bivariate tests. The reasons for looking at three or more variables vary according to the aims and design of a study. Consequently, we will begin by outlining four design features which only involve three variables at a time. Obviously these features may include more than three variables and the features themselves can be combined to form more complicated designs, but we shall discuss them largely as if they were separate designs. However, as has been done before, we will use one set of data to illustrate their analysis, all of which can be carried out with a general statistical model called *multivariate analysis of variance and covariance* (MANOVA and MANCOVA). This model can be accessed through SPSS-X but requires the Advanced Statistics option if SPSS/PC+ is being used. Although the details of the model are difficult to understand and to convey simply (and so will not be attempted here), its basic principles are similar to those of other parametric tests we have previously discussed such as the *t*-test, one-way analysis of variance, and simple regression.

Multivariate designs

Factorial design

We are often interested in the effect of two variables on a third, particularly if we believe that the two variables may influence one another. To take a purely hypothetical case, we may expect the gender of the patient to interact with the kind of treatment they are given for feeling depressed. Women may respond more positively to psychotherapy where they have an opportunity to talk about their feelings while men may react more favourably to being treated with an antidepressant drug. In this case, we are

Figure 9.1 An example of an interaction between two variables

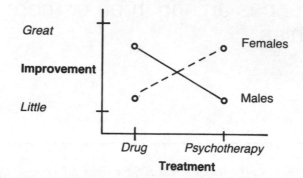

anticipating that the kind of treatment will *interact* with gender in alleviating depression. An interaction is when the effect of one variable is not the same under all the conditions of the other variable. It is often more readily understood when it is depicted in the form of a graph, as in Figure 9.1. However, whether these effects are statistically significant can only be determined by testing them and not just by visually inspecting them. The vertical axis shows the amount of improvement in depression that has taken place after treatment, while the horizontal one can represent either of the other two variables. In this case it reflects the kind of treatment received. The effects of the third variable, gender, are depicted by two different kinds of points and lines in the graph itself. Males are indicated by a dot and a continuous line while females are signified by a small circle and a broken line.

An interaction is indicated when the two lines representing the third variable are not parallel. Consequently, a variety of interaction effects can exist, three of which are shown in Figure 9.2 as hypothetical possibilities. In Figure 9.2a, men show less improvement with psychotherapy than with drugs while women derive greater benefit from psychotherapy than from the drug treatment. In Figure 9.2b, men improve little with either treatment, while women, once again, benefit considerably more from psychotherapy than from drugs. Finally, in Figure 9.2c, both men and women improve more with psychotherapy than with drugs, but the improvement is much greater for women than it is for men.

The absence of an interaction can be seen by the lines representing the third variable as remaining more or less parallel to one another, as is the case in the three examples in Figure 9.3. In Figure 9.3a, both men and women show a similar degree of improvement with both treatments. In Figure 9.3b, women improve more than men under both conditions while both treatments are equally effective. In Figure 9.3c, women show greater benefit than men with both treatments, and psychotherapy is better than drugs.

Figure 9.2 Examples of other interactions

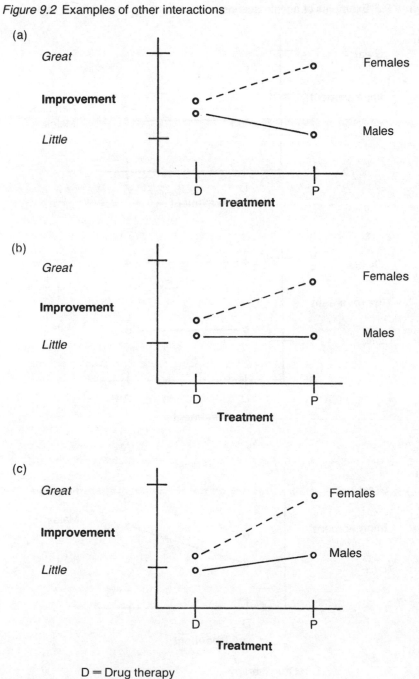

(a)

Great

Improvement

Little

D P
Treatment

Females

Males

(b)

Great

Improvement

Little

D P
Treatment

Females

Males

(c)

Great

Improvement

Little

D P
Treatment

Females

Males

D = Drug therapy

P = Psychotherapy

Figure 9.3 Examples of no interactions

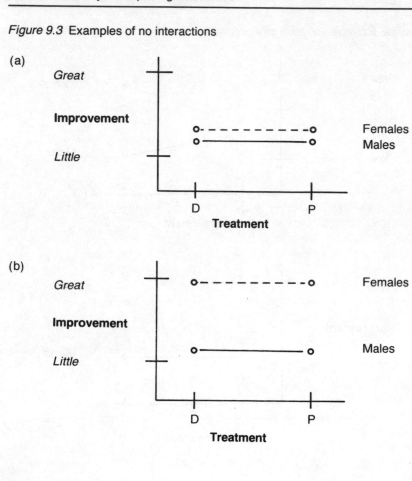

(a)

Great

Improvement

Little

Females
Males

D   P
Treatment

(b)

Great

Improvement

Little

Females

Males

D   P
Treatment

(c)

Great

Improvement

Little

Females

Males

D   P
Treatment

D = Drug therapy

P = Psychotherapy

The results of treatment and gender on their own are known as *main effects*. In these situations, the influence of the other variable is disregarded. If, for example, we wanted to examine the effect of gender, we would only look at improvement for men and women, ignoring that of treatment. If we were interested in the effect of the kind of treatment, we would simply compare the outcome of patients receiving psychotherapy with those being given drugs, paying no heed to gender.

The variables which are used to form the comparison groups are termed *factors*. The number of groups which constitute a factor are referred to as the *levels* of that factor. Since gender consists of two groups, it is called a two-level factor. The two kinds of treatment also create a two-level factor. If a third treatment had been included such as a control group of patients receiving neither drugs nor psychotherapy, we would have a three-level factor. Studies which investigate the effects of two or more factors are known as *factorial* designs. A study comparing two levels of gender and two levels of treatment is described as a *2 × 2* factorial design. If three rather than two levels of treatment had been compared, it would be a 2 × 3 factorial design. Incidentally, a study which only looks at one factor is called a oneway design, although it would be more consistent to call it a one-factor design.

The factors in these designs may be ones that are *manipulated,* such as differing dosages of drugs, different teaching methods, or varying levels of induced anxiety. Where they have been manipulated and where subjects have been randomly assigned to different levels, the factors may also be referred to as *independent* variables since they are more likely to be unrelated to, or independent of, other features of the experimental situation such as the personality of the subjects. Variables which are used to assess the effect of these independent variables are known as *dependent* variables since the effect on them is thought to depend on the level of the variable which has been manipulated. Thus, for example, the improvement in the depression experienced by patients (i.e. the dependent variable) is believed to be partly the result of the treatment they have received (i.e. the independent variable). Factors can also be variables which have not been manipulated, such as gender, age, ethnic origin, and social class. Because they cannot be separated from the individual who has them, they are sometimes referred to as *subject* variables. A study which investigated the effect of such subject variables would also be called a factorial design.

One of the main advantages of factorial designs, other than the study of interaction effects, is that they provide a more sensitive or powerful statistical test of the effect of the factors than designs which investigate just one factor at a time. To understand why this is the case, it is necessary to describe how a oneway and a twoway (i.e. a factorial) analysis of variance differ. In oneway analysis of variance, the variance in the means of the groups (or levels) is compared with the variance within them averaged across all the groups:

$$F = \frac{\text{variance between-groups}}{\text{variance within-groups}}$$

The between-groups variance is calculated by comparing the group mean with the overall or grand mean, while the within-groups variance is worked out by comparing the individual scores in the group with its mean. If the group means differ, then their variance should be greater than the average of those within them. This situation is illustrated in Figure 9.4 where the means of the three groups (M_1, M_2, and M_3) are quite widely separated causing a greater spread of between-groups variance (V_B) while the variance within the groups (V_1, V_2, and V_3) is considerably less when averaged (V_W).

Now the variance within the groups is normally thought of as error since this is the only way in which we can estimate it, while the between-groups variance is considered to consist of this error plus the effect of the factor which is being investigated. While some of the within-groups variance may be due to error, such as that of measurement and of procedure, the rest of it will be due to factors which we have not controlled such as gender, age, and motivation. In other words, the within-groups variance will contain error as well as variance due to other factors, and so will be larger than if it were just to contain error variance. Consequently, it will provide an over-estimate of error. In a two-factor design, on the other hand, the variance due to the other factor can be removed from this overestimate of the error variance, thereby giving a more accurate calculation of it. If, for example,

Figure 9.4 Schematic representation of a significant oneway effect

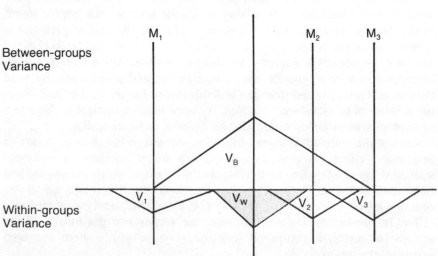

we had just compared the effectiveness of the drug treatment with psychotherapy in reducing depression, then some of the within-groups variance would have been due to gender but treated as error, and may have obscured any differential effect due to treatment.

Covariate design

Another way of reducing error variance is by removing the influence of a non-categorical variable (i.e. one which is not nominal) which we believe to be biasing the results. This is particularly useful in designs where subjects are not randomly assigned to factors, such as in the Job-Survey study, or where random assignment did not result in the groups being equal in terms of some other important variable, such as how depressed patients were before being treated. A covariate is a variable which is linearly related to the one in which we are most directly interested, usually called the *dependent* or *criterion* variable.

We will give two examples of the way in which the effect of covariates may be controlled. Suppose, for instance, we wanted to find out the relationship between job satisfaction and the two factors of gender and ethnic group in the Job-Survey data and we knew that job satisfaction was positively correlated with income, so that people who were earning more were also more satisfied with their jobs. It is possible that both gender and ethnic group will also be related to income. Women may earn less than men and non-white workers may earn less than their white counterparts. If so, then the relationship of these two factors to job satisfaction is likely to be biased by their association with income. To control for this, we will remove the influence of income by covarying it out. In this case, income is the covariate. If income were not correlated with job satisfaction, then there would be no need to do this. Consequently, it is only advisable to control a covariate when it has been found to be related to the dependent variable.

In true experimental designs, we try to control the effect of variables other than the independent ones by randomly assigning subjects to different treatments or conditions. However, when the number of subjects allocated to treatments is small (say, about ten or less), there is a stronger possibility that there will be chance differences between them. If, for example, we are interested in comparing the effects of drugs with psycho-therapy in treating depression, it is important that the patients in the two conditions should be similar in terms of how depressed they are before treatment begins (i.e. at *pre-test*). If the patients receiving the drug treatment were found at pre-test to be more depressed than those having psychotherapy despite random assignment, then it is possible that because they are more depressed to begin with, they will show less improvement than the psychotherapy patients. If pre-test depression is positively correlated with depression at the end of treatment (i.e. at *post-test*), then the effect of these initial differences can be removed statistically by covarying them out. The covariate in this example would be the pre-test depression scores.

Three points need to be made about the selection of covariates. First, as mentioned before, they should only be variables which are related to the dependent variable. Variables which are unrelated to it do not need to be covaried out. Second, if two covariates are strongly correlated with one another (say 0.8 or above), it is only necessary to remove one of them since the other one seems to be measuring the same variable(s). Third, with small numbers of subjects only a few covariates at most should be used, since the more covariates there are in such situations, the less powerful the statistical test becomes.

Multiple-measures design

In many designs we may be interested in examining differences in more than one dependent or criterion measure. In the Job-Survey study, for example, we may want to know how differences in gender and ethnic group are related to job autonomy and routine as well as satisfaction. In the depression study, we may wish to assess the effect of treatment in more than one way. How depressed the patients themselves feel may be one measure. Another may be how depressed they appear to be to someone who knows them well, such as a close friend or informant. One of the advantages of using multiple measures is to find out how restricted or widespread a particular effect may be. In studying the effectiveness of treatments for depression, for instance, we would have more confidence in the results if the effects were picked up by a number of similar measures rather than just one. Another advantage is that although groups may not differ on individual measures, they may do so when a number of related individual measures are examined jointly. Thus, for example, psycho-therapy may not be significantly more effective than the drug treatment when outcome is assessed by either the patients themselves or by their close friends, but it may be significantly better when these two measures are analysed together.

Mixed between–within design

The multiple-measures design needs to be distinguished from the repeated-measures design which we encountered at the end of Chapter 7. A multiple-measures design has two or more dependent or criterion variables such as two separate measures of depression. A repeated-measures design, on the other hand, consists of one or more factors being investigated on the same group of subjects. Measuring job satisfaction or depression at two or more points in time would be an example of such a factor. Another would be evaluating the effectiveness of drugs and psychotherapy on the same patients by giving them both treatments. If we were to do this, we would have to make sure that half the patients were randomly assigned to receiving psychotherapy first and the drug treatment second, while the other patients would be given the two treatments in the reverse order. It is necessary to counterbalance the sequence of the two conditions to control for *order effects*. It would also be advisable to check that the sequence in which the treatments were administered did not affect the results. The order effect would constitute a between-subject factor since any one subject would only receive one of the two orders. In other words, this design would become a mixed one which included both a between-subject factor (order) and a within-subject one (treatment). One of the advantages of this design is that it restricts the amount of variance due to individuals, since the same treatments are compared on the same subjects.

Another example of a mixed between–within design is where we assess the dependent variable before as well as after the treatment, as in the study on depression comparing the effectiveness of psychotherapy with drugs. This design has two advantages. The first is that the pre-test enables us to determine whether the groups were similar in terms of the dependent variable before the treatment began. The second is that it allows us to determine if there has been any change in the dependent variable before and after the treatment has been given. In other words, this design enables us to discern whether any improvement has taken place as a result of the treatment and whether this improvement is greater for one group than the other.

Combined design

As was mentioned earlier, the four design features can be combined in various ways. Thus, for instance, we can have two independent factors (gender and treatment for depression), one covariate (age), two dependent measures (assessment of depression by patient and informant), and one repeated measure (pre- and post-test). These components will form the basis of the following illustration, which shall be referred to as the Depression Project. The data for it are shown in Table 9.1. There are three treatments: a no-treatment control condition (coded 1 and with eight subjects); a psychotherapy treatment (coded 2 and with ten subjects); and a drug treatment (coded 3 and with twelve subjects). Females are coded as 1 and males as 2. A high score on depression indicates a greater degree of it. The patient's assessment of their depression before and after treatment is referred to as **patpre** and **patpost** respectively, while the assessment provided by an informant before and after treatment is known as **infpre** and **infpost**.

Table 9.1 The Depression-Project data

id	treat	gend	age	patpre	infpre	patpost	infpost
01	1	1	27	25	27	20	19
02	1	2	30	29	26	25	27
03	1	1	33	26	25	23	26
04	1	2	36	31	33	24	26
05	1	1	41	33	30	29	28
06	1	2	44	28	30	23	26
07	1	1	47	34	30	30	31
08	1	2	51	35	37	29	28
09	2	1	25	21	24	9	15
10	2	2	27	20	21	9	12
11	2	1	30	23	20	10	8
12	2	2	31	22	28	14	18
13	2	1	33	25	22	15	17
14	2	2	34	26	23	17	16
15	2	1	35	24	26	9	13
16	2	2	37	27	25	18	20
17	2	1	38	25	21	11	8
18	2	2	42	29	30	19	21
19	3	1	30	34	37	23	25
20	3	2	33	31	27	15	13
21	3	1	36	32	35	20	21
22	3	2	37	33	35	20	18
23	3	1	39	40	38	33	35
24	3	2	41	34	31	18	19
25	3	1	42	34	36	23	27
26	3	2	44	37	31	14	11
27	3	1	45	36	38	24	25
28	3	2	47	38	35	25	27
29	3	1	48	37	39	29	28
30	3	2	50	39	37	23	24

We shall now turn to methods of analysing the results of this kind of study using MANOVA or MANCOVA.

Multivariate analysis

Factorial design

The example we have given is the more common one in which there are unequal numbers of subjects on one or more of the factors. Although it is possible to equalize them by randomly omitting two subjects from the psychotherapy treatment and four from the drug one, this would be a waste of valuable data and so is not recommended. There are three different ways of analysing the results of factorial designs (Overall and Spiegel 1969). All three methods produce the same result when there are equal numbers of subjects in each cell. When they are unequal, as in this case, one of them has to be selected as the preferred method since the results they give differ.

The first method, referred to as the *regression* or *unweighted-means* approach, assigns equal weight to the means in all cells regardless of their size. In other words, interaction effects have the same importance as main ones. This is the approach to be recommended in a true experimental design such as this one where subjects have been randomly assigned to treatments. The second method, known as the *classic experimental* or *least-squares* approach, places greater weight on cells with larger numbers of subjects and is recommended for non-experimental designs in which the number of subjects in each cell may reflect its importance. This approach gives greater weight to main effects than to interaction ones. In SPSS, the least-squares approach is only available with the **anova** statistical procedure. The commands for carrying out such an analysis will be described at the end of this chapter. The third method, called the *hierarchical* approach, allows the investigator to determine the order of the effects. If one factor is thought to precede another, then it can be placed first. This approach should be used in non-experimental designs where the factors can be ordered in some sequential manner. If, for example, we are interested in the effect of ethnic group and income on job satisfaction, then ethnic group would be entered first since income cannot determine to which ethnic group we belong.

To determine the effect of treatment, gender, and their interaction on post-test depression as seen by the patient, the following commands are needed:

```
manova patpost by treat (1,3) gender (1,2)
 /method=sstype(unique)
 /print=cellinfo(means) homogeneity(bartlett,cochran)
 /design.
```

The dependent variable (**patpost**) is listed immediately after the **manova** command followed by the two independent variables (**treat** and **gender**) and their minimum and maximum levels in parentheses (**1,3** and **1,2**). The **method** subcommand requests the regression approach in which each cell makes a unique contribution to the sum of squares. The **print** subcommand provides the means and standard deviations of each cell (**cellinfo**), and a test to determine whether the variances are the same or homogeneous (**homogeneity**). The **design** subcommand states that it is a between-subjects one which includes both main effects (treatment and gender) and their interaction (treatment by gender). This subcommand is always placed last. It should be noted that the full stop at the end of the list of sub-commands applies only to SPSS/PC+; it should be omitted if SPSS-X is being used. Throughout this chapter, this same convention holds.

The means and standard deviations for the three treatments for males and females are shown in Table 9.2. Also included are two tests for homo-geneity of variance, both of which are not significant. This means there are

Table 9.2 Means and standard deviations of post-test depression in the three treatments for men and women (Depression-Project SPSS/PC+ output)

Cell Means and Standard Deviations
Variable . . PATPOST

FACTOR	CODE	posttest depression:patient Mean	Std. Dev.	N
TREAT	control			
GENDER	female	25.500	4.796	4
GENDER	male	25.250	2.630	4
TREAT	therapy			
GENDER	female	10.800	2.490	5
GENDER	male	15.400	4.037	5
TREAT	drug			
GENDER	female	25.333	4.761	6
GENDER	male	19.167	4.355	6
For entire sample		20.033	6.754	30

Univariate Homogeneity of Variance Tests

Variable . . PATPOST   posttest depression:patient

      Cochrans C(4,6) =   .24455, P = 1.000 (approx.)
      Bartlett-Box F (5,677) =   .50600, P = .722

no significant differences between the variances of the groups, an assumption on which this test is based. If the variances had been grossly unequal, then it may have been possible to reduce this through transforming the data by taking the log or square root of the dependent variable. This can easily be done with the **compute** command: for example, the natural or Naperian log (base e) of **patpost** (called **lnpapost** here) is produced by:

compute lnpapost=ln(patpost).

Its square root (**sqrppost**) is given by:

compute sqrppost=sqrt(patpost).

It is necessary to check that the transformations have produced the desired effect.

The tests of significance for determining the unique sum of squares for each effect are shown in Table 9.3. These indicate that there is a significant effect for the treatment factor ($p < 0.00005$) and a significant interaction effect for treatment and gender ($p=0.016$). If we plot this interaction, we can see that depression after the drug treatment is higher for women than men, while after psychotherapy it is higher for men than women. The **constant** effect is usually not presented in ANOVA and MANOVA tables and can be ignored. It is a measure of the deviation of each score from the grand mean, which as we can see from Table 9.2, is about 20. The mean square of an effect is its sum of squares divided by its number of degrees of

Table 9.3 Tests of significance for main and interaction effects of a factorial design (Depression-Project SPSS/PC+ output)

Tests of Significance for PATPOST using UNIQUE sums of squares

Source of Variation	SS	DF	MS	F	Sig. of F
WITHIN CELLS	387.92	24	16.16		
CONSTANT	11959.54	1	11959.54	739.92	.000
TREAT	767.94	2	383.97	23.76	.000
GENDER	2.68	1	2.68	.17	.688
TREAT BY GENDER	159.61	2	79.80	4.94	.016

freedom. Thus, for example, the mean square of the treatment effect is 767.94 divided by 2, which is 383.97. The *F* value for an effect is its mean square divided by that of the within-cells or error term. For the treatment effect, therefore, this would be 383.97 divided by 16.16, which is 23.76.

Having found that there is an overall significant difference in depression for the three treatments, we need to determine where this difference lies. One way of doing this is to test for differences between two treatments at a time. If we had not anticipated certain differences between treatments, we would apply *a priori* tests such as Scheffé to determine their statistical significance, whereas if we had predicted them we would use unrelated *t*-tests (see Chapter 7). An alternative method for analysing predicted differences is to make *planned contrasts*. The advantage of doing this is to make the test a more powerful one of potential differences.

Although SPSS provides a number of methods for doing so, we shall only outline the one in which we define the contrasts. In doing this, it is important to ensure that the contrasts are not linear combinations of one another. In other words, a contrast is a linear combination of other ones if it can be derived from them. If, for example, we compare the control treatment with the drug treatment and the control treatment with the psychotherapy treatment, then these two contrasts are not linearly dependent since they are unrelated to one another. However, if we then went on to compare the drug with the psychotherapy treatment, this contrast would not be linearly independent of the previous two contrasts since it can be calculated from the previous two comparisons as follows:

psychotherapy–drug difference=(control–drug difference)−(control–psychotherapy difference)

We might wish to test the following two contrasts which are not linear combinations of one another. First, we could compare the mean of the drug and the psychotherapy treatments with that of the control condition, since we would anticipate that patients receiving some form of treatment should improve more than those not having any. Second, we might hypothesize that there would be no difference between the drug and the psychotherapy treatments. To do this, we need to use the following subcommands placed after the **method** subcommand:

```
/method=sstype(unique)
/contrast(treat)=special(1   1   1
                         2  -1  -1
                         0   1  -1)
/partition(treat)
/design=treat(1) treat(2).
```

The first row is the mean, or constant, effect and indicates the groups to be included. The second row compares the mean of the control group (2) with that of the other two combined $(-1 -1)$. Note that the numbers in the rows have to sum to zero. This contrast could also have been indicated by 1 -0.5 -0.5. The third row compares the mean of the psychotherapy condition (1) with that of the drug one (-1). The **partition** subcommand specifies the degrees of freedom to be used for each of the contrasts. The name of the variable or factor to be partitioned is placed in parentheses immediately after it. The default value consists of one degree of freedom for each level of the factor, which is the option to be used in this case. The partitions to be requested are listed in the **design** subcommand. The first one [**treat(1)**] compares the control group with the other two treatments combined, while the second one [**treat(2)**] examines the difference between the two treatments. The output for these commands is displayed in Table 9.4.

Both contrasts are significant. To interpret what these differences indicate, we need to know what the means are for the relevant comparisons. Using the information in Table 9.2, we can calculate the means for the contrasted groups. To do this for the drug and psychotherapy treatments combined, it is important to remember that allowance has to be made for the fact that there are different numbers of subjects in these two conditions. In other words, the mean for each condition is multiplied by the number of subjects in it to give a total score. The total scores for the two conditions are summed and divided by the total number of subjects. This will give the mean for the combined group. The mean of the combined

Table 9.4 Tests of significance for specified contrasts (Depression-Project SPSS/PC+ output)

Tests of Significance for PATPOST using UNIQUE sums of squares

Source of Variation	SS	DF	MS	F	Sig. of F
WITHIN CELLS	387.92	24	16.16		
CONSTANT	11959.54	1	11959.54	739.92	.000
TREAT (1)	347.06	1	347.06	21.47	.000
TREAT (2)	456.67	1	456.67	28.25	.000

group (18.1) is lower than that for the control group (25.4), while the mean of the drug treatment (22.25) is higher than that for the psychotherapy condition (13.1). In other words, patients without treatment see themselves as more depressed than those with treatment, and those receiving the drug treatment are more depressed than those having psychotherapy. The constant effect is ignored since it simply reflects whether the unweighted mean of the three groups differs from zero. The unweighted mean, unlike the weighted mean, takes no account of the fact that there are different numbers of subjects in each of the three treatments. The unweighted mean is about 20.24, while the weighted mean is about 20.03.

Covariate design

If the patients' pre-test depression scores differ for gender, treatment, or their interaction and if the pre-test scores are related to the post-test ones, then the results of the previous test will be biased by this. To determine if there are such differences, we need to run a factorial analysis on the patients' pre-test depression scores. If we do this, we find that there is a significant effect for treatments (see the output in Table 9.5),'which means that the pre-test depression scores differ between treatments.

Covariate analysis is based on the same assumptions as the previous factorial analysis plus three additional ones. First, there must be a linear relationship between the dependent variable and the covariate. If there is no such relationship, then there is no need to conduct a covariate analysis. This assumption can be tested by plotting a scatter diagram (see Chapter 8) to see if the relationship appears non-linear. If the correlation is statistically significant, then it is appropriate to carry out a covariate analysis. The statistical procedure **manova** also provides information on this (see p. 205). If the relationship is non-linear, it may be possible to transform it so that it becomes linear using a logarithmic transformation of one variable. The procedure for effecting such a transformation with SPSS has been described on page 200.

The second assumption is that the slope of the regression lines in each

Table 9.5 Tests of significance for effects on pre-test depression (Depression-Project SPSS/PC+ output)

Tests of Significance for PATPRE using UNIQUE sums of squares

Source of Variation	SS	DF	MS	F	Sig. of F
WITHIN CELLS	248.58	24	10.36		
CONSTANT	26119.68	1	26119.68	2521.78	.000
TREAT	686.47	2	343.24	33.14	.000
GENDER	4.23	1	4.23	.41	.529
TREAT BY GENDER	3.47	2	1.74	.17	.847

group or cell is the same. If they are the same, this implies that there is no interaction between the independent variable and the covariate and that the average within-cell regression can be used to adjust the scores of the dependent variable. This information is also provided by **manova**. If this condition is not met, then the Johnson–Neyman technique should be considered. This method is not available on SPSS but a description of it may be found elsewhere (Huitema 1980).

The third assumption is that the covariate should be measured without error. For some variables such as gender and age, this assumption can usually be justified. For others, however, such as measures of depression, this needs to be checked. This can be done by computing the alpha reliability coefficient for multi-item variables (such as job satisfaction) or test–retest correlations where this information is available. A coefficient of 0.8 or above is usually taken as indicating a reliable measure. This assumption is more important in non- than in true-experimental designs, where its violation may lead to either Type I or II errors. In true-experimental designs, the violation of this assumption only leads to loss of power. As there are no agreed or simple procedures for adjusting covariates for unreliability, these will not be discussed.

The following commands are necessary to test the effect of treatment on the patients' post-test depression scores controlling for their pre-test ones:

```
manova patpost by treat(1,3) with patpre
 /method=sstype(unique)
 /pmeans
 /design
 /analysis=patpost
 /design=treat, treat by patpre.
```

The dependent variable (**patpost**) is listed first on the **manova** command, followed with the word **by**, the independent variable (**treat**), and its minimum and maximum levels (**1,3**). The covariate (**patpre**) comes last and is preceded by the word **with**. The **pmeans** subcommand in SPSS gives us the predicted and adjusted means. The **design** subcommand specifies that it is a between-subject one. The **analysis** and the second **design**

Table 9.6 Test of homogeneity of slope of regression line within cells (Depression-Project SPSS/PC+ output)

Tests of Significance for PATPOST using UNIQUE sums of squares					
Source of Variation	*SS*	*DF*	*MS*	*F*	*Sig. of F*
WITHIN+RESIDUAL	550.90	25	22.04		
CONSTANT	3137.48	1	3137.48	142.38	.000
TREAT	7.11	2	3.56	.16	.852
TREAT BY PATPRE	4.12	2	2.06	.09	.911

Table 9.7 Significance of the relationship between the covariate and post-test depression (Depression-Project SPSS/PC+ output)

Regression analysis for WITHIN CELLS error term (CONT.)
Dependent variable . . PATPOST   posttest depression:patient

COVARIATE	B	Beta	Std. Err.	t-Value	Sig. of t
PATPRE	1.08138	.73354	.196	5.503	.000
COVARIATE	Lower −95%	CL- Upper			
PATPRE	.677	1.485			

subcommands test whether the regression lines are the same in each of the cells. The output for these last two subcommands is presented in Table 9.6. The interaction between the independent variable of treatment and the covariate of **patpre** is not significant since *p* is 0.911. This means that the slope of the regression line in each of the cells is similar and therefore the second assumption is met.

The output in Table 9.7 shows what the relationship is between the covariate (**patpre**) and the dependent variable (**patpost**); in this case, the relationship is significant. Consequently, it is appropriate to proceed with the covariate analysis.

The analysis-of-covariance table is displayed in Table 9.8. This shows that there is a significant treatment effect when pretreatment depression is covaried out.

An inspection of the adjusted means for the three treatments presented in Table 9.9 shows that controlling for pretreatment depression has little effect on the mean for the control group, which remains at about 25. However, it makes a considerable difference to the means of the two treatment conditions, reversing their order so that patients who received psychotherapy report themselves as being more depressed than those given the drug treatment. The Bryant–Paulson *post-hoc* test for determining whether this difference is significant is described in Stevens (1986). The estimated means are also presented in Table 9.9. These are the same as the

Table 9.8 Analysis-of-covariance table (Depression-Project SPSS/PC+ output)

Tests of Significance for PATPOST using UNIQUE sums of squares

Source of Variation	SS	DF	MS	F	Sig. of F
WITHIN CELLS	256.38	26	9.86		
REGRESSION	298.65	1	298.65	30.29	.000
CONSTANT	41.43	1	41.43	4.20	.051
TREAT	339.16	2	169.58	17.20	.000

Regression analysis for WITHIN CELLS error term

Table 9.9 Observed and adjusted means of post-test depression in the three treatments (Depression-Project SPSS/PC+ output)

Adjusted and Estimated Means
Variable .. PATPOST   posttest depression: patient

CELL	Obs. Mean	Adj. Mean	Est. Mean	Raw Resid.	Std. Resid.
1	25.375	25.147	25.375	.000	.000
2	13.100	19.279	13.100	.000	.000
3	22.250	16.299	22.250	.000	.000

observed ones and will only differ from them when not all of the effects in a design are specified.

Multiple-measures design

So far, we have only analysed one of the two dependent measures, the patient's self-report of depression. Analysing the two dependent measures together has certain advantages. First, it reduces the probability of making Type I errors (deciding there is a difference when there is none) when making a number of comparisons. The probability of making this error is usually set at 0.05 when comparing two groups on one dependent variable. If we made two such independent comparisons, then the *p* level would increase to about 0.10. Since the comparisons are not independent, this probability is higher. Second, analysing the two dependent measures together provides us with a more sensitive measure of the effects of the independent variables.

The following commands are necessary to carry out such an analysis:

```
manova patpost infpost by treat(1,3)
 /method=sstype(unique)
 /print=cellinfo(means) homogeneity(boxm) error(cor)
 /design.
```

The **print** subcommand gives the means of the two dependent variables for each cell, Box's *M* multivariate test for homogeneity of variance, and Bartlett's test of sphericity [**error(cor)**].

The result for Box's *M* test is presented in Table 9.10. This determines whether the variances of the two dependent variables are similar. Two statistics are given for this test – the *F* and the chi-square approximation. The chi-square test should be used when all the group sizes are greater than twenty, the number of groups is less than six and the number of dependent variables is also less than six (Stevens 1986). Otherwise, the *F* test should be used, as in this case where the group sizes are smaller than twenty. For this example, both tests are not significant, which means that the variances do not differ significantly from one another.

Table 9.10 Box's *M* test (Depression-Project SPSS/PC+ output)

Multivariate test for Homogeneity of Dispersion matrices

Boxs M =	7.98483
F WITH (6,9324) DF =	1.18201, P = .312 (Approx.)
Chi-square with 6 DF =	7.09720, P = .312 (Approx.)

Table 9.11 shows the output for Bartlett's test of sphericity which assesses whether the dependent measures are correlated. If the test is significant, as it is here, it means the two dependent measures are related. In this situation, it is more appropriate to use the multivariate test of significance to determine whether there are significant differences between the treatments. The result of this test is presented in Table 9.12 and shows the treatment effect to be significant when the two measures are taken together.

The univariate *F*-tests for the treatment effect, which are presented in Table 9.13, show that the treatments differ on both the dependent measures when they are analysed separately. To determine which treatments differ significantly from one another, it would be necessary to carry out a series of unrelated *t*-tests or *post-hoc* tests as discussed previously.

Table 9.11 Bartlett's test of sphericity (Depression-Project SPSS/PC+ output)

Statistics for WITHIN CELLS correlations

Determinant =	.18419
Bartlett test of sphericity = 43.14008 with 1 D. F.	
Significance =	.000
F(max) criterion =	1.37962 with (2,27) D. F.

Table 9.12 Multivariate tests of significance for the treatment effect (Depression-Project SPSS/PC+ output)

EFFECT .. TREAT
Multivariate Tests of Significance (S = 2, M = −1/2, N = 12)

Test Name	Value	Approx. F	Hypoth. DF	Error DF	Sig. of F
Pillais	.61765	6.03196	4.00	54.00	.000
Hotellings	1.51298	9.45613	4.00	50.00	.000
Wilks	.39350	7.72394	4.00	52.00	.000
Roys	.59904				

Table 9.13 Univariate tests of significance for the two dependent measures (Depression-Project SPSS/PC+ output)

Univariate F-tests with (2,27) D. F.

Variable	Hypoth. SS	Error SS	Hypoth. MS	Error MS	F	Sig. of F
PATPOST	767.94167	555.02500	383.97083	20.55648	18.67882	.000
INFPOST	652.14167	765.72500	326.07083	28.36019	11.49749	.000

Mixed between–within design

The commands for determining whether there is a significant difference between the three conditions in improvement in depression as assessed by the patient before (**patpre**) and after (**patpost**) treatment are:

```
manova patpre patpost by treat(1,3)
 /wsfactor=time(2)
 /wsdesign=time
 /rename=constant change
 /print=transform cellinfo(means)
 /method=sstype(unique)
 /design.
```

Since this analysis incorporates one measure which is repeated twice (**patpre** and **patpost**), it is necessary to indicate this with two within-subject subcommands (**wsfactor** and **wsdesign**) in SPSS/PC+. In SPSS-X, you can omit the **wsdesign** subcommand. Since there are only two variables which are going to be transformed, there will only be two transformed dependent variables. It is important to realize that unless they are renamed the transformed variables will have the same names as the untransformed ones. To remind us what these transformed variables are, they have been renamed using the **rename** subcommand. The first transformation is the constant (which is the mean of the pre- and the post-treatment scores) while the second corresponds to the change in depression over time. Since there is

Table 9.14 The second renamed transformed variable (Depression-Project SPSS/PC+ output)

Order of Variables for Analysis

    Variates   Covariates

    CHANGE

    1 Dependent Variable
    0 Covariates

Note: TRANSFORMED variables are in the variates column.
       These TRANSFORMED variables correspond to the 'TIME' WITHIN-SUBJECT effect.

Table 9.15 Test of significance for treatment (Depression-Project SPSS/PC+ output)

Tests of Between-Subjects Effects
Tests of Significance for CONSTANT using UNIQUE sums of squares

Source of Variation	SS	DF	MS	F	Sig. of F
WITHIN CELLS	681.38	27	25.24		
CONSTANT	36713.87	1	36713.87	1454.80	.000
TREAT	1278.77	2	639.38	25.34	.000

effectively only one dependent measure (**change**), it is not necessary to request multivariate or univariate tests of significance, nor Bartlett's test of sphericity. The output showing the second transformed variable to be analysed is presented in Table 9.14.

There is a significant effect for treatment, as indicated in the output in Table 9.15. This information is of limited use in this case since we do not know whether the treatments differ primarily on the pre- or the post-treatment scores.

More useful information is presented in Table 9.16 which shows a significant effect due to time (i.e. the change between the pre- and the post-treatment scores) and a significant interaction between time and treatment, as displayed in Table 9.16.

If we look at the means of the patients' pre-test and post-test depression scores in Table 9.17, we can see that the amount of improvement shown by the three groups of patients is not the same. Least improvement has occurred in the group receiving no treatment (30.125−25.375=4.75), while patients being administered the drug treatment exhibit the most improvement (35.417−22.250=13.167).

Statistical differences in the amount of improvement shown in the three treatments could be further examined using **oneway** analysis of variance where the dependent variable is the computed difference between pre- and post-test patient depression.

Table 9.16 Tests of significance for the within-subject 'time' effect (Depression-Project SPSS/PC+ output)

Tests involving 'TIME' Within-Subject Effect.
Tests of Significance for CHANGE using UNIQUE sums of squares

Source of Variation	SS	DF	MS	F	Sig. of F
WITHIN CELLS	129.03	27	4.78		
TIME	1365.35	1	1365.35	285.70	.000
TREAT BY TIME	175.65	2	87.82	18.38	.000

Table 9.17 Means and standard deviations of pre-test and post-test depression for the three treatments (Depression-Project SPSS/PC+ output)

Cell Means and Standard Deviations
Variable .. PATPRE   pre-test depression:patient

FACTOR	CODE	Mean	Std. Dev.	N
TREAT	control	30.125	3.720	8
TREAT	therapy	24.200	2.781	10
TREAT	drug	35.417	2.843	12
For entire sample		30.267	5.699	30

Variable .. PATPOST   posttest depression:patient

FACTOR	CODE	Mean	Std. Dev.	N
TREAT	control	25.375	3.583	8
TREAT	therapy	13.100	3.985	10
TREAT	drug	22.250	5.413	12
For entire sample		20.033	6.754	30

Combined design

As pointed out earlier on, it is possible to combine some of the above analyses. To show how this can be done, we shall look at the effect of two between-subject factors (treatment and gender) and one within-subject one (pre- to post-test or time) on two dependent variables (depression as assessed by the patient and an informant), covarying out the effects of age which we think might be related to the pre- and post-test measures. The following commands could be used to carry this out:

```
compute age2=age.
manova patpre patpost infpre infpost by treat(1,3) gender(1,2)
 with age age2
 /wsfactor=time(2)
 /wsdesign=time
 /rename=constpat diffpat constinf diffinf age age2
 /print=homogeneity(boxm) transform error(cor) signif(univ)
 /method=sstype(unique)
 /design.
```

Since the covariate is the same for the repeated factor which consists of two measures, it is necessary to have as many covariates as measures, which in this case is two. In other words, we have to create a replicate of the covariate, which is done with the **compute** command (i.e. **compute age2=age**). The within-subject design is specified by the **wsfactor** and **wsdesign** subcommands in SPSS/PC+. The **wsdesign** subcommand is omitted in SPSS-X. The between-subject design is requested by the last **design** subcommand. The four transformed variables to be used in the two analyses have been renamed, while the two covariates which have not been changed have kept their names. In conducting a multivariate analysis of covariance, it is necessary to check that the covariate (**age**) is significantly correlated with the two dependent variables, which it is as the output in Table 9.18 shows.

Table 9.18 Relationship between the covariate age and the two transformed variables (Depression-Project SPSS/PC+ output)

Regression analysis for WITHIN CELLS error term (CONT.)
Dependent variable .. CONSTPAT

COVARIATE	B	Beta	Std. Err.	t-Value	Sig. of t
AGE	.36439	.71863	.074	4.956	.000

COVARIATE	Lower −95%	CL- Upper
AGE	.212	.516

Regression analysis for WITHIN CELLS error term (CONT.)
Dependent variable .. CONSTINF

COVARIATE	B	Beta	Std. Err.	t-Value	Sig. of t
AGE	.29224	.58309	.085	3.442	.002

COVARIATE	Lower −95%	CL- Upper
AGE	.117	.468

Since we are interested in the time within-subject effect and not the constant one, these two transformed and renamed variables are displayed in Table 9.19.

Table 9.19 The renamed and transformed within-subject effect for time (Depression-Project SPSS/PC+ output)

Order of Variables for Analysis

Variates	*Covariates*
DIFFPAT	AGE2
DIFFINF	

2 Dependent Variables
1 Covariate

Note. TRANSFORMED variables are in the variates column.
These TRANSFORMED variables correspond to the 'TIME' WITHIN-SUBJECT effect.

Although the results for four effects are given in this analysis (i.e. time, treatment by time, gender by time, and treatment by gender by time), only those for the triple interaction will be displayed. The output for the multivariate tests are reproduced in Table 9.20, which show a significant effect.

Table 9.20 Multivariate tests for the interaction between treatment, gender, and time (Depression-Project SPSS/PC+ output)

EFFECT .. TREAT BY GENDER BY TIME
Multivariate Tests of Significance (S = 2, M = −½, N = 10½)

Test Name	Value	Approx. F	Hypoth. DF	Error DF	Sig. of F
Pillais	.57382	4.82814	4.00	48.00	.002
Hotellings	1.23762	6.80692	4.00	44.00	.000
Wilks	.44050	5.82700	4.00	46.00	.001
Roys	.54767				

The univariate tests in Table 9.21 demonstrate the interaction effect to be significant ($p < 0.0005$) for the patient measure only (**diffpat**). It is not significant ($p=0.164$) for the informant measure (**diffinf**). To interpret these results, it would be necessary to compute the mean pre- and post-treatment patient-depression scores, adjusted for age, for men and women in the three treatments. Additional analyses would have to be conducted to test these interpretations, as described previously.

Table 9.21 Univariate tests for the interaction effect between treatment, gender, and time (Depression-Project SPSS/PC+ output)

EFFECT .. TREAT BY GENDER BY TIME (CONT.)
Univariate F-tests with (2,24) D. F.

Variable	Hypoth. SS	Error SS	Hypoth. MS	Error MS	F	Sig. of F
DIFFPAT	60.28333	58.33333	30.14167	2.43056	12.40114	.000
DIFFINF	27.57917	169.64167	13.78958	7.06840	1.95088	.164

Classic experimental approach for unequal cell sizes

This option is not available on **manova** but is the default method in **anova** (analysis of variance). Since it is useful for analysing non-experimental or survey data where it is preferable to weight the cells according to their sample size, the commands for carrying it out will be outlined. To illustrate it, we will use the Job-Survey data. If we wanted to analyse the effect of ethnic group and gender on job satisfaction, while controlling for the effect of age, we would give the following commands:

anova satis by ethnicgp(1,4) gender(1,2) with age
 /statistic 3.

The set-up of the **anova** command is similar to that of **manova** with the

Table 9.22 Group means of job satisfaction (Job-Survey SPSS/PC+ output)

```
                         · · · CELL MEANS · · ·
                      SATIS          job satisfaction
                   BY ETHNICGP       ethnic group
                      GENDER         gender

TOTAL POPULATION
     10.91
   (   67)
ETHNICGP
       1            2            3            4
     10.68        10.94        11.29        12.00
   (   34)      (   17)      (   14)      (    2)
GENDER
       1            2
     11.08        10.71
   (   36)      (   31)

                  GENDER
                     1            2
ETHNICGP
       1           11.15        10.00
                 (   20)      (   14)

       2           10.29        11.40
                 (    7)      (   10)

       3           11.25        11.33
                 (    8)      (    6)

       4           14.00        10.00
                 (    1)      (    1)
```

dependent variable (**satis**) listed first, followed by the two independent variables (**ethnicgp** and **gender**) and the number of levels in parentheses for each of them (**1,4** and **1,2**) and ending with the covariate (**age**). The **statistic** subcommand prints the means for the groups and the number of subjects on which they are based. In SPSS-X the keyword **mean** can be substituted for **3** to obtain the cell means.

The group means and numbers of subjects on which they are based are shown in Table 9.22, and the output from this two-way design is displayed in Table 9.23. Although the covariate of age is significantly related to job satisfaction ($p=0.002$), neither the main effects of ethnic group ($p=0.717$) nor gender ($p=0.703$) are significant; and their twoway interaction is also not significant ($p=0.781$).

Table 9.23 Analysis-of-covariance table (Job-Survey SPSS/PC+ output)

```
· · · ANALYSIS OF VARIANCE · · ·
              SATIS      job satisfaction
        BY    ETHNICGP   ethnic group
              GENDER     gender
        WITH AGE
```

Source of Variation	Sum of Squares	DF	Mean Square	F	Signif. of F
Covariates	100.538	1	100.538	10.037	.002
AGE	100.538	1	100.538	10.037	.002
Main Effects	15.109	4	3.777	.377	.824
ETHNICGP	13.573	3	4.524	.452	.717
GENDER	1.475	1	1.475	.147	.703
2-way Interactions	10.846	3	3.615	.361	.781
ETHNICGP GENDER	10.846	3	3.615	.361	.781
Explained	126.494	8	15.812	1.579	.151
Residual	580.969	58	10.017		
Total	707.463	66	10.719		

70 Cases were processed.
 3 Cases (4.3 PCT) were missing.

Exercises

1. What are the two main advantages in studying the effects of two rather than one independent variable?

2. What is meant when two variables are said to interact?

3. How would you determine whether there was a significant interaction between two independent variables?

4. A colleague is interested in the relationship between alcohol, anxiety, and gender on performance. Subjects are randomly assigned to receiving one of four increasing dosages of alcohol. In addition, they are divided into three groups of low, moderate, and high anxiety. Which is the dependent variable?

5. How many factors are there in this design?

6. How many levels of anxiety are there?

7. How would you describe this design?

8. If there are unequal numbers of subjects in each group and if the variable names for alcohol, anxiety, gender, and performance are **alcohol**, **anxiety**, **gender**, and **perform** respectively, what is the first part of the appropriate SPSS command for examining the effect of the first three variables on performance?

9. You are interested in examining the effect of three different methods of

teaching on learning to read. Although subjects have been randomly assigned to the three methods, you think that differences in intelligence may obscure any effects. How would you try to control statistically for the effects of intelligence?

10. What is the first part of the SPSS command for examining the effect of three teaching methods on learning to read, covarying out the effect of intelligence when the names for these three variables are **methods**, **read**, and **intell** respectively and the teaching method factor is **methods**?

11. You are studying what effect physical attractiveness has on judgements of intelligence, likeability, honesty, and self-confidence. Subjects are shown a photograph of either an attractive or unattractive person and are asked to judge the extent to which this person has these four characteristics. How would you describe the design of this study?

12. If the names of the five variables in this study are **attract**, **intell**, **likeable**, **honesty**, and **confid** respectively, what is the first part of the SPSS command you would use for analysing the results of this study?

13. What kind of design would this be called if subjects had been presented with photographs of both the attractive and the unattractive person?

14. What would the appropriate SPSS commands be for analysing the results of this study?

15. Suppose that in the Depression Study described in this chapter, patients had been followed up three months after the experiment had ended to find out how depressed they were. What would the appropriate SPSS subcommand be for comparing pre- with post-treatment depression and post-treatment with follow-up depression?

Chapter ten

Multivariate analysis: exploring relationships among three or more variables

In this chapter we will be concerned with a variety of approaches to the examination of relationships when more than two variables are involved. Clearly, these concerns follow on directly from those of Chapter 8, in which we focused upon bivariate analysis of relationships. In the present chapter, we will be concerned to explore the reasons for wishing to analyse three or more variables in conjunction – that is, why *multivariate analysis* is an important aspect of the examination of relationships among variables.

The basic rationale for multivariate analysis is to allow the researcher to discount the alternative explanations of a relationship that can arise when a survey/correlational design has been employed. The experimental researcher can discount alternative explanations of a relationship through the combination of a control group (or through a number of experimental groups) and random assignment (see Chapter 1). The absence of these characteristics, which in large part derives from the failure or inability to manipulate the independent variable in a survey/correlational study, means that a number of potentially confounding factors may exist. Thus, for example, we may find a relationship between people's self-assigned social class (whether they describe themselves as middle or working class) and their voting preference (Conservative or Labour). However, there are a number of problems that can be identified with interpreting such a relationship as causal. Could the relationship be spurious? This possibility could arise because people of higher incomes are both more likely to consider themselves middle class *and* to vote Conservative. Also, even if the relationship is not spurious, does the relationship apply equally to young and old? We know that age affects voting preferences, so how does this variable interact with self-assigned social class in regard to voting behaviour? Such a finding would imply that the class–voting relationship is moderated by age. The problem of spuriousness arises because we cannot make some people think they are middle class and others working class and then randomly assign subjects to the two categories. If we wanted to establish whether a moderated relationship exists, whereby age moderated the class-voting relationship, with an experimental study, we would use a factorial design (see Chapter 9). Obviously, we are not able to create such experimental conditions, so when we investigate this kind of issue through surveys, we have to recognize the limitations of inferring causal relationships from our data. In each of the two questions about the class–voting relationship, a third variable – income and age respectively – potentially contaminates the relationship and forces us to be sceptical about it.

The procedures to be explained in this chapter are designed to allow such contaminating variables to be discounted. This is done by imposing 'statistical controls' which allow the third variable to be 'held constant'. In this way we can examine the relationship between two variables by *partialling out* and thereby *controlling* the effect of a third variable. If, for example, we believe that income confounds the relationship between self-assigned social class and voting, we examine the relationship between social class and voting for each income level in our sample. The sample might reveal four income levels, so we examine the class–voting relationship for each of these four income levels. We can then ask whether the relationship between class and voting persists for each income level or whether it has been eliminated for all or some of these levels. The third variable (i.e. the one that is controlled) is often referred to as the *test factor* (for example, Rosenberg 1968), but the term *test variable* is preferred in the following discussion.

The imposition of statistical controls suffers from a number of disadvantages. In particular, it is only possible to control for those variables which occur to you as potentially important and which are relatively easy to measure. Other variables will constitute further contaminating factors, but the effects of which are unknown. Further, the time order of variables collected by means of a survey/correlational study cannot be established through multivariate analysis, but has to be inferred. In order to make inferences about the likely direction of cause and effect, the researcher must look to probable directions of causation (for example, education precedes current occupation) or to theories which suggest that certain variables are more likely to precede others. As suggested in Chapter 1, the generation of causal inferences from survey/correlational research can be hazardous, but in the present chapter we will largely side-step these problems which are not capable of easy resolution in the absence of a panel study.

The initial exposition of multivariate analysis will solely emphasize the examination of three variables. It should be recognized that many examples of multivariate analysis, particularly those involving correlation and regression techniques, go much further than this. Many researchers refer to the relationship between two variables as the *zero-order relationship*; when a third variable is introduced, they refer to the *first-order relationship*, that is the relationship between two variables when one variable is held constant; and when two extra variables are introduced, they refer to the *second-order relationship* when two variables are held constant.

Multivariate analysis through contingency tables

In this section, we will examine the potential of contingency tables as a means of exploring relationships among three variables. Four contexts in which such analysis can be useful are provided: testing for spuriousness, testing for intervening variables, testing for moderated relationships, and examining multiple causation. Although these four notions are treated in connection with contingency table analysis, they are also relevant to the correlation and regression techniques which are examined later.

Testing for spuriousness

The idea of spuriousness was introduced in Chapter 1 in the context of a discussion about the nature of causality. In order to establish that there exists a relationship between two variables it is necessary to show that the relationship is non-spurious. A spurious relationship exists when the relationship between two variables is not a 'true' relationship, in that it only appears because a third variable causes each of the variables making up the pair. In Table 10.1 a bivariate contingency table is presented which derives from an imaginary study of 500 manual workers in twelve firms. The table seems to show a relationship between the presence of variety in work and job satisfaction. Thus, for example, 80 per cent of those performing varied

Table 10.1 Relationship between work variety and job satisfaction (imaginary data)

		Work variety	
		Varied work	Not varied work
Job satisfaction	Satisfied	(200) 1 ⟶ 80% $d_1 =$	(60) 2 ⟶ 24% 56%
	Not satisfied	(50) 3 ⟶ 20% $d_2 =$	(190) 4 ⟶ 76% 56%

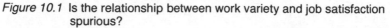

Figure 10.1 Is the relationship between work variety and job satisfaction
spurious?

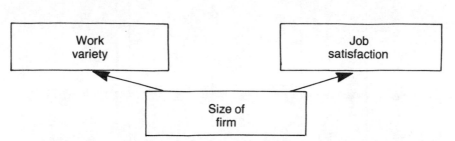

work are satisfied, as against only 24 per cent of those whose work is not
varied. There is, therefore, a difference (d_1) of 56 per cent (i.e. $80 - 24$)
between those performing varied work and those not performing varied
work in terms of job satisfaction. Contingency tables are not normally
presented with the differences between cells inserted, but since these form
the crux of the multivariate contingency-table analysis, this additional
information is provided in this and subsequent tables in this section.

Could the relationship between these two variables be spurious? Could
it be that the size of the firm (the test variable) in which each respondent
works has 'produced' the relationship (see Figure 10.1)? It may be that size
of firm affects both the amount of variety of work reported and levels of
job satisfaction. In order to examine this possibility, we partition our
sample into those who work in large firms and those who work in small
firms. There are 250 respondents in each of these two categories. We then
examine the relationship between amount of variety in work and job satisfaction for each category. If the relationship is spurious we would expect
the relationship between amount of variety in work and job satisfaction
largely to disappear. Table 10.2 presents such an analysis. In a sense, what
one is doing here is to present two separate tables: one examining the
relationship between amount of variety in work and job satisfaction for
respondents from large firms and one examining the same relationship for
small firms. This notion is symbolized by the double line separating the
analysis for large firms from the analysis for small firms.

What we find is that the relationship between amount of variety in work
and job satisfaction has largely disappeared. Compare d_1 in Table 10.1
with both d_1 and d_2 in Table 10.2. Whereas d_1 in Table 10.1 is 56 per cent,
implying a large difference between those whose work is varied and those
whose work is not varied in terms of job satisfaction, the corresponding
percentage differences in Table 10.2 are 10 and 11 per cent for d_1 and d_2
respectively. This means that when size of firm is controlled, the difference
in terms of job satisfaction between those whose work is varied and those
whose work is not varied is considerably reduced. This analysis implies that

Table 10.2 A spurious relationship: the relationship between work variety and job satisfaction, controlling for size of firm (imaginary data)

	Large firms		Small firms	
	Varied work	Not varied work	Varied work	Not varied work
Job satisfaction				
Satisfied	1 (190) 95% $d_1 =$	2 (42) 85% 10%	3 (10) 20% $d_2 =$	4 (18) 9% 11%
Not satisfied	5 (10) 5% $d_3 =$	6 (8) 15% 10%	7 (40) 80% $d_4 =$	8 (182) 91% 11%

Table 10.3 A non-spurious relationship: the relationship between work variety and job satisfaction, controlling for size of firm (imaginary data)

Job satisfaction	Large firms		Small firms	
	Varied work	*Not varied work*	*Varied work*	*Not varied work*
Satisfied	1 (166) 83% $d_1 =$ 55%	2 (14) 28% 55%	3 (34) 68% $d_2 =$ 45%	4 (46) 23% 45%
Not satisfied	5 (34) 17% $d_3 =$ 55%	6 (36) 72% 55%	7 (16) 32% $d_4 =$ 45%	8 (154) 77% 45%

there is not a true relationship between variety in work and job satisfaction, because when size of firm is controlled the relationship between work variety and job satisfaction is almost eliminated. We can suggest that size of firm seems to affect both variables. Most respondents reporting varied work come from large firms ([cell1 + cell5] − [cell3 + cell7]) and most respondents who are satisfied come from large firms ([cell1 + cell2] − [cell3 + cell4]).

What would Table 10.2 look like if the relationship between variety in work and job satisfaction was *not* spurious when size of firm is controlled? Table 10.3 presents the same analysis but this time the relationship is not spurious. Again, we can compare d_1 in Table 10.1 with both d_1 and d_2 in Table 10.3. In Table 10.1, the difference between those who report variety in their work and those who report no variety is 56 per cent (i.e. d_1), whereas in Table 10.3 the corresponding differences are 55 per cent for large firms (d_1) and 45 per cent for small firms (d_2) respectively. Thus, d_1 in Table 10.3 is almost exactly the same as d_1 in Table 10.1, but d_2 is 11 percentage points smaller (i.e. 56 − 45). However, this latter finding would not be sufficient to suggest that the relationship is spurious because the difference between those who report varied work and those whose work is not varied is still large for both respondents in large firms and those in small firms. We do not expect an exact replication of percentage differences when we carry out such controls. Similarly, as suggested in the context of the discussion of Table 10.2, we do not need percentage differences to disappear completely in order to infer that a relationship is spurious. When there is an in-between reduction in percentage differences (for example, to around half of the original difference), the relationship is probably partially spurious, implying that part of it is caused by the third variable and the other part is indicative of a 'true' relationship. This would have been the interpretation if the original d_1 difference of 56 per cent had fallen to around 28 per cent for respondents from both large firms and from small firms.

Testing for intervening variables

The quest for intervening variables is different from the search for potentially spurious relationships. An intervening variable is one that is both a product of the independent variable and a cause of the dependent variable. Taking the data examined in Table 10.1, the sequence depicted in Figure 10.2 might be imagined. The analysis presented in Table 10.4 strongly suggests that the level of people's interest in their work is an intervening variable. As with Tables 10.2 and 10.3, we partition the sample into two groups (this time those who report that they are interested and those reporting no interest in their work) and examine the relationship between work variety and job satisfaction for each group. Again, we can compare d_1

Figure 10.2 Is the relationship between work variety and job satisfaction affected by an intervening variable?

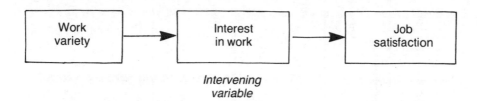

in Table 10.1 with d_1 and d_2 in Table 10.4. In Table 10.1 d_1 is 56 per cent, but in Table 10.4 d_1 and d_2 are 13 per cent and 20 per cent respectively. Clearly, d_1 and d_2 in Table 10.3 have not been reduced to zero (which would suggest that the whole of the relationship was through interest in work), but they are also much lower than the 56 per cent difference in Table 10.1. If d_1 and d_2 in Table 10.4 had remained at or around 56 per cent, we would conclude that interest in work is not an intervening variable.

The sequence in Figure 10.2 suggests that variety in work affects the degree of interest in work that people experience which in turn affects their level of job satisfaction. This pattern differs from that depicted in Figure 10.1 in that if the analysis supported the hypothesized sequence, it suggests that there *is* a relationship between amount of variety in work and job satisfaction, but the relationship is not direct. The search for intervening variables is often referred to as *explanation* and it is easy to see why. If we find that a test variable acts as an intervening variable, we are able to gain some explanatory leverage on the bivariate relationship. Thus, we find that there is a relationship between amount of variety in work and job satisfaction and then ask why that relationship might exist. We speculate that it may be because those who have varied work become more interested in their work, which in turn heightens their job satisfaction.

It should be apparent that the computation of a test for an intervening variable is identical to a test for spuriousness. How, then, do we know which is which? If we carry out an analysis like those of Tables 10.2, 10.3, and 10.4, how can we be sure that what we are taking to be an intervening variable is not in fact an indication that the relationship is spurious? The answer is that there should be only one logical possibility, that is, only one that makes sense. If we take the trio of variables in Figure 10.1, to argue that the test variable – size of firm – could be an intervening variable would mean that we would have to suggest that a person's level of work variety affects the size of the firm in which he or she works – an unlikely scenario. Similarly, to argue that the trio in Figure 10.2 could point to a test for spuriousness would mean that we would have to accept that the test

223

Table 10.4 An intervening variable: the relationship between work variety and job satisfaction, controlling for interest in work (imaginary data)

Job satisfaction	Interested		Not interested	
	Varied work	Not varied work	Varied work	Not varied work
Satisfied	1 (185) 93% $d_1=$	2 (40) 80% 13%	3 (15) 30% $d_2=$	4 (20) 10% 20%
Not satisfied	5 (15) 7% $d_3=$	6 (10) 20% 13%	7 (35) 70% $d_4=$	8 (180) 90% 20%

variable – interest in work – can affect the amount of variety in a person's work. This too makes much less sense than to perceive it as an intervening variable.

One further point should be registered. It is clear that controlling for interest in work in Table 10.4 has not totally eliminated the difference between those reporting varied work and those whose work is not varied in terms of job satisfaction. It would seem, therefore, that there are aspects of the relationship between amount of variety in work and job satisfaction that arc not totally explained by the test variable, interest in work.

Testing for moderated relationships

A moderated relationship occurs when a relationship is found to hold for some categories of a sample but not others. Diagrammatically this can be displayed as in Figure 10.3. We may even find that the character of a relationship can differ for categories of the test variable. We might find that for one category those who report varied work exhibit greater job satisfaction, but for another category of people the reverse may be true (i.e. varied work seems to engender lower levels of job satisfaction than work that is not varied).

Table 10.5 looks at the relationship between variety in work and job satisfaction for men and women. Once again, we can compare d_1 (56 per cent) in Table 10.1 with d_1 and d_2 in Table 10.5, which are 85 per cent and 12 per cent respectively. The bulk of the 56 percentage-point difference between those reporting varied work and those reporting that work is not varied in Table 10.1 appears to derive from the relationship between variety in work and job satisfaction being far stronger for men than women and there being more men (300) than women (200) in the sample. Table 10.5 demonstrates the importance of searching for moderated relationships in that they allow the researcher to avoid inferring that a set of findings pertains to a sample as a whole, when in fact it only really applies to a

Figure 10.3 Is the relationship between work variety and job satisfaction moderated by gender?

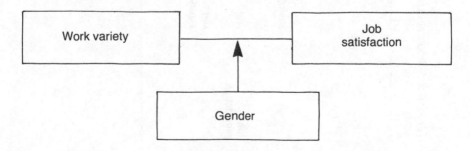

Table 10.5 A moderated relationship: the relationship between work variety and job satisfaction, controlling for gender (imaginary data)

		Men		Women	
		Varied work	Not varied work	Varied work	Not varied work
Job satisfaction	Satisfied	1 (143) 95% $d_1 =$	2 (15) 10% 85%	3 (57) 57% $d_2 =$	4 (45) 45% 12%
	Not satisfied	5 (7) 5% $d_3 =$	6 (135) 90% 85%	7 (43) 43% $d_4 =$	8 (55) 55% 12%

portion of that sample. The term *interaction effect* is often employed to refer to the situation in which a relationship between two variables differs substantially for categories of the test variable. This kind of occurrence was also addressed in Chapter 9. The discovery of such an effect often inaugurates a new line of enquiry in that it stimulates reflection about the likely reasons for such variations.

The discovery of moderated relationships can occur by design or by chance. When they occur by design, the researcher has usually anticipated the possibility that a relationship may be moderated (though he or she may, of course, be wrong). They can occur by chance when the researcher conducts a test for an intervening variable or a test for spuriousness and finds a marked contrast in findings for different categories of the test variable.

Multiple causation

Dependent variables in the social sciences are rarely determined by one variable alone, so that two or more potential independent variables can usefully be considered in conjunction. Figure 10.4 suggests that whether someone is allowed participation in decision-making at work also affects his or her level of job satisfaction. It is misleading to refer to participation in decision-making as a test variable in this context, since it is really a second independent variable. What, then, is the impact of amount of variety in work on job satisfaction when we control the effects of participation?

Again, we compare d_1 in Table 10.1 (56 per cent) with d_1 and d_2 in Table 10.6. The latter are 19 and 18 per cent respectively. This suggests that although the effect of amount of variety in work has not been reduced to zero or nearly zero, its impact has been considerably reduced. Participation in decision-making appears to be a more important cause of variation in job satisfaction. Compare the percentages in cells 1 and 3 in Table 10.6, for example: among those respondents who report that they perform varied work, 93 per cent of those who experience participation

Figure 10.4 Work variety and participation at work

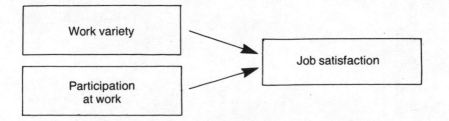

Table 10.6 Two independent variables: the relationship between work variety and job satisfaction, controlling for participation at work (imaginary data)

Job satisfaction	Participation		Little or no participation	
	Varied work	Not varied work	Varied work	Not varied work
Satisfied	1 (185) 93% $d_1 =$	2 (37) 74% 19%	3 (15) 30% $d_2 =$	4 (23) 12% 18%
Not satisfied	5 (15) 7% $d_3 =$	6 (13) 26% 19%	7 (35) 70% $d_4 =$	8 (177) 88% 18%

exhibit job satisfaction, whereas only 30 per cent of those who do not experience participation are satisfied.

One reason for this pattern of findings is that most people who experience participation in decision-making also have varied jobs, that is (cell1 + cell5) − (cell2 + cell6). Likewise, most people who do not experience participation have work which is not varied, that is (cell4 + cell8) − (cell3 + cell7). Could this mean that the relationship between variety in work and job satisfaction is really spurious, when participation in decision-making is employed as the test variable? The answer is that this is unlikely, since it would mean that participation in decision-making would have to cause variation in the amount of variety in work, which is a less likely possibility (since technological conditions tend to be the major influence on variables like work variety). Once again, we have to resort to a combination of intuitive logic and theoretical reflection in order to discount such a possibility. We will return to this kind of issue in the context of an examination of the use of multivariate analysis through correlation and regression.

Using SPSS-X and SPSS/PC+ to perform multivariate analysis through contingency tables

The use of SPSS to generate the kinds of table examined above is a simple extension of the **crosstabs** procedure described in Chapter 8. Taking the Job-Survey data, if we wanted to examine the relationship between **skill** and **ethnicgp**, holding **gender** constant (i.e. as a test variable), the following command would be required:

crosstabs tables=skill by ethnicgp by gender.

If SPSS-X is being used, it is necessary to remember to omit the full stop. This command will generate two contingency tables in which **skill** and **ethnicgp** are cross-tabulated – one for men and one for women. The test variable must be the last variable entered in the list. Identical ways of listing variables as those mentioned in Chapter 8 can be employed. The same **options** as those described in relation to **crosstabs** in Chapter 8 are relevant. Moreover, the **statistics** subcommand will provide statistical tests for *each* table. Thus, separate chi-square tests can be conducted for each table and such measures of strength of association as phi, eta, and Cramer's V can be supplied for each table. Of course, the researcher must decide which of these measures is appropriate (that is, according to the kinds of data in question in terms of whether they are nominal, ordinal, interval, or dichotomous).

Multivariate analysis and correlation

Although the use of contingency tables provides a powerful tool for multivariate analysis, it suffers from a major limitation, namely that complex analyses with more than three variables require large samples, especially when the variables include a large number of categories. Otherwise, there is the likelihood of very small frequencies in many cells (and indeed the likelihood of many empty cells) when a small sample is employed. By contrast, correlation and regression can be used to conduct multivariate analyses on fairly small samples, although their use in relation to very small samples is limited. Further, both correlation and regression provide easy-to-interpret indications of the relative strength of relationships. On the other hand, if one or more variables are nominal, multivariate analysis through contingency tables is probably the best way forward for most purposes.

The partial correlation coefficient

One of the main ways in which the multivariate analysis of relationships is conducted in the social sciences is through the *partial correlation coefficient*. This test allows the researcher to examine the relationship between two variables while holding one other or more variables constant. It allows tests for spuriousness, tests for intervening variables, and multiple causation to be investigated. The researcher must stipulate the anticipated logic that underpins the three variables in question (for example, test for spuriousness) and can then investigate the effect of the test variable on the original relationship. Moderated relationships are probably better examined by computing Pearson's r for each category of the test variable (for example, for both men and women, or young, middle-aged, and old) and then comparing the r values.

The partial correlation coefficient is computed by first calculating the Pearson's r for each of the pairs of possible relationships involved. Thus, if the two variables concerned are x and y, and t is the test variable (or second independent variable in the case of investigating multiple causation), the partial correlation coefficient computes Pearson's r for x and y, x and t, and y and t. Because of this, it is necessary to remember that all the restrictions associated with Pearson's r apply to variables involved in the possible computation of the partial correlation coefficient (for example, variables must be interval).

There are three possible effects that can occur when partial correlation is undertaken: the relationship between x and y is unaffected by t; the relationship between x and y is totally explained by t; and the relationship between x and y is partially explained by t. Each of these three possibilities can be illustrated with Venn diagrams (see Figure 10.5). In the first case (a), t is only related to x, so the relationship between x and y is unchanged, because t can only have an impact on the relationship between x and y if it affects both variables. In the second case (b), all of the relationship between x and y (the shaded area) is encapsulated by t. This would mean

Figure 10.5 The effects of controlling for a test variable

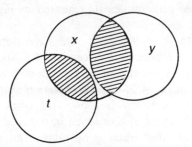

(a)

t only affects *x*, so that *r* is unaffected when *t* is controlled.

(b)

Controlling for *t* totally explains the relationship between *x* and *y*.

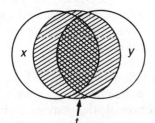

(c)

Controlling for *t* partially explains the relationship between *x* and *y*.

that the relationship between *x* and *y* when *t* is controlled would be zero. What usually occurs is that the test variable, *t*, partly explains the relationship between *x* and *y*, as in the case of (c) in Figure 10.5. In this case, only part of the relationship between *x* and *y* is explained by *t* (the shaded area which is overlapped by *t*). This would mean that the partial correlation coefficient will be lower than the Pearson's *r* for *x* and *y*. This is the most normal outcome of calculating the partial correlation coefficient. If the first order correlation between *x* and *y* when *t* is controlled is considerably less than the zero-order correlation between *x* and *y*, the researcher must decide (if he or she has not already done so) whether: (a) the *x*–*y* relationship is spurious, or at least largely so; or (b) whether *t* is an intervening variable between x and y; or (c) whether t is best thought of as a causal variable which is related to x and which largely eliminates the effect of x on y. These are the three possibilities represented in Figures 10.3, 10.4, and 10.6 respectively.

As an example, consider the data in Table 10.7. We have data on eighteen individuals relating to three variables: age, income (in £'000), and a questionnaire scale measuring support for the market economy, which goes from a minimum of 5 to a maximum of 25. The correlation between income and support for the market economy is 0.64. But could this relationship be spurious? Could it be that age should be introduced as a test variable, since we might anticipate that older people are both more likely to earn more *and* to support the market economy? This possibility can be anticipated because age is related to income (0.76) and to support (0.83). When we compute the partial correlation coefficient for income and support controlling the effects of age, the level of correlation falls to 0.32. This means that a large proportion of the relationship is spurious. It is a large proportion because, whereas a correlation coefficient of 0.64 implies (using r^2) that 41 per cent of the variation in support for the market economy is due to income, a partial correlation coefficient of 0.32 implies that only 10 per cent of the variation is due to income when age is controlled. In other words, a large proportion of the relationship between income and support for the market economy is spurious. A similar kind of reasoning would apply to the detection of intervening variables and multiple causation.

Table 10.7 Income, age, and support for the market economy (imaginary data)

Subject	Age	Income (£'000s)	Support for market economy
1	20	9	11
2	23	8	9
3	28	12.5	12
4	30	10	14
5	32	15	10
6	34	12.5	13
7	35	13	16
8	37	14.5	14
9	37	14	17
10	41	16	13
11	43	15.5	15
12	47	14	14
13	50	16.5	18
14	52	12.5	17
15	54	14.5	15
16	59	15	19
17	61	17	22
18	63	16.5	18

Partial correlation with SPSS

Partial correlation can easily be generated with SPSS-X, but is unavailable with SPSS/PC+. Taking the Job-Survey data, if we wanted to compute the relationship between both **satis** and **absence** and both **routine** and **autonomy**, holding **income** constant, the following command will be used:

partial corr variables=satis absence with routine autonom
by income (1)

This will compute partial correlations for **satis** and both **routine** and **autonom** and between **absence** and both **routine** and **autonom**. The figure **1** in this command means that first-order partial correlation coefficients will be generated. In the case of all four correlations, **income** will be held constant. If two variables are to be controlled, the following command will produce *both* first- and second-order partial correlation coefficients:

partial corr variables=satis absence with routine autonom
by income age (1,2)

This command produces (a) first-order partial coefficients holding **income** constant; (b) first-order partial coefficients holding **age** constant; and (c) second-order partial coefficients holding *both* **age** and **income** constant. If only the second-order partial correlation coefficients were required, only the figure **2** should appear in brackets at the end of the command.

The SPSS output provides one-tailed significance tests, which can be interpreted in the same way as the statistical significance of Pearson's *r*. It also presents the number of degrees of freedom associated with the test of statistical significance. When first-order partial correlation is being requested, the number of degrees of freedom is the number of cases – three. Two-tailed tests can be generated by inserting /**significance =twotail** after the **partial corr** command. It is important to realize that the **partial corr** procedure handles missing values differently from **correlations**. The latter deletes cases with missing values on a pairwise basis: this means that a matrix of correlations will be based on different sample sizes since the number of missing values differs from variable to variable. If, for example, we imagine a sample of forty and four variables – *a, b, c,* and *d* – *a, b,* and *c* have no cases with missing values, but *d* has two cases with missing values. Thus, the correlation coefficients for *a* and *b, b* and *c,* and *a* and *c* will be based on forty cases, but those for *a* and *d, b* and *d,* and *c* and *d* will be based on thirty-eight cases. By contrast, the **partial corr** procedure deletes listwise. This means that if we wanted to calculate the partial correlation coefficients for *a* and *b, b* and *d,* and *a* and *d,* controlling for *c* in each case, *all* of the computations would be based on the thirty-eight cases for which there are complete data for all variables. Even though the partial correlation of *a* and *b,* with *c* controlled, relates to variables for which there are no cases with missing values, because d is part of the list of variables and contains cases with missing values, the computation of the coefficients is based on thirty-eight. If the pairwise approach is preferred (this is more properly called *analysiswise* since more than two variables are involved in partial correlation), /**missing=analysis** should be inserted. In addition, /**statistics corr** will produce zero-order correlation coefficients and their significance levels. Thus,

partial corr variables=satis absence by routine with income(1)
 /**statistics corr**
 /**missing=analysis**

will provide: zero-order correlations involving all variables in the list; the first-order partial correlation between **satis** and **routine** and between **absence** and **routine** with **income** controlled in each case; *analysiswise* deletion of cases with missing values. When zero-order correlation is requested as well, the number of degrees of freedom (rather than the number of cases as generated by **correlations**) is provided.

Partial correlation and ordinal variables

Kendall's rank partial correlation coefficient (which is based on Kendall's tau – see Chapter 8) allows an analysis that is essentially identical to the partial correlation coefficient to be conducted in relation to three ordinal variables. Unfortunately, this statistic is not available to users of SPSS. However, since the partial rank correlation coefficient is relatively easy to compute, the relevant information for its computation will be provided. Imagine we have three variables – a, b, and c – and we want to examine the relationship between a and b holding c constant. We would then proceed as follows:

(a) Compute Kendall's tau for each pair using the **nonpar corr** command within SPSS, i.e. a and b, a and c, and b and c.
(b) Multiply the tau coefficient for a and c by the coefficient for b and c. Subtract the product from the coefficient for a and b.
(c) Take the square of the tau coefficient for a and c from 1 and multiply the result by the subtraction of the square of the tau coefficient for b and c from 1.
(d) Take the square root of the product of step (c).
(e) Divide the product of step (b) by the product of step (d).

If we take a simple example:

(a) Let us say that the three coefficients are 0.60, 0.70, and 0.80 respectively.
(b) We multiply 0.70 by 0.80 and subtract the product from 0.60, i.e. 0.60 $- (0.70 \times 0.80) = 0.04$.
(c) We subtract the square of 0.70 from 1 and 0.80 from 1 and multiply

the results of the two subtractions, i.e. $(1 - 0.49)(1 - 0.64) = 0.1836$.
(d) We then take the square root of 0.1836, i.e. 0.428.
(e) We then divide 0.04 by $0.428 = 0.09$.

Thus, the correlation between a and b with c controlled would be 0.09. There is no test of statistical significance to accompany this coefficient.

Regression and multivariate analysis

Nowadays, regression, in the form of *multiple regression*, is the most widely used method for conducting multivariate analysis, particularly when more than three variables are involved. In Chapter 8 we previously encountered regression as a means of expressing relationships among pairs of variables. In this chapter, the focus will be on the presence of two or more independent variables.

Consider first of all a fairly simple case in which there are three variables, that is two independent variables. The nature of the relationship between the dependent variable and the two independent variables is expressed in a similar manner to the bivariate case explored in Chapter 8. The analogous equation for multivariate analysis is

$$y = a + b_1 x_1 + b_2 x_2 + e$$

where x_1 and x_2 are the two independent variables, a is the intercept, b_1 and b_2 are the regression coefficients for the two independent variables, and e is an *error term* which points to the fact that a proportion of the variance in the dependent variable, y, is unexplained by the regression equation. As in Chapter 8, the error term is ignored since it is not used for making predictions.

In order to illustrate the operation of multiple regression we can return to the data in Table 10.7. The regression equation for these data is

support $= 5.9125 + 0.2126$age $+ 0.0008$income

where 5.9125 is the intercept (a), 0.2126 is the regression coefficient for the first independent variable, age (x_1), and 0.0008 is the regression coefficient for the second independent variable, income (x_2). Each of the two regression coefficients estimates the amount of change that occurs in the dependent variable (support for the market economy) for a one-unit change in the independent variable. Moreover, the regression coefficient expresses the amount of change in the dependent variable with the effect of all other independent variables in the equation partialled out (i.e. controlled). Thus, if we had an equation with four independent variables, each of the four regression coefficients would express the unique contribution of the relevant variable to the dependent variable (with the effect in each case of the three other variables removed). This feature is of considerable importance, since the independent variables in a multiple-regression equation are almost always related to each other.

Thus, every extra year of a person's age increases support for the market economy by 0.2126, and every extra £1,000 increases support by 0.0008. Moreover, the effect of age on support is with the effect of income removed, and the effect of income on support is with the effect of age removed. If we wanted to predict the likely level of support for the market economy of someone aged 40 with an income of £17,500, we would substitute as follows:

$$y = 5.9125 + (0.2126)(40) + (0.0008)(17.5)$$
$$= 5.9125 + 8.5 + 0.014$$
$$= 14.43$$

Thus, we would expect that someone with an age of 40 and an income of £17,500 would have a score of 14.43 on the scale of support for the market economy.

While the ability to make such predictions is of some interest to social scientists, the strength of multiple regression lies primarily in its use as a means of establishing the relative importance of independent variables to the dependent variable. However, we cannot say that simply because the regression coefficient for age is larger than that for income that this means that age is more important to support for the market economy than is income. This is because age and income derive from different units of measurement that cannot be directly compared. In order to effect a comparison it is necessary to standardize the units of measurement involved. This is done by multiplying each regression coefficient by the product of dividing the standard deviation of the relevant independent variable by the standard deviation of the dependent variable. The result is known as a *standardized regression coefficient* or *beta weight*. This coefficient is easily computed through SPSS. Standardized regression coefficients in a regression equation employ the same standard of measurement and can therefore be compared to establish which of two or more independent variables is the more important factor in relation to the dependent variable. They essentially tell us how many standard-deviation units the dependent variable will change for a one unit change in the independent variable.

We can now take an example from the Job-Survey data in order to illustrate some of these points. Let us say that we want to treat **satis** as the dependent variable and **autonom**, **routine**, **age** and **income** as the independent variables. The three independent variables were chosen because they are all known to be related to **satis**, as revealed by the relevant correlation coefficients. However, it is important to ensure that the independent variables are not too highly related to each other. The Pearson's *r* between each pair of independent variables should not exceed 0.80; otherwise the independent variables that show a relationship at or in excess of 0.80 may be suspected of exhibiting *multicollinearity*. Multicollinearity is usually regarded as a problem because it means that the regression coefficients may be unstable. This implies that they are likely to be subject to considerable variability from sample to sample. In any case, when two variables are very highly correlated, there seems little point in treating them as separate entities. Multicollinearity is often quite difficult to detect where there are more than two independent variables and SPSS provides a useful means of detection which will be examined below.

When the previous multiple-regression analysis is carried out, the following equation is generated:

satis = − 2.43137 + 0.59450autonom + 0.00125income − 0.15508routine

Age has been eliminated from the analysis by the procedure chosen for including variables in the analysis (the *stepwise* procedure), because it failed to meet the program's statistical criteria for inclusion in the analysis. If it had been 'forced' into the equation, the impact of **age** on **satis** would be shown to be almost zero. Thus, if we wanted to predict the likely **satis** score of someone with an **autonom** score of 16, an **income** of £8,000, and a **routine** score of 8, the calculation would proceed as follows:

satis = − 2.43137 + (0.5945) (16) + (0.00125) (8000) − (0.15508) (8)
= − 2.43137 + 9.512 + 10 − 1.24064
= 15.84

However, it is the relative impact of each of these variables on **satis** that provides the main area of interest for many social scientists. Table 10.8 presents the regression coefficients for the three independent variables remaining in the equation and the corresponding standardized regression coefficients. Although **autonom** provides the largest unstandardized and standardized regression coefficients, the case of **income** demonstrates the hazardousness of using unstandardized coefficients in order to infer the size of the impact of independent variables on the dependent variable. **Income** provides the smallest unstandardized coefficient (0.00125), but the second largest standardized coefficient (0.37754). As pointed out earlier, the magnitude of an unstandardized coefficient is affected by the nature of the

Table 10.8 Comparison of unstandardized and standardized regression coefficients with **satis** as the dependent variable

Independent variables	Unstandardized regression coefficients	Standardized regression coefficients
Autonom	0.59450	0.50354
Income	0.00125	0.37754
Routine	−0.15508	−0.19559
[Intercept]	−2.43137	—

measurement scale for the variable itself. **Income** has a range from 0 to 10,500, whereas a variable like **routine** has a range of only 4 to 20. When we see the standardized regression coefficients we can conclude that **autonom** has the greatest impact on **satis** and **income** the next highest. **Routine** has the next highest impact which is negative, indicating that more **routine** engenders less **satis**. Finally, in spite of the fact that the Pearson's r between **age** and **satis** is moderate (0.35), when the three other variables are controlled it does not have a sufficient impact on **satis** to avoid the program's default criteria for exclusion of a variable in the equation.

We can see here some of the strengths of multiple regression and the use of standardized regression coefficients. In particular, the latter allow us to examine the effects of each of a number of independent variables on the dependent variable. Thus, the standardized coefficient for **autonom** means that for each one unit change in **autonom**, there is a standard deviation change in **satis** of 0.50354, with the effects of **income** and **routine** on **satis** partialled out.

Although we cannot compare unstandardized regression coefficients within a multiple regression equation, we can compare them across equations when the same measures are employed. We may, for example, want to divide a sample into men and women and to compute separate multiple-regression equations for each. To do this, we would need to make use of the **select if** command in SPSS. Thus, for example, an equation for men might be

$$y = 2.43 + 3.84x_1 + 0.67x_2 + e_1$$

and for women

$$y = 1.89 + 2.98x_1 + 2.42x_2 + e_2$$

In this case, we can say that for men, x_1 is larger than for women, while x_2 is much larger for women than men. However, it is important to realize that the variables must be identical for such contrasts to be drawn. On the other hand, it is important to be aware of such subsample differences, since they may have implications for the kinds of conclusions that are generated. An alternative approach would be to include gender as a third independent variable in the equation, since dichotomous variables can legitimately be employed in multiple regression (see the discussion of 'dummy variables' below). The decision about which option to choose will be determined by the points that the researcher wishes to make about the data at hand.

One of the questions that we may ask is how well the independent variables explain the dependent variable. In just the same way that we were able to use r^2 (the coefficient of determination) as a measure of how well the line of best fit represents the relationship between the two variables, we can compute the multiple coefficient of determination (R^2) for the collective effect of all of the independent variables. The R^2 value for the equation as a whole is 0.71, implying that only 29 per cent of the variance in **satis** (i.e. $100 - 71$) is not explained by the three variables in the equation. In addition, SPSS will produce an *adjusted* R^2. The technical reasons for this variation should not overly concern us here, but the basic idea is that the adjusted version provides a more conservative estimate than the ordinary R^2 of the amount of variance in **satis** that is explained. The adjusted R^2 takes into account the number of independent variables involved. The magnitude of R^2 is bound to be inflated by the number of independent variables associated with the regression equation. The adjusted R^2 corrects for this by adjusting the level of R^2 to take account of the number of independent variables.

Another aspect of how well the regression equation fits the data is the *standard error of the estimate.* This statistic allows the researcher to determine the limits of the confidence that he or she can exhibit in the prediction from a regression coefficient. The notion of the standard error of the estimate is similar to the notion of the standard error of the mean that was introduced in Chapter 7. The standard error of the estimate of each regression coefficient in a multiple-regression equation reflects the accuracy of that equation. If successive similar-sized samples are taken from the population, estimates of each regression coefficient will vary from sample to sample. The standard error of the estimate allows the researcher to determine the band of confidence for each coefficient. Thus, if b is the regression coefficient and s.e. is the standard error, we can be 95 per cent certain that the population regression coefficient will lie between $b +$ 1.96(s.e.) and $b - 1.96$(s.e.). This confidence band can be established because of the properties of the normal distribution which were discussed in Chapter 6 and if the sample is random. Thus, the confidence interval for the regression coefficient for **autonom** will be between $0.5940 +$ 1.96(0.09110) and $0.5940 - 1.96(0.09110)$, i.e. between 0.77256 and 0.415444. This confidence interval indicates that we can be 95 per cent certain that the population regression coefficient will lie between 0.77256 and 0.415444. This calculation can be extremely useful when the researcher is seeking to make predictions and requires some sense of their likely accuracy.

Statistical significance and multiple regression

A useful statistical test that is related to R^2 is the F ratio. The F ratio test generated by SPSS is based on the *multiple correlation* (R) for the analysis. The multiple correlation, which is of course the square root of the multiple coefficient of determination, expresses the correlation between the dependent variable (**satis**) and all of the independent variables collectively (i.e. **autonom, routine, income,** and **age**). The multiple R for the multiple-regression analysis under consideration is 0.84. The F-ratio test allows the researcher to test the null hypothesis that the multiple correlation is zero in the population from which the sample (which should be random) was taken. For our computed equation, $F=54.84157$ (see Table 10.10 below) and the significance level is described by SPSS as 0.0000 (which means $p<0.00005$), suggesting that it is extremely improbable that R in the population is zero.

The calculation of the F ratio is useful as a test of statistical significance for the equation as a whole, since R reflects how well the independent variables collectively correlate with the dependent variable. If it is required to test the significance of the individual regression coefficients, a different test is required. A number of approaches to this question can be found. Two approaches which can be found in SPSS may be proffered. First, a statistic that is based on the F ratio calculates the significance of the change in the value of R^2 as a result of the inclusion of each variable in the equation. Since each variable is entered into the equation in turn, the individual contribution of each variable to R^2 is calculated and the statistical significance of that contribution can be assessed. In the comput-ation of the multiple-regression equation, a procedure for deciding the sequence of the entry of variables into the equation called *stepwise* was employed. An explanation of this procedure will be given in the next section, but in the mean time it may be noted that it means that each variable is entered according to the magnitude of its contribution to R^2. Thus, an examination of the SPSS output (given in Table 10.10 below) shows that the variables were entered in the sequence: **autonom**, **income**, **routine** (**age** was not entered). The respective contributions to R^2 were 0.53150, 0.15452, and 0.02768. These add up to the unadjusted R^2 value of 0.71370. Clearly, **income** was by far the major contributor to R^2. The first two contributions to R^2 were significant at 0.0000 (which can be inter-preted as $p<0.00005$), and the third at 0.014 (i.e. $p<0.05$).

In addition, SPSS will produce a test of the statistical significance of individual regression coefficients through the calculation of a t value for each coefficient and an associated two-tailed significance test. As the output in Table 10.10 below indicates, the significance levels for **autonom** and **income** were 0.0000, and for **routine** 0.0140. These confirm the previous analysis using the F ratio in suggesting that the coefficients for **income, autonomy**, and **routine** are highly unlikely to be zero in the popul-ation.

Dummy variables

It is quite conceivable that the researcher may be interested in the impli-cations of non-interval variables for a dependent variable. It is possible to include such variables in multiple-regression analysis through the creation of *dummy variables*. We could, for example, treat **gender** as a dummy

Table 10.9 Creation of a dummy variable (**ethnicgp**)

Category	Dummy variables		
	x_1	x_2	x_3
White	1	0	0
Asian	0	1	0
West Indian	0	0	1
African	0	0	0

variable. Normally, this would be done by coding men as 1 and women as 0 (or vice versa), but the existing coding in which the categories are coded as 1 and 2 respectively is perfectly acceptable. But how do we proceed when a nominal or ordinal variable comprises more than two categories? The procedure is that if we have k categories we produce $k-1$ dummy variables. Thus, for example, the **ethnicgp** variable comprises five distinct categories, only four of which appear in the sample: white, Asian, West Indian, and African. In order to include these in a multiple-regression analysis, three (i.e. $4-1$) categories must be created. For example,

x_1 is white (coded as 1) or not white (coded as 0)
x_2 is Asian (coded as 1) or not Asian (coded as 0)
x_3 is West Indian (coded as 1) or not West Indian (coded as 0).

In this way, all four categories are represented by the three dummy variables. There is no need for a fourth dummy variable (one based on African or not African) because all of the information regarding **ethnicgp** is encapsulated in the three other dummy variables. Each category has a unique combination of ones or zeroes through which it is represented. The category 'African' is represented by the combination 0 0 0 (see Table 10.9). Thus, if we formulated a multiple-regression equation in which **ethnicgp** and **income** were the independent variables, it would take the form

$$y = a + bx_1(\text{white}) + cx_2(\text{Asian}) + dx_3(\text{West Indian}) + fx_4(\text{income}) + e$$

The assignment of codes – 1 and 0 – is entirely arbitrary and is meant to denote whether the characteristic in question is present or absent. The resulting unstandardized and standardized regression coefficients can be interpreted in the same manner as if they were based on interval variables.

Multiple regression and SPSS

The regression program within SPSS comprises a bewildering assortment of options and an equally bewildering array of output. In this section, it is proposed to cut a channel through this complexity by dealing with the

Table 10.10 Sample multiple-regression SPSS-X output (Job-Survey data)

· · · MULTIPLE REGRESSION · · ·

Variable list number 1
Equation number 1   Dependent variable.. Satis
Beginning block number 1   Method: Stepwise
Variable(s) entered on step number 1.. Autonom

Substitute mean for missing data

			Analysis of variance			
Multiple R	.72904			DF	Sum of Squares	Mean Square
R Square	.53150	R Square change	.53150	Regression 1	388.64728	388.64728
Adjusted R square	.52462	F Change	77.14557	Residual 68	342.57331	5.03784
Standard error	2.24451	Signif F change	.0000			

F = 77.14557   Signif F = .0000

------ VARIABLES IN THE EQUATION ------

Variable	B	SE B	BETA	TOLERANCE	T	Sig T
Autonom	.86074	.09800	.72904	1.00000	8.783	.0000
(Constant)	2.75962	.95810			2.880	.0053

------ VARIABLES NOT IN THE EQUATION ------

Variable	Beta in	Partial	Tolerance	Min Toler	T	Sig T
Income	.41878	.57430	.88105	.88105	5.742	.0000
Age	.17844	.25056	.92367	.92367	2.118	.0378
Routine	-.28757	-.36690	.76263	.76263	-3.228	.0019

Equation number 1   Dependent variable.. Satis
Variable(s) entered on step number 2.. Income

			Analysis of variance			
Multiple R	.82826			DF	Sum of Squares	Mean Square
R Square	.68602	R Square change	.15452	Regression 2	501.63304	250.81652
Adjusted R square	.67665	F Change	32.97237	Residual 67	229.58755	3.42668
Standard error	1.85113	Signif F change	.0000			

F = 73.19520   Signif F = 0.0

— — — — — VARIABLES IN THE EQUATION — — — — —

Variable	B	SE B	BETA	TOLERANCE	T	Sig T
Autonom	.69021	.08611	.58461	.88105	8.016	.0000
Income	1.386332E-03	2.41430E-04	.41878	.88105	5.742	.0000
(Constant)	-6.47977	1.79260			-3.615	.0006

— — — — — VARIABLES NOT IN THE EQUATION — — — — —

Variable	Beta in	Partial	Tolerance	Min Toler	T	Sig T
Age	-.07250	-.10316	.63578	.60644	-.843	.4025
Routine	-.19559	-.29689	.72345	.72345	-2.526	.0140

Variable(s) entered on step number 3..   Routine

Multiple R	.84481	R Square change	.02768
R Square	.71370	F Change	6.37980
Adjusted R square	.70068	Signif F change	.0140
Standard error	1.78101		

Analysis of variance

	DF	Sum of Squares	Mean Square
Regression	3	521.86966	173.95655
Residual	66	209.35093	3.17198

F = 54.84157   Signif F = .0000

Equation number 1   Dependent variable..   Satis

— — — — — VARIABLES IN THE EQUATION — — — — —

Variable	B	SE B	BETA	TOLERANCE	T	Sig T
Autonom	.59450	.09110	.50354	.72862	6.526	.0000
Income	1.249790E-03	2.38492E-04	.37754	.83578	5.240	.0000
Routine	-.15508	.06140	-.19559	.72345	-2.526	.0140
(Constant)	-2.43137	2.35447			-1.033	.3055

— — — — — VARIABLES NOT IN THE EQUATION — — — — —

Variable	Beta in	Partial	Tolerance	Min Toler	T	Sig T
Age	.01045	.01434	.53910	.50579	.116	.9083

For block number 1   PIN = 0.050 limits reached.

simple multiple-regression equation that was the focus for the preceding section and to show how it was generated using SPSS. The output is presented in Table 10.10. The set of commands employed to generate this output is as follows:

```
regression variables=income age satis routine autonom
 /statistics=defaults tol cha
 /dependent=satis/step
 /missing=meansubstitution.
```

The first line of SPSS commands signals that a regression analysis is to be conducted and stipulates all of the variables that are to be included in the analysis.

The second line stipulates a number of statistics that can be generated. The **defaults** comprise a huge number of computations and need not be specified unless further information is requested (as is the case in the second line); in other words, the information is provided unless there is an indication to the contrary. The **defaults** are made up of four components. In presenting these four components and their associated statistics, only those which have been covered in this book will be mentioned:

(1) Multiple R, R^2, and the adjusted R^2 – see the *circled* elements in Table 10.10.

(2) The F ratio for the model and the significance level of F are produced. Also, an analysis-of-variance table is produced, which can be interpreted in the same way as the ANOVA procedure described in Chapter 7. The analysis-of-variance table has not been discussed in the present chapter because it is not necessary to an understanding of regression for our present purposes. The F-ratio statistic and the significance level in Table 10.10 have been enclosed in a *straight-line rectangle* to highlight them.

(3) The unstandardized and standardized regression coefficients (**B** and **BETA** respectively in the output), the t value for the unstandardized regression coefficients, the standard error of each unstandardized regression coefficient (**SE B**), and significance levels for each t value – see the information within the *dotted* areas.

(4) A number of statistics are generated at each step regarding variables that are either not yet in the equation at each step or which in fact never enter the equation (such as **age**).

All of these statistics are generated by the request for the default statistics. In addition, the following additional information was requested:

(5) **Cha**. This provides the change in R^2 at each step, the associated F value, and the significance of F. These elements are indicated by the *hyphenated straight lines* in Table 10.10. **Tol** will produce useful information that is relevant to the detection of multicollinearity. This item stands for the *tolerance* of each variable that is in the equation. It is derived from 1 minus the multiple R for each independent variable. The multiple

R for each independent variable is made up of its correlation with all of the other independent variables. When the tolerance is low, the multiple correlation is high and the possibility of multicollinearity is raised. The tolerances for **autonom, routine**, and **income** were 0.72862, 0.83578 and 0.72345 respectively (see under the heading **TOLERANCE** in step 3), suggesting that multicollinearity is unlikely. If the tolerances were close to zero, the possibility of multicollinearity would have been considerable.

The third line then indicates which of these is to be the dependent variable; by implication, all of the other variables listed in the third line will be treated as independent variables.

In addition, the third line stipulates that a procedure for including variables in the equation called *stepwise* (**step**) is to be used. This is one of a number of approaches that can be used in deciding how and whether independent variables should be entered in the equation and is probably the most commonly used approach. Although popular, the stepwise method is none the less controversial because its use affords priority to statistical criteria of inclusion rather than theoretical ones. Independent variables are entered only if they meet the package's statistical criteria and the order of inclusion is determined by the contribution of each variable to the explained variance. Each variable is entered in steps, with the variable that exhibits the highest correlation with the dependent variable being entered at the first step (i.e. **autonom**). This variable must also meet the program's criteria for inclusion in terms of the required *F*-ratio value. The variable that exhibits the largest partial correlation with the dependent variable (with the effect of the first independent variable partialled out) is then entered (i.e. **income**). This variable must then meet the program's *F*-ratio default criteria. **Age** does not meet the necessary criteria and is therefore not included in the equation. In addition, as each new variable is included, variables that are already in the equation are re-assessed to see if they still meet the necessary statistical criteria. If they do not, they are removed from the equation. The capacity of this procedure to exclude variables from the equation can be overridden by the insertion of **enter** in the fourth line, which 'forces' each variable into the equation, regardless of whether it meets the program's statistical criteria. Normally, it would not be desirable to force variables into the equation in this way. However, when a path analysis (see next section) is being conducted, it will probably be necessary to force variables into the equation since the researcher will want all possible relationships in the model to be represented.

The fourth line indicates how cases with missing values are to be handled. In the above example it is proposed to substitute for a missing value for a case, the mean for that variable. The substitution of means for missing values is unlikely to be acceptable if there are many missing values affecting the relevant variables. If no instruction regarding missing values is provided, **listwise** deletion of cases will occur, whereby all cases with a missing value for any one of the variables specified in the first of the four lines above will be deleted.

If dummy variables are to be created, the following use of **if** for **ethnicgp** can be followed to produce such variables:

```
if (ethnicgp eq 1) x1 = 1
if (ethnicgp ne 1) x1 = 0
if (ethnicgp eq 2) x2 = 1
if (ethnicgp ne 2) x2 = 0
if (ethnicgp eq 3) x3 = 1
if (ethnicgp ne 3) x3 = 0
```

This procedure will create the three dummy variables described in Table 10.9.

Much more could be written about the SPSS regression output and the numerous options that exist for users, but for the sake of simplicity we have attempted to provide the chief points that we think will be necessary in order to fit most circumstances. All of the commands used in this section can, of course, be used for bivariate regression. In Chapter 8, it was suggested that the researcher might initially want to use **plot**, since these procedures can generate some of the necessary information. However, if a more detailed analysis were required, the reader would need to use the SPSS regression procedures described in this section.

Path analysis

The final area to be examined in this chapter, *path analysis,* is an extension of the multiple-regression procedures explored in the previous section. In fact, path analysis entails the use of multiple regression in relation to explicitly formulated causal models. Path analysis cannot establish causality; it cannot be used as a substitute for the researcher's views about the likely causal linkages among groups of variables. All it can do is to examine the pattern of relationships between three or more variables, but can neither confirm not reject the hypothetical causal imagery.

The aim of path analysis is to provide quantitative estimates of the causal connections between sets of variables. The connections proceed in one direction and are viewed as making up distinct paths. These ideas can best be explained with reference to the central feature of a path analysis – the path diagram. The path diagram makes explicit the likely causal connections between variables. An example is provided in Figure 10.6 which takes four variables employed in the Job Survey: **age, income, autonom,** and **satis**. The arrows indicate expected causal connections between variables. The model moves from left to right implying causal priority to those variables closer to the left. Each *p* denotes a causal path and hence a path coefficient that will need to be computed. The model

Figure 10.6 Path diagram for **satis**

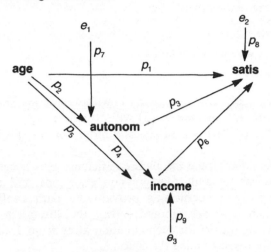

proposes that **age** has a *direct* effect on **satis** (p_1). However, *indirect* effects of **age** on **satis** are also proposed: **age** affects **income** (p_5) which in turn affects **satis** (p_6); **age** affects **autonom** (p_2) which in turn affects **satis** (p_3); and **age** affects **autonom** (p_2) again, but this time affects **income** (p_4) which in turn affects **satis** (p_6). In addition, **autonom** has a direct effect on **satis** (p_3) and an indirect effect whereby it affects **income** (p_4) which in turn affects **satis** (p_6). Finally, **income** has a direct effect on **satis** (p_6), but no indirect effects. Thus, a direct effect occurs when a variable has an effect on another variable without a third variable intervening between them; an indirect effect occurs when there is a third intervening variable through which two variables are connected.

In addition, **income, autonom,** and **satis** have further arrows directed to them from outside the nexus of variables. These refer to the amount of unexplained variance for each variable respectively. Thus, the arrow from e_1 to **autonom** (p_7) refers to the amount of variance in **autonom** that is not accounted for by **age**. Likewise, the arrow from e_2 to **satis** (p_8) denotes the amount of error arising from the variance in **satis** that is not explained by **age, autonom,** and **income**. Finally, the arrow from e_3 to **income** (p_9) denotes the amount of variance in **income** that is unexplained by **age** and **autonom**. These error terms point to the fact that there are other variables that have an impact on **autonom** and **satis**, but which are not included in the path diagram.

In order to provide estimates of each of the postulated paths, path coefficients are computed. A path coefficient is a standardized regression coefficient. The path coefficients are computed by setting up three *structural equations,* that is equations which stipulate the structure of hypothesized relationships in a model. In the case of Figure 10.6, three structural equations will be required – one for **autonom**, one for **satis**, and one for **income**. The three equations will be:

(1) **autonom** $= x_1$**age** $+ e_1$

(2) **satis** $= x_1$**age** $+ x_2$**autonom** $+ x_3$**income** $+ e_2$

(3) **income** $= x_1$**age** $+ x_2$**autonom** $+ e_3$

The standardized coefficient for **age** in (1) will provide p_2. The coefficients for **age**, **autonom**, and **income** in (2) will provide p_1, p_3, and p_6 respectively. Finally, the coefficients for **age** and **autonom** in (3) will provide p_5 and p_4 respectively.

Thus, in order to compute the path coefficients, it is necessary to treat the three equations as multiple-regression equations and the resulting standardized regression coefficients provide the path coefficients. The intercepts in each case are ignored. Also, the three error terms are calculated by taking the R^2 for each equation away from 1 and taking the square root of the result of this subtraction.

To compute equation (1) with SPSS, the following commands should be employed:

```
regression variables=autonom age
 /dependent=autonom
 /step/enter.
```

For equation (2):

```
regression variables=age autonom income
 /dependent=satis
 /step/enter.
```

For equation (3):

```
regression variables=age autonom income
 /dependent=income
 /step/enter.
```

When conducting a path analysis the critical issues to search for in the SPSS output are the standardized regression coefficients for each variable (under the heading **BETA** on the last page of output for each equation) and the R^2 (for the error-term paths). If we take the results of the third equation, we find that the standardized coefficients for **autonom** and **age** are 0.21524 and 0.56690 respectively and the R^2 is 0.40810. Thus, for p_4, p_5, and p_9 in the path diagram (Figure 10.7) we substitute 0.22, 0.57, and 0.77 (the latter being the square root of 1 - 0.40810). All of the relevant path coefficients have been inserted in Figure 10.7.

Since the path coefficients are standardized, it is possible to compare them directly. We can see that **age** has a very small negative direct effect on **satis**, but it has a number of fairly pronounced indirect effects on **satis**. In particular, there is a strong sequence that goes from **age** to **income** ($p_5 =$ 0.57) to **satis** ($p_6 = 0.47$).

Many researchers recommend calculating the overall impact of a variable like **age** on **satis**. This would be done as follows. We take the direct effect of **age** (−0.08) and add to it the indirect effects. The indirect effects are gleaned by multiplying the coefficients for each path from **age** to **satis**. The path from **age** to **income** to **satis** would be calculated as (0.57) (0.47) = 0.26. For the path from **age** to **autonom** to **satis** we have (0.28) (0.58) = 0.16. Finally, the sequence from **age** to **autonom** to **income** to **satis** yields (0.28) (0.22) (0.47) = 0.02. Thus the total indirect effect of **age** on **satis** is 0.26 + 0.16 + 0.02 = 0.44. For the total effect of **age** on **satis**, we add the direct effect and the total indirect effect, i.e. −0.08 + 0.44 = 0.36. This exercise suggests that the indirect effect of **age** on **satis** is inconsistent with its direct effect, since the former is slightly negative and the indirect effect is positive. Clearly, an appreciation of the intervening variables **income** and **autonom** is essential to an understanding of the **age**–**satis** relationship.

The effect of **age** on **satis** could be compared with other variables in the path diagram. Thus, the effect of **autonom** is made up of the direct effect (0.58) plus the indirect effect of **autonom** to **income** to **satis**, i.e. 0.58 + (0.22) (0.47), which equals 0.67. The effect of **income** on **satis** is made up only of the direct effect, which is 0.47, since there is no indirect effect from **income** to **satis**. Thus, we have three *effect coefficients*, as they are often called (for example, Pedhazur 1982) – 0.36, 0.67, and 0.47 for **age**, **autonom**, and **income** respectively – implying that **autonom** has the largest overall effect on **satis**.

Figure 10.7 Path diagram for **satis** with path coefficients

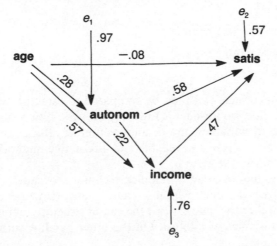

Figure 10.8 Path diagram for **absence**

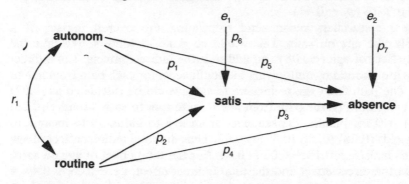

Sometimes, it is not possible to specify the causal direction between all of the variables in a path diagram. In Figure 10.8 **autonom** and **routine** are deemed to be correlates; there is no attempt to ascribe causal priority to one or the other. The link between them is indicated by a curved arrow with two heads. Each variable has a direct effect on **absence** (p_5 and p_4). In addition, each variable has an indirect effect on **absence** through **satis**: **autonom** to **satis** (p_1) and **satis** to **absence** (p_3); **routine** to **satis** (p_2) and **satis** to **absence** (p_3). In order to generate the necessary coefficients, we would need the Pearson's *r* for **autonom** and **routine** and the standardized regression coefficients from two equations:

(1) **satis** $= x_1$**autonom** $+ x_2$**routine** $+ e_1$

(2) **absence** $= x_1$**autonom** $+ x_2$**routine** $+ x_3$**satis** $+ e_2$

We could then compare the total causal effects of both **autonom, routine,** and **satis**. The total effect would be made up of the direct effect plus the total indirect effect. The total effect of each of these three variables on **absence** would be:

Total effect of **autonom** $= (p_5) + (p_1)(p_3)$

Total effect of **routine** $= (p_4) + (p_2)(p_3)$

Total effect of **satis** $= p_3$

These three total effects can then be compared to establish which has the greater overall effect on **absence**. However, with complex models involving a large number of variables, the decomposition of effects using the foregoing procedures can prove unreliable and alternative methods have to be employed (Pedhazur 1982).

Path analysis has become a popular technique because it allows the relative impact of variables within a causal network to be estimated. It forces the researcher to make explicit the causal structure that is believed to undergird the variables of interest. On the other hand, it suffers from the problem that it cannot confirm the underlying causal structure. It tells us what the relative impact of the variables upon each other is, but cannot validate that causal structure. Since a cause must precede an effect, the time order of variables must be established in the construction of a path diagram. We are forced to rely on theoretical ideas and our common-sense notions for information about the likely sequence of the variables in the real world. Sometimes these conceptions of time ordering of variables will be faulty and the ensuing path diagram will be misleading. Clearly, while path analysis has much to offer, its potential limitations should also be appreciated. In this chapter, it has only been feasible to cover a limited range of issues in relation to path analysis and the emphasis has been upon the use of examples to illustrate some of the relevant procedures, rather than a formal presentation of the issues. Readers requiring more detailed treatments should consult Land (1969), Pedhazur (1982), and Davis (1985).

Exercises

1. A researcher hypothesizes that women are more likely than men to support legislation for equal pay between the sexes. The researcher decides to conduct a social survey and draws a sample of 1,000 individuals among whom men and women are equally represented. One set of questions asked directs the respondent to indicate whether he or she approves of such legislation. The findings are provided in Table 10E.1. Is the researcher's belief that women are more likely than men to support equal pay legislation confirmed by the data in the table?

2. Following from Question 1, the researcher controls for age and the results of the analysis are provided in Table 10E.2. What are the implications of this analysis for the researcher's view that men and women differ in support for equal-pay legislation?

3. What SPSS commands would be required to examine the relationship between **ethnicgp** and **commit**, controlling for **gender**?

Table 10E.1 The relationship between approval of equal-pay legislation and gender

	Men	Women
	%	
Approve	58	71
Disapprove	42	29
	100	100
N =	500	500

Table 10E.2 The relationship between approval of equal-pay legislation and gender holding age constant

| | Under 35 | | 35 and over | |
| | Men | Women | Men | Women |
	%		%	
Approve	68	92	48	54
Disapprove	32	8	52	46
	100	100	100	100
N =	250	250	250	250

4. A researcher is interested in the correlates of the number of times that people attend religious services during the course of a year. On the basis of a sample of individuals, he finds that income correlates fairly well with frequency of attendance (Pearson's $r=0.59$). When the researcher controls for the effects of age the partial correlation coefficient is found to be 0.12. Why has the size of the correlation fallen so much?

5. What SPSS-X command would you need to correlate **income** and **satis**, controlling for **age**?

6. Using SPSS-X, what commands and steps would you need to take in order to produce a partial rank correlation coefficient, whereby the relationship between **skill** and **prody** controlling for **qual** is examined? Interpret the result of this analysis.

7. Consider the following regression equation and other details:

$$y = 7.3 + 2.3x_1 + 4.1x_2 - 1.4x_3 \quad R^2=0.78 \; F21.43, \, p<0.01$$

(a) What value would you expect y to exhibit if $x_1=9$, $x_2=22$, and $x_3=17$?
(b) How confident would you feel about this prediction?
(c) Which of the three independent variables exhibits the largest effect on y?
(d) What does the negative sign for x_3 mean?

8. What SPSS commands would you need to provide the data for the multiple-regression equations on p. 250? In considering the commands, you should bear in mind that the information is required for a path analysis. Also, the commands should be for a stepwise analysis with listwise deletion of missing cases and should request the default statistics and the details about the change in R^2.

9. Turning to the first of the two equations referred to in Question 8 (i.e. the one with **satis** as the dependent variable),
(a) How much of the variance in **satis** do the two variables account for?
(b) Are the individual regression coefficients for **autonom** and **routine** statistically significant?
(c) What is the standardized regression coefficient for **routine**?

10. Examine Figure 10.8 (see p. 250). Using the information generated for Questions 8 and 9, which variable has the largest overall effect on **absence** – is it **autonom, routine**, or **satis**?

Chapter eleven

Aggregating variables: exploratory factor analysis

Many of the concepts we use to describe human behaviour seem to consist of a number of different aspects. Take, for example, the concept of job satisfaction. When we say we are satisfied with our job, this statement may refer to various feelings we have about our work, such as being keen to go to it every day, not looking for other kinds of jobs, being prepared to spend time and effort on it, and having a sense of achievement about it. If these different components contribute to our judgement of how satisfied we are with our job, we would expect them to be interrelated. In other words, how eager we are to go to work should be correlated with the feeling of accomplishment we gain from it and so on. Similarly, the concept of job routine may refer to a number of interdependent characteristics such as how repetitive the work is, how much it makes us think about what we are doing, the number of different kinds of tasks we have to carry out each day, and so on. Some people may enjoy repetitive work while others may prefer a job which is more varied. If this is the case, we would expect job satisfaction to be unrelated to job routine. To determine this, we could ask people to describe their feelings about their jobs in terms of these characteristics and see to what extent those aspects which reflect satisfaction are correlated with one another and are unrelated to those which represent routine. Characteristics which go together constitute a *factor* and *factor analysis* refers to a number of related statistical techniques which help us to determine them.

These techniques are used for three main purposes. First, as implied above, they can assess the degree to which items, such as those measuring job satisfaction and routine, are tapping the same concept. If people respond in similar ways to questions concerning job satisfaction as they do to those about job routine, this implies that these two concepts are not seen as being conceptually distinct by these people. If, however, their answers to the job-satisfaction items are unrelated to their ones to the job-routine items, this suggests that these two feelings can be distinguished. In other words, factor analysis enables us to assess the *factorial validity* of the questions which make up our scales by telling us the extent to which they seem to be measuring the same concepts or variables.

Second, if we have a large number of variables, factor analysis can determine the degree to which they can be reduced to a smaller set. Suppose, for example, we were interested in how gender and ethnic group were related to attitudes towards work. To measure this, we generate from our own experience twelve questions similar to those used in the Job Survey to reflect the different feelings we think people hold towards their jobs. At this stage, we have no idea that they might form three distinct concepts (i.e. job satisfaction, autonomy, and routine). To analyse the relationship of gender and ethnic group to these items, we would have to conduct twelve separate analyses. There would be two major disadvantages to doing this. First, it would make it more difficult to understand the findings since we would have to keep in mind the results of twelve different tests. Second, the more statistical tests we carry out, the more likely we are to find that some of them will be significant by chance. It is not possible to determine the likelihood of this if the data come from the same sample.

The third use to which factor analysis has been put is related to the previous one but is more ambitious in the sense that it is aimed at trying to make sense of the bewildering complexity of social behaviour by reducing it to a more limited number of factors. A good example of this is the factor-analytic approach to the description of personality by psychologists such as Eysenck and Cattell (for example, Eysenck and Eysenck 1969; Cattell 1973). There is a large number of ways in which the personalities of people vary. One indication of this is the hundreds of words describing personality characteristics which are listed in a dictionary. Many of these terms seem to refer to similar aspects: for example, the words 'sociable', 'outwardgoing', 'gregarious', and 'extraverted' all describe individuals who like the company of others. If we ask people to describe themselves or someone they know well in terms of these and other words, and we factor analyse this information, we will find that these characteristics will group themselves into a smaller number of factors. In fact, a major factor that emerges is one called sociability or extraversion. Some people, then, see factor analysis as a tool for bringing order to the way we see things by determining which of them are related and which of them are not.

Two uses of factor analysis can be distinguished. The one most commonly reported is the *exploratory* kind in which the relationships between various variables are examined without determining the extent to which the results fit a particular model. *Confirmatory* factor analysis, on the other hand, compares the solution found against a hypothetical one. If, for example, we expected the four items measuring job satisfaction in the Job Survey to form one factor, then we could assess the degree to which they did so by comparing the results of our analysis with a hypothetical solution in which this was done perfectly. Although there are techniques for making these kinds of statistical comparisons (for example, Long 1983;

Jöreskog and Sörbom 1986) they are only available as an extra option with SPSS-X. Consequently, we shall confine our discussion to the exploratory use of factor analysis. It should be noted that factor analysis is a standard component of SPSS-X, but is only available in SPSS/PC+ as a set of procedures within the Advanced Statistics option. We will illustrate its use with an analysis of the job satisfaction and routine items in the Job Survey, in which we will describe the decisions to be made, followed by the commands to carry these out.

Correlation matrix

The initial step is to compute a correlation matrix for the eight items which make up the two scales of job satisfaction and routine. If there are no significant correlations between these items, then this means that they are unrelated and that we would not expect them to form one or more factors. In other words, it would not be worthwhile to go on to conduct a factor analysis. Consequently, this should be the first stage in deciding whether to carry one out. The correlation matrix for these items, together with their significance levels, is presented in Table 11.1.

All but one of the items are significantly correlated at less than the 0.05 level, either positively or negatively, with one another, which suggests that they may constitute one or more factors.

Sample size

Second, how reliable the factors are which emerge from a factor analysis depends on the size of the sample, although there is no consensus on what this should be. There is agreement, however, that there should be more subjects than variables. Gorsuch (1983), for example, has proposed an absolute minimum of five subjects per variable and not less than 100 individuals per analysis. Although factor analysis can be carried out on samples smaller than this to describe the relationships between the variables, not much confidence should be placed that these same factors would emerge in a second sample. Consequently, if the main purpose of a study is to find out what factors underlie a group of variables, it is essential that the sample should be sufficiently large to enable this to be done reliably.

Principal components or factors?

The two most widely used forms of factor analysis are *principal components* and *factor* analysis (called *principal-axis factoring* in SPSS). There are also other kinds of methods which are available on SPSS such as alpha, image, and maximum-likelihood factoring but these are used much less

255

Table 11.1 Correlation and significance-level matrices for items (Job-Survey SPSS/PC+ output)

- - - - F A C T O R   A N A L Y S I S - - - -

Analysis Number 1 Listwise deletion of cases with missing values

Correlation Matrix:

	SATIS1	SATIS2	SATIS3	SATIS4	ROUTINE1	ROUTINE2	ROUTINE3	ROUTINE4
SATIS1	1.00000							
SATIS2	.43949	1.00000						
SATIS3	.43851	.31244	1.00000					
SATIS4	.44248	.47440	.56741	1.00000				
ROUTINE1	−.46823	−.52223	−.28931	−.42153	1.00000			
ROUTINE2	−.46484	−.47181	−.19333	−.41693	.69200	1.00000		
ROUTINE3	−.39267	−.43339	−.28664	−.41467	.79382	.61968	1.00000	
ROUTINE4	−.35075	−.46251	−.22857	−.29975	.72544	.49617	.63604	1.00000

Correlation 1-tailed Significance Matrix:
'.' is printed for diagonal elements.

	SATIS1	SATIS2	SATIS3	SATIS4	ROUTINE1	ROUTINE2	ROUTINE3	ROUTINE4
SATIS1	.							
SATIS2	.00009	.						
SATIS3	.00009	.00474	.					
SATIS4	.00008	.00002	.00000	.				
ROUTINE1	.00003	.00000	.00836	.00017	.			
ROUTINE2	.00003	.00002	.05709	.00020	.00000	.		
ROUTINE3	.00046	.00011	.00890	.00022	.00000	.00001	.	
ROUTINE4	.00168	.00004	.03041	.00651	.00000	.00000	.00000	.

frequently. Because of this and the need to keep the discussion brief, we will only outline the first two techniques. When talking about both these methods we shall refer to them collectively as factor analysis, as is the usual convention. However, when specifically discussing the method of factor analysis we shall call it principal-axis factoring, as SPSS does, to distinguish it from the general method.

Factor analysis is primarily concerned with describing the variation or variance which is shared by the scores of people on three or more variables. This variance is referred to as *common variance* and needs to be distinguished from two other kinds of variance. *Specific variance* describes the variation which is specific or unique to a variable and which is not shared with any other variable. *Error variance*, on the other hand, is the variation due to the fluctuations which inevitably result from measuring something. If, for example, you weigh yourself a number of times in quick succession, you will find that the readings will vary somewhat, despite the fact that your weight could not have changed in so short a time. These fluctuations in measurement are known as error variance. So the total variance that we find in the scores of an instrument (such as an item or test) to assess a particular variable can be divided or partitioned into common, specific, and error variance:

Total variance=Common variance+Specific variance+Error variance

Since factor analysis cannot distinguish specific from error variance, they are combined to form *unique variance*. In other words, the total variance of a test consists of its common and its unique variance.

This idea may be illustrated with the relationship between three variables, *x*, *y*, and *z*, as displayed in the Venn diagram in Figure 11.1 The overlap between any two of the variables and all three of them represents common variance (the shaded areas), while the remaining unshaded areas constitute the unique variance of each of the three variables.

Figure 11.1 Common and unique variance

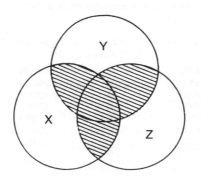

Figure 11.2 Scree test of eigenvalues (Job-Survey SPSS/PC+ output)

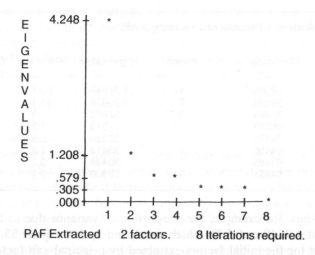

PAF Extracted   2 factors.   8 Iterations required.

be retained are those which lie before the point at which the eigenvalues seem to level off. This occurs after the first two factors in this case, both of which incidentally have eigenvalues of greater than one. In other words, both criteria suggest the same number of factors in this example. Which criterion to use may depend on the size of the average communalities and the number of variables and subjects. The Kaiser criterion has been recommended for situations where the number of variables is less than thirty and the average communality is greater than 0.70 or when the number of subjects is greater than 250 and the mean communality is greater than or equal to 0.60 (Stevens 1986). If the number of factors to be extracted differs from that suggested by the Kaiser criterion, then this has to be specified with the appropriate SPSS subcommand.

The two principal-component factors are shown in Table 11.4, while the two principal-axis ones are displayed in Table 11.5. The relationship between each item or test and a factor is expressed as a correlation or *loading*.

The items have been listed, by request, in terms of the size of their loadings on the factor to which they are most closely related. Thus, for example, the item **routine1** loads most highly on the first of the two factors in both analyses, although its correlation with them varies somewhat. In other words, the two analyses produce somewhat different solutions. All but one (**satis3**) of the eight items correlate most highly with the first factor.

Table 11.4 Item loadings on first two principal components (Job-Survey SPSS/PC+ output)

Factor Matrix:	FACTOR 1	FACTOR 2
ROUTINE1	.87341	.30955
ROUTINE3	.81358	.29568
ROUTINE2	.77101	.24197
ROUTINE4	.74404	.36377
SATIS2	−.70623	.08660
SATIS1	−.67255	.30585
SATIS4	−.67103	.50586
SATIS3	−.52373	.69088

Rotation of factors

The first factors extracted from an analysis are those which account for the maximum amount of variance. As a consequence, what they represent might not be easy to interpret since items will not correlate as highly with them as they might. In fact, most of the items will fall on the first factor, although their correlations with it may not be that high. In order to increase the interpretability of factors, they are rotated to maximize the loadings of some of the items. These items can then be used to identify the meaning of the factor. A number of ways have been developed to rotate factors, some of which are available on SPSS. The two most commonly used methods are *orthogonal* rotation which produces factors which are unrelated to or independent of one another, and *oblique* rotation in which the factors are correlated.

There is some controversy as to which of these two kinds of rotation is the more appropriate. The advantage of orthogonal rotation is that the

Table 11.5 Item loadings on first two principal axes (Job-Survey SPSS/PC+ output)

Factor Matrix:	FACTOR 1	FACTOR 2
ROUTINE1	.89950	.30938
ROUTINE3	.79335	.23001
ROUTINE2	.72399	.14921
ROUTINE4	.70313	.25687
SATIS2	−.63709	.09454
SATIS4	−.63588	.46495
SATIS1	−.60582	.22723
SATIS3	−.48142	.53148

information the factors provide is not redundant, since a person's score on one factor is unrelated to his or her score on another. If, for example, we found two orthogonal factors which we interpreted as being of job satis-faction and routine, then what this means is that in general, how satisfied people are with their jobs is not related to how routine they see them as being. The disadvantage of orthogonal rotation, on the other hand, is that the factors may have been forced to be unrelated, whereas in real life they may be related. In other words, an orthogonal solution may be more artificial and not necessarily an accurate reflection of what occurs naturally in the world. This may be less likely with oblique rotation, although it should be borne in mind that the original factors in an analysis are made to be orthogonal.

Orthogonal rotation

An orthogonal rotation of the two principal-component factors is shown in Table 11.6. The method for doing this was *varimax*. In terms of the orthogonally rotated solution, five and not seven items load on the first factor, while three of them correlate most highly with the second one. The items which load most strongly on the first factor are listed or grouped together first and are ordered in terms of the size of their correlations. The items which correlate most strongly with the second factor form the second group on the second factor. If there had been a third factor, then the items which loaded most highly on it would constitute the third group on the third factor, and so on. Although the data are made up, if we were to obtain a result like this with real data it would suggest that the way in which people answered the job-routine items was not related to the way they responded to the job-satisfaction ones, with the exception of **satis2**. In

Table 11.6 Item loadings on orthogonally rotated factors (Job-Survey SPSS/PC+ output)

Varimax Rotation 1, Extraction 2, Analysis 1 — Kaiser Normalization.

Varimax converged in 3 iterations.

Rotated Factor Matrix:

	FACTOR 1	FACTOR 2
ROUTINE1	.89431	−.24264
ROUTINE3	.83723	−.21999
ROUTINE4	.81881	−.12443
ROUTINE2	.77165	−.23992
SATIS2	−.53136	.47319
SATIS3	−.03735	.86615
SATIS4	−.26377	.79787
SATIS1	−.37887	.63429

other words, the two groups of items seem to be factorially distinct. The loadings of items on factors can be positive or negative: for example, the **satis2** item has a negative correlation with the first factor while the four job-routine items are positively related to it. In fact, this item appears to be a reflection of both these factors, since it correlates quite highly with the two of them. Consequently, if we wanted to have a purer measure of job satisfaction, it would be advisable to omit it from this scale.

In general, the meaning of a factor is determined by the items which load most highly on it. Which items to ignore when interpreting a factor is arguable. It may not be appropriate to use the significance level of the factor loading since this depends on the size of the sample. In addition, the appropriate level to use is complicated by the fact that a large number of correlations have been computed on data which come from the same subjects. Conventionally, items or variables which correlate less than 0.3 with a factor are omitted from consideration since they account for less than 9 per cent of the variance and so are not very important. An alternative criterion to use is the correlation above which no item correlates highly with more than one factor. The advantage of this rule is that factors are interpreted in terms of items unique to them. Consequently, their meaning should be less ambiguous. According to these two rules, factor 1 comprises all four of the routine items whereas factor 2 contains only **satis3** and **satis4**. However, the use of these two conventions in conjunction engenders a highly stringent set of criteria for deciding which variables should be included in which factors. Many researchers ignore the second convention and emphasize all loadings in excess of 0.3 regardless of whether any variables are thereby implicated in more than one factor.

The amount or percentage of variance that each of the orthogonally rotated factors accounts for is not given by SPSS but can easily be calculated. To work out the amount of variance explained by a factor, square the correlations of each of its items and add them together. If we do this for the first factor, the amount of variance is about 3.26. The percentage of variance is simply this amount divided by the number of items ($3.26/8=0.41$) and multiplied by 100 (i.e. 41 per cent).

Oblique rotation

Oblique rotation produced by the *oblimin* method in SPSS gives three matrices. The first, a *structure* matrix, consists of correlations between the variables and the factors. The second, the *pattern* matrix, is made up of weights which reflect the unique variance each factor contributes to a variable. This is the matrix which is generally used to interpret the factors. The oblique factors shown in Table 11.7 are from this matrix. The results are similar to the orthogonal rotation except that the loadings between the items and factors are higher.

Table 11.7 Item loadings on obliquely rotated factors (Job-Survey SPSS/PC+ output)

Structure Matrix:

	FACTOR 1	FACTOR 2
ROUTINE1	.92655	−.42930
ROUTINE3	.86563	−.39491
ROUTINE4	.82403	−.29762
ROUTINE2	.80707	−.40026
SATIS2	−.63236	.57640
SATIS3	−.25161	.85392
SATIS4	−.45393	.83593
SATIS1	−.52473	.70093

Table 11.8 Correlations between oblique factors (Job-Survey SPSS/PC+ output)

Factor Correlation Matrix:

	FACTOR 1	FACTOR 2
FACTOR 1	1.00000	
FACTOR 2	−.45121	1.00000

The third matrix shows the correlations between the factors and is presented in Table 11.8.

Since they are moderately intercorrelated (−0.45), oblique rotation may be more appropriate in this case. It is difficult to estimate the amount of variance accounted for by oblique factors since the variance is shared between the correlated factors. Thus, for example, as the two factors are correlated in this instance, part of the variance of the first factor would also be part of the second.

SPSS-X and SPSS/PC+ factor-analysis commands

The following commands were used to compute the output for the principal-components analysis:

```
missing values ethnicgp to qual (0) absence (0).
recode satis2 satis4 (1=5) (2=4) (4=2) (5=1).
factor variables=satis1 to satis4 routine1 to routine4
 /extraction=pc
 /print=initial correlation sig extraction rotation
 /format=sort
 /plot=eigen
 /rotation=varimax
 /rotation=oblimin.
```

It is important to remember to specify the missing values of the items, as is done here, otherwise the zeros will be read as real values. **Satis2** and **satis4** have been recoded so that the direction of the scoring of the job-satisfaction items is the same. The variables to be analysed are listed after the **variables** subcommand. Since the four job-satisfaction items are consecutively located in the data file, there is no need to name the inter-mediate ones (i.e. **satis2** and **satis3**). The principal-components analysis (**pc**) is the default one and so does not have to be specified. To ask for principal-axis factoring (**paf**), replace **pc** with **paf**. If SPSS-X is being used, the full stops should be excluded from the ends of the commands.

Included in the output printed by default are: (1) the initial commun-alities, eigenvalues, and per-cent variance (**initial**), as displayed in Tables 11.2 and 11.3; (2) the loadings of the items on the unrotated factors (**extraction**), as presented in Tables 11.4 and 11.5; and (3) the loadings on the rotated factors, as shown in Tables 11.6 and 11.7, and the factor corre-lations in Table 11.8 (**rotation**). It is necessary to use the **print** sub-command specifically to request the correlation matrix of the original items (**correlation**) and their statistical significance (**sig**) reproduced in Table 11.1. To order or **sort** the items which correlate most highly with a factor in terms of the size of their loadings, the **format** subcommand is used. The scree plot (**eigen**) shown in Figure 11.2 was produced with the **plot** subcommand. The **rotation** subcommand asked for the **varimax** rotation followed by the **oblimin** one.

Although not illustrated here, if the number of factors we wanted to extract differed from the default option of Kaiser's criterion, we would use the **criteria** subcommand, which takes the following form:

/criteria=factors(1)

The number of factors to be extracted is specified in parentheses. In this case, it is one. It is sometimes necessary to increase the number of iterations required to arrive at a factor solution. An *iteration* may be thought of as an attempt to estimate the total common variance of a variable or item to be accounted for by the main factors. Successive attempts are made (iterations) until the estimates change little. If we were to find that the default maximum number of twenty-five iterations were insufficient to produce an acceptable solution, we could increase it to, say, fifty using the **criteria** subcommand:

/criteria=iterate(50)

Exercises

1. You have developed a questionnaire to measure anxiety which consists of ten items. You want to know whether the items constitute a single factor. To find this out, would it be appropriate to carry out a factor analysis on the ten items?

2. If you were to carry out a factor analysis on ten items or variables, what would be the minimum number of subjects or cases you would use?

3. What is the unique variance of a variable?

4. How does principal-components analysis differ from principal-axis factoring?

5. How many factors are there in a factor analysis?

6. Which factor accounts for most of the variance?

7. Why are not all the factors extracted?

8. Which criterion is most commonly used to determine the number of factors to be extracted?

9. What is meant by a loading?

10. Why are factors rotated?

11. What is the advantage of orthogonal rotation?

12. Is it possible to calculate the amount of variance explained by oblique factors?

Appendix

There has been a number of different versions of SPSS-X. In this book, we have used what at the time of writing was the latest version, i.e. Release 3.0. However, since some readers may only have access to earlier versions, it was felt necessary to highlight the differences from the commands used in the text between Release 3.0 and earlier versions. These differences generally are few in number and relatively minor.

File handle command

In SPSS-X releases prior to 3.0, a **file handle** command is required to precede **data list**. This command tells SPSS-X the name of the data file that is to be processed. The first half of the command contains the keywords **file handle**, the name of the file (for example, **jsr.dat**) and / (forward slash):

file handle jsr.dat/

The second half of this command is specific to different implementations of SPSS-X. To find out what the rest of the command is, you should consult your Computer Centre. Note that the name of the data file used here is the same as in the **data list** command:

file handle jsr.dat/ [second half of command]
write outfile=jss.dat table

When saving either tabular or system files, it is necessary to precede the **write** and **save** commands respectively with a **file handle** command. Thus, for example, to save a tabular file called **jss.dat**, the following commands would be required:

file handle jss.dat/ [second half of command]
write outfile=jss.dat table

These commands would follow the **formats** command.

Variable labels

With versions of SPSS-X prior to 2.2, the maximum character length is 40; thereafter it is 120.

Value labels

With versions of SPSS-X prior to 2.2, the maximum character length is 40; thereafter it is 120.

Descriptive statistics

In releases of SPSS-X prior to 3.0, the **condescriptive** command is used instead of **descriptives** to produce various descriptive statistics.

Scatter diagrams

Prior to SPSS-X Release 2.0, the command for generating scatter diagrams was **scattergram** rather than **plot**. In order to produce a scatter diagram and the associated regression and correlation information, the following commands would be required:

scattergram satis routine
 /statistics 1 2 3

Pearson's correlation

Prior to Release 3.0, the **corr** command was called **pearson corr**. To correlate **satis** with **routine**, for example, the following command is used:

pearson corr satis routine

To obtain a two-tailed significance test, the following subcommand is required:

 /options 3

Means

Prior to Release 3.0, the **means** command was called **breakdown**. The rest of the **means** command is identical to that of **breakdown**.

MANOVA

Adjusted means

Prior to Release 3.0, the subcommand for producing adjusted means is:

```
/print=pmeans
```

Repeated measures

Prior to Release 3.0, it is necessary to include both a **wsdesign** and **analysis(repeated)** subcommand. The full command for comparing job satisfaction over three months (see p. 145) would be:

```
manova satis1 satis2 satis3
 /wsfactor=month(3)
 /wsdesign=month
 /print=cellinfo(means) transform signif(univ averf)
 /analysis(repeated)
```

Statistics and options subcommands

In releases of SPSS-X prior to 3.0, the keyword approach cannot be used.

Answers to exercises

Chapter 1

1. These forms of analysis concentrate upon one, two, and three or more variables respectively.

2. It is necessary in order to ensure that members of experimental and control groups are as alike as possible. If members of the experimental and control groups are alike any contrasts that are found between the two groups cannot be attributed to differences in the membership of the two groups; instead, it is possible to infer that it is the experimental stimulus (Exp) that is the source of the differences between the two groups.

3. The reasoning is faulty. First, those who read the quality dailies and those who read the tabloids will differ from each other in ways other than the newspapers that they read. In other words, people cannot be treated as though they have been randomly assigned to two experimental treatments – qualities and tabloids. Second, the causal inference is risky because it is possible that people with a certain level of political knowledge are more likely to read certain kinds of newspaper, rather than the type of newspaper affecting the level of political knowledge.

Chapter 2

1. Since various other religious affiliations have not been included, it is important to have a further option in which these can be placed. This can be called 'Other'.

2. The most convenient way of coding this information is to assign a number to each option, such as 1 for Agnostic, 2 for Atheist, and so on.

3. This information should be coded as missing. In other words, you need to assign a number to data that are missing.

4. If this happened very infrequently, then one possibility would be to code this kind of response as missing. Since the answer is not truly missing, an alternative course of action would be to record one of the two answers. There are a number of ways this could be done. First, the most common category could be chosen. Second, one of the two answers could be selected at random. Third, using other information we could try and predict which of the two was the most likely one. If there were a large number of such multiple answers, then a separate code could be used to signify them.

5. If we provide an identification number for each subject and if Agnostics are

coded as 1 and Atheists as 2, your data file should look something like this:

```
01    1 25
02    1 47
03    2 33
04    2 18
```

In other words, the information for the same subject is placed in a separate row, while the information for the same variable is placed in the same column(s).

6. Two columns since there are eleven options including 'Missing' and 'Other'.

7. The **data list** command does this.

8. There are usually no more than eighty columns to a line.

9.

data list file=ps.dat records=1
 /id 1–2 attend1 qual1 3–6

There are various ways of writing the second line such as:

 /id attend1 qual1 1–6

or

 /id 1–2 attend1 4 qual1 6

10.
data list file='a:ps.dat'
 /id 1–2 attend1 qual1 3–6.

11.

data list file=psd records=1
 /id 1–2 attend1 qual1 3–6 satis1 8–9 attend2 qual2 10–13
 satis2 15–16 attend3 qual3 17–20 satis3 22–23

12. Eight characters.

Chapter 3

1.

select if (ethnicgp eq 4).

2.

select if (gender eq 2 and age 1e 25 and ethnicgp eq 2
 or ethnicgp eq 4).

3.

select if (satis1 gt 0 and satis2 gt 0 and satis3 gt 0
 and satis4 gt 0).

4.

temporary
select if (ethnicgp eq 2 and gender eq 1)

5. It is not possible to use relational operators such as **and** with the **process if** command in SPSS/PC. Consequently, it would be necessary to use the following **select if** command which permanently selects the subjects specified:

select if (ethnicgp eq 2 and gender eq 1).

6.

recode skill (1,2=1) (3,4=2).

7.

recode income (1 thru 4999) (5000 thru 9999) (10000 thru hi).

8.

compute days=weeks∗7.

9.

variable labels patpre 'pretest depression-patient'.

10.

value labels treat 1 'control' 2 'therapy' 3 'drug'.

11.

```
data list file=jsr.dat
  /satis1 21-22.
missing values satis1 (0).
variable labels satis1 'job satisfaction item 1'.
value labels satis1 1 'strongly disagree' 2 'disagree' 3 'undecided'
  4 'agree' 5 'strongly agree'.
frequencies variables=satis1.
```

12.

```
title 'Job Survey scored data'.
subtitle 'Command file for analysing jss.dat'.
data list file=jss.dat
  /id ethnicgp gender 1-6 income 7-12 age years 13-18 commit 19-20
  satis autonom routine 21-29 attend skill prody qual 30-37
  absence 38-40.
missing values ethnicgp to qual (0) absence (99).
variable labels ethnicgp 'ethnic group'
  years 'years worked'
  commit 'organizational commitment'
  satis 'job satisfaction'
  autonom 'job autonomy'
  routine 'job routine'
  attend 'attendance at meeting'
  skill 'rated skill'
  prody 'rated productivity'
  qual 'rated quality'
  absence 'days absent'.
value labels ethnicgp 1 'white' 2 'asian' 3 'west indian' 4 'african' 5 'other'
  /gender 1 'male' 2 'female'
  /attend 1 'attended' 2 'not attended'
```

/skill 1 'unskilled' 2 'semi-skilled' 3 'fairly skilled'
  4 'highly skilled'
/prody qual 1 'very poor' 2 'poor' 3 'average' 4 'good'
  5 'very good'.

Chapter 4

1. (b)

2. It forces the researcher to think about the breadth of the concept and the possibility that it comprises a number of distinct components.

3. Ordinal.

4. Interval.

5. External reliability.

6.
reliability variables=autonom1 to autonom4
  /scale (testscore)=autonom1 to autonom4
  /model=alpha.
(Remember to omit the full stop if SPSS-X is being used.)

7. Internal reliability.

8. (a)

Chapter 5

1.

frequencies variables=prody
  /statistics default median.
(Remember to omit the full stop if using SPSS-X.)

2. 17.4 per cent

3. The chief problem is that the last case (number 20) has a very outlying value (2,700 employees). Indeed, it is over four times the next highest value (640). Therefore, both the mean and range would be distorted by this outlying value.

4. (c)

5.

frequencies variables=income/ntiles=4
  /statistics default.

6. 6 (i.e. 14−8).

7. It takes all values in a distribution into account and is easier to interpret in relation to the mean which is more commonly employed as a measure of central tendency than the median.

8. Between 4.23 and 17.446. Some 95.44 per cent of cases will probably lie within this range.

Chapter 6

1. A representative sample is one which accurately mirrors the population from which it was drawn. A random sample is a type of sample which aims to enhance the likelihood of achieving a representative sample. However, due to a number of factors (such as sampling error or non-response), it is unlikely that a random sample will be a representative sample.

2. Because it enhances the likelihood that the groups (i.e. strata) in the population will be accurately represented.

3. When a population is highly dispersed, the time and cost of interviewing can be reduced by multistage cluster sampling.

4. No. Quite aside from the problems of non-response and sampling error, it is unlikely that the Yellow Pages provide a sufficiently complete and accurate sampling frame.

5. Since there are only two possible outcomes (heads or tails) and the coin was flipped four times, the probability of finding the particular sequence you did would be one out of sixteen ($2\times2\times2\times2$) or 0.0625.

6. No. Even if the coin were unbiased, you would still have a one in sixteen chance that you would obtain four heads in a row.

7. The probability of obtaining any sequence of two heads and two tails is six out of sixteen or 0.375 since six such sequences are possible. In other words, this is the most likely outcome.

8. Since there are only two outcomes to each question (true and false), the most likely score for someone who has no general knowledge is 50 points (0.5×100 which is the mean of the probability distribution).

9. Once again, there are only two outcomes for each person (butter or margarine). The probability of guessing correctly is 0.5. Since fifty people took part, the mean or most likely number of people guessing correctly would be twenty-five.

10. The null hypothesis would be that there was no difference in talkativeness between men and women.

11. The non-directional hypothesis would be that men and women differ in talkativeness. In other words, the direction of the difference is not stated.

Chapter 7

1. A one-sample chi-square test should be used since there are more than two groups (i.e. October, November, and December) and the number of books sold in any one month by that shop cannot vary. In other words, the number of books in this case is a frequency count.

2. The null hypothesis is that there would be no change in the number of books sold over the three months. In other words, the number sold in each month would be roughly equal.

3.

npar tests chisquare=months.

Unless told otherwise (i.e. by default), this command assumes that all three values of the variable **months** (i.e. October, November, and December) are to be used and that the expected frequency of books sold is equal in the three months.

4. We would use a two-tailed level of significance in this case and in others involving a comparison of three or more cells since it is not possible to determine between which two cells any significant difference would lie. In addition, we have not specified the direction we were expecting in the number of books sold over the three months. Although not stated in the *SPSS-X User's Guide* or the *SPSS/PC+ Manual*, the two-tailed level is given by SPSS.

5. Since the value of 0.25 is greater than the conventional criterion or cut-off point of 0.05, we would conclude that the number of books sold did not differ significantly between the three months. A probability value of 0.25 means that we could expect to obtain this result by chance one out of four times. To be more certain that our result is not due to chance, it is customary to expect the finding to occur at or less than five times out of a hundred.

6. A finding with a probability level of 0.0001 would not mean that there had been a greater change in the number of books than one with a probability level of 0.037. It would simply mean that the former finding was less likely to occur (once in 10,000 times) than the latter one (thirty-seven out of a thousand times).

7. A binomial test would be used to determine if there had been a significant change between, say, October and November.

8.

npar tests binomial=months (1,2).

Since only two of the three cells or categories are being tested, it is necessary to specify which these are by placing their numerical codes in parentheses.

9. If we specify the direction of the change in the number of books sold between any two months, we would use a one-tailed level of significance.

10. You would simply divide the two-tailed level by 2, which in this case would give a one-tailed level of 0.042.

11. It would be inappropriate to analyse this data with a binomial test since it does not take account of the number of men and women who reported not having this experience. In other words, it does not compare the proportion of men with the proportion of women reporting this experience. Consequently, it is necessary to use a chi-square test for two samples. Note, however, that it would have been possible to have used a binomial test if the *proportion* of people falling in love in one sample were compared with that in the other. However, it may be simpler to use chi-square.

12.

crosstabs tables=gender by love
  /option 14
  /statistic 1.

In SPSS-X, the **options** subcommand can be substituted with **/cells expected** and the **1** on the **statistics** subcommand can be replaced with **chisq.**

13. Since the number of close friends a person has is an interval/ratio measure and the data being compared come from two unrelated samples (men and women), an unrelated *t*-test should be used.

14. The pooled variance estimate is used to interpret the results of a *t*-test when the variances do not differ significantly from one another.

15. You would use a repeated-measure test since the average number of books sold is an interval/ratio measure which can vary between the ten shops, and the cases (i.e. the ten shops) are the same for the three time-periods. If you were simply interested in whether the total number of books sold by the ten shops changed significantly over the three months, you would use a one-sample chi-square test.

Chapter 8

1. (a)

crosstabs tables=prody by gender
/**options 4.** [or **cells column** may also be used with SPSS-X]

(b) Chi-square would probably be the best choice.
(c) With $x^2=1.18298$ and $p > 0.05$, the relationship would be regarded as non-significant.
(d) 35.2 per cent.

2. The reasoning is faulty. Chi-square cannot establish the strength of a relationship between two variables. Also, statistical significance is not the same as substantive significance, so that the researcher would be incorrect in believing that the presence of a statistically significant chi-square value indicates that the relationship is important.

3. (a)

correlations variables=income years satis age
/**statistics 1** [or **statistics descriptives** may be used with SPSS-X]
/**options 3.** [or **print=twotail** may be used with SPSS-X]

(b) the correlation between **age** and **years** ($r=0.80$).
(c) 64 per cent.

4. There is a host of errors. The researcher should not have employed *r* to assess the correlation, since social class is an ordinal variable. The amount of variance explained is 53.3 per cent, not 73 per cent. Finally, the causal inference (i.e. that social class explains the number of books read) is risky with a correlational/survey design of this kind.

5. The statistical significance of *r* is affected not just by the size of *r*, but also by the size of the sample. As sample size increases, it becomes much easier for *r* to be statistically significant. The reason, therefore, for the contrast in the findings is that the sample size for the researcher's study, in which $r=0.55$ and $p > 0.05$, is smaller than the one which found a smaller correlation but was statistically highly significant.

6. (a) Since these two variables are ordinal, a measure of rank correlation will probably be most appropriate. Since there are quite a few tied ranks, Kendall's tau may be more appropriate than Spearman's rho.

(b) With SPSS-X the commands would be:

nonpar corr variables=prody commit
/print=Kendall

With SPSS/PC+, the commands would be:

crosstabs tables=prody by commit
/statistics 6.

(c) tau=.25, $p < 0.005$. This suggests that there is a weak correlation but one can be confident that a correlation of at least this size will be found in the population from which the sample was taken.

7. (a) The intercept.
   (b) The regression coefficient. For each extra year, **autonom** increases by 0.0623.
   (c) Not terribly well. Only 8 per cent of the variance in **autonom** is explained by **age**.
   (d) 10.29
   (e)

plot format=regression
/plot=autonom with age.

Chapter 9

1. One advantage is that a more accurate measure of error variance is provided. The other is to examine interaction effects between the two variables.

2. An interaction is when the effect of one variable is not the same under all the conditions of the other variable.

3. You would conduct either an analysis of variance (ANOVA) or multivariate analysis of variance (MANOVA) to determine whether the interaction between the two variables was significant.

4. Performance is the dependent variable since the way in which it is affected by alcohol, anxiety, and gender is being investigated.

5. There are three factors, i.e. alcohol, anxiety, and gender.

6. There are three levels of anxiety.

7. It can be described as a 4×3×2 factorial design.

8.

manova perform by alcohol (1,4) anxiety (1,3) gender (1,2)
/method=sstype(unique)
/print=cellinfo(means)
/design.

9. First, you would find out if there were any differences in intelligence between the three conditions, using oneway analysis of variance. If there were no significant differences, then you could assume that the effect of intelligence is likely to be equal in the three conditions and that there is no need to control for it statistically. If you

had found that there were significant differences in intelligence between the three conditions, you would need to determine whether there was any relationship between intelligence and the learning-to-read measure. If such a relationship existed, you could control for the effect of intelligence by conducting an analysis of covariance.

10.

anova read by methods(1,3) with intell

11. It is a between-subjects design with multiple measures.

12.

manova intell likeable honesty confid by attract(1,2)

13. It is a within-subjects or repeated measures design with multiple measures.

14. In specifying your dependent variables you would have to distinguish the ratings of the attractive face from those of the unattractive one. This has been done below by shortening the name of the dependent variables to their first three letters (for example, **int**) and adding a three-letter suffix to distinguish the rating of the attractive face (**att**) from the unattractive one (**una**).

manova intatt intuna likatt likuna honatt honuna conatt conuna
 /wsfactor=attract(2)
 /wsdesign=attract.

Note that the dependent variables (for example, **int**) for the two conditions (i.e. **att** and **una**) are listed together (**intatt intuna**).

15. A **contrast** subcommand needs to be used to do this:

 /contrast(time)=special(1 1 1, -1 1 0, 0 -1 1)

Chapter 10

1. To a large extent, in that 71 per cent of women support equal-pay legislation, as against 58 per cent of men.

2. Table 2 suggests that the relationship between sex and approval for equal-pay legislation is moderated by age. For respondents under the age of 35, there is greater overall support for legislation, and the difference between men and women is greater than in Table 10E.1. Among those who are 35 and over, the overall level of approval is lower and the difference between men and women is much less than in the table. Clearly, the relationship between sex and approval for equal-pay legislation applies to the under-35s in this imaginary example, rather than those who are 35 or over.

3.

crosstabs tables=commit by ethnicgp by gender.

Remember to omit the full stop with SPSS-X.

4. The main possibility is that the relationship between income and attendance at religious services is spurious. Age is probably related to both income and attendance. However, it should also be noted that the relationship between income and attendance does not disappear entirely when age is controlled.

5.

partial corr income by satis with age(1)

6. There is no direct mechanism for producing Kendall's partial rank correlation coefficient with SPSS. Initially, we would need a matrix of Kendall's tau correlations for the three variables concerned. With SPSS-X, the command would be:

nonpar corr variables=skill prody qual
/print=kendall

It is then necessary to follow the procedures described on p. 234 to compute a partial rank correlation coefficient. The correlation between **skill** and **prody** is 0.1944; when **qual** is controlled, the correlation is 0.1943. In other words, the partial rank correlation coefficient between **skill** and **prody** is hardly different from the zero-order coefficient.

7. (a) 90.4.
   (b) Quite confident. The multiple coefficient of determination (R^2) suggests that a large proportion of y is explained by the three variables (78 per cent) and the equation as a whole is statistically significant, suggesting that the multiple correlation between the three independent variables and y is unlikely to be zero in the population.
   (c) This was a trick question. Since the three regression coefficients presented in the equation are unstandardized, it is not possible to compare them to determine which independent variable has the largest effect on y. In order to make such an inference, standardized regression coefficients would be required.
   (d) For every one unit change in x_3, y decreases by 1.4.

8. Equation (1)

regression variables=satis autonom routine
/statistics=defaults cha
/dependent=satis
/stepwise/enter.

Equation (2)

regression variables=absence satis autonom routine
/statistics=defaults cha
/dependent=absence
/stepwise/enter.

9. (a) According to the adjusted R^2, 59 per cent of the variance in **satis** is explained by **autonom** and **routine**.
   (b) Yes. The t values for **autonom** and **routine** are significant at $p < 0.0001$ and $p < 0.01$ respectively.
   (c) -0.29254

10. The largest effect coefficient is for **satis** (-0.50). The effect coefficients for **autonom** and **routine** were -0.115 and -0.015 respectively.

Chapter 11

1. No. If you were to do this, you would be examining the way in which your anxiety items were grouped together. In other words, you may be analysing the factor structure of anxiety itself. To find out if your ten items assessed a single factor of anxiety, you would need to include items which measured other variables such as sociability.

2. At least 50–100 cases.

3. This is the variance which is not shared with other variables.

4. Principal-components analysis analyses all the variance of a variable while principal-axis factoring analyses the variance it shares with the other variables.

5. There are as many factors as variables.

6. The first factor always accounts for the largest amount of variance.

7. This would defeat the aim of factor analysis which is to reduce the number of variables which need to be examined. The smaller factors may account for less variance than that of a single variable.

8. Kaiser's criterion which extracts factors with an eigenvalue of greater than one.

9. A loading is a measure of association between a variable and a factor.

10. Factors are rotated to increase the loading of some items and to decrease that of others so as to make the factors easier to interpret.

11. The advantage of orthogonal rotation is that since the factors are uncorrelated with one another, they provide the minimum number of factors required to account for the relationships between the variables.

12. No. Since the variance may be shared between two or more factors, it is not possible to estimate it.

Bibliography

Blauner, R. (1964) *Alienation and Freedom: The Factory Worker and his Industry*, Chicago: University of Chicago Press.

Bohrnstedt, G.W. and Knoke, D. (1982) *Statistics for Social Data Analysis*, Itasca, IL: F.E. Peacock.

Boneau, C. (1960) 'The effects of violations of assumptions underlying the *t* test', *Psychological Bulletin* 57: 49–64.

Brayfield, A. and Rothe, H. (1951) 'An index of job satisfaction', *Journal of Applied Psychology* 35: 307–11.

Bridgman, P.W. (1927) *The Logic of Modern Physics*, London: Macmillan.

Bruning, J.L. and Kintz, B.L. (1977) *Computational Handbook of Statistics* (2nd edition), Glenview, IL: Scott, Foresman.

Bryman, A. (1985) 'Professionalism and the clergy', *Review of Religious Research* 26: 253–60.

—— (1986) *Leadership and Organizations*, London: Routledge.

—— (1988a) *Quantity and Quality in Social Research*, London: Unwin Hyman.

—— (1988b) 'Introduction: "inside" accounts and social research in organizations', in A. Bryman (ed.) *Doing Research in Organizations*, London: Routledge.

—— (1989) *Research Methods and Organization Studies*, London: Unwin Hyman.

Campbell, D.T. and Fiske, D.W. (1959) 'Convergent and discriminant validation by the multitrait-multimethod index', *Psychological Bulletin* 56: 81–105.

Cattell, R.B. (1966) 'The meaning and strategic use of factor analysis', in R.B. Cattell (ed.) *Handbook of Multivariate Experimental Psychology*, Chicago: Rand McNally.

—— (1973) *Personality and Mood by Questionnaire*, San Francisco: Jossey-Bass.

Child, J. (1973) 'Predicting and understanding organization structure', *Administrative Science Quarterly* 18: 168–85.

Cohen, L. and Holliday, M. (1982) *Statistics for Social Scientists*, London: Harper & Row.

Conover, W.J. (1980) *Practical Nonparametric Statistics* (2nd edition), New York: Wiley.

Cramer, D. (1988) 'Self-esteem and facilitative close relationships: a cross-lagged panel correlation analysis', *British Journal of Social Psychology* 27: 115–26.

Cronbach, L.J. and Meehl, P.E. (1955) 'Construct validity in psychological tests', *Psychological Bulletin* 52: 281–302.

Davis, J.A. (1985) *The Logic of Causal Order*, Sage University Paper Series on Quantitative Applications in the Social Sciences, series no. 55, Beverly Hills, CA: Sage.

Durkheim, E. (1952) *Suicide: A Study in Sociology*, London: Routledge & Kegan Paul.

Eysenck, H.J. and Eysenck, S.B.G. (1969) *Personality Structure and Measurement*, London: Routledge & Kegan Paul.

Freeman, L.C. (1965) *Elementary Applied Statistics: For Students of Behavioral Science*, New York: Wiley.

Games, P. and Lucas, P. (1966) 'Power of the analysis of variance of independent groups on non-normal and normally transformed data', *Educational and Psychological Measurement* 26: 311–27.

Glock, C.Y. and Stark, R. (1965) *Religion and Society in Tension*, Chicago: Rand McNally.

Gorsuch, R.L. (1983) *Factor Analysis*, Hillsdale, NJ: Lawrence Erlbaum.

Goyder, J. (1988) *The Silent Minority: Non-Respondents on Social Surveys*, Oxford: Polity Press.

Hall, R.H. (1968) 'Professionalization and bureaucratization', *American Sociological Review* 33: 92–104.

Hirschi, T. (1969) *Causes of Delinquency*, Berkeley, CA: University of California Press.

Huff, D. (1973) *How to Lie with Statistics*, Harmondsworth, Middx.: Penguin.

Huitema, B. (1980) *The Analysis of Covariance and Alternatives*, New York: Wiley.

Jackson, P.R. (1983) 'An easy to use BASIC program for agreement among many raters', *British Journal of Clinical Psychology* 22: 145–6.

Jenkins, G.D., Nadler, D.A., Lawler, E.E., and Cammann, C. (1975) 'Structured observations: an approach to measuring the nature of jobs', *Journal of Applied Psychology* 60: 171–81.

Jöreskog, K.G. and Sörbom, D. (1986) *LISREL VI: Analysis of Linear Structural Relationships by Maximum Likelihood, Instrumental Variables and Least Squares Methods* (4th edition), Mooresville, IN: Scientific Software Inc.

Labovitz, S. (1970) 'The assignment of numbers to rank order categories', *American Sociological Review* 35: 515–24.

—— (1971) 'In defense of assigning numbers to ranks', *American Sociological Review* 36: 521–2.

Land, K.C. (1969) 'Principles of path analysis', in E.F. Borgatta and G.F. Bohrnstedt (eds) *Sociological Methodology 1969*, San Francisco: Jossey-Bass.

Lazarsfeld, P.F. (1958) 'Evidence and inference in social research', *Daedalus* 87: 99–130.

Locke, E.A. and Schweiger, D.M. (1979) 'Participation in decision-making: one more look', in B.M. Staw (ed.) *Research in Organizational Behavior*, Vol. 1, Greenwich, CT: JAI Press.

Long, J.S. (1983) *Confirmatory Factor Analysis: A Preface to LISREL*, Beverly Hills, CA: Sage.

Lord, F.M. (1953) 'On the statistical treatment of football numbers', *American Psychologist* 8: 750–1.

Maxwell, S.E. (1980) 'Pairwise multiple comparisons in repeated measures designs', *Journal of Educational Statistics* 5: 269–87.

Merton, R.K. (1967) *On Theoretical Sociology*, New York: Free Press.

Mitchell, T.R. (1985) 'An evaluation of the validity of correlational research conducted in organizations', *Academy of Management Review* 10: 192–205.

Norusis, M.J./SPSS Inc. (1988a) *SPSS/PC+ Advanced Statistics V2.0*, Chicago: SPSS Inc.

—— (1988b) *SPSS/PC+ V2.0 Base Manual*, Chicago: SPSS Inc.

—— (1988c) *SPSS/PC+ V3.0 Update Manual*, Chicago: SPSS Inc.

O'Brien, R.M. (1979) 'The use of Pearson's r with ordinal data', *American Sociological Review* 44: 851–7.

Overall, J.E. and Spiegel, D.K. (1969) 'Concerning least squares analysis of experimental data', *Psychological Bulletin* 72: 311–22.

Pedhazur, E.J. (1982) *Multiple Regression in Behavioral Research: Explanation and Prediction* (2nd edition), New York: Holt, Rinehart & Winston.

Rosenberg, M. (1968) *The Logic of Survey Analysis*, New York, Basic Books.

Siegel, S. (1956) *Nonparametric Statistics for the Behavioral Sciences*, New York: McGraw-Hill.

Snizek, W.E. (1972) 'Hall's professionalism scale: an empirical reassessment', *American Sociological Review* 37: 10–14.

SPSS Inc. (1988) *SPSS-X User's Guide* (3rd edition), Chicago, Illinois.

Stevens, J. (1986) *Applied Multivariate Statistics for the Social Sciences*, Hillsdale, NJ: Lawrence Erlbaum.

Stevens, J.P. (1979) 'Comment on Olson: choosing a test statistic in multivariate analysis of variance', *Psychological Bulletin* 86: 728–37.

Stevens, S.S. (1946) 'On the theory of scales of measurement', *Science* 103: 677–80.

Tukey, J.W. (1977) *Exploratory Data Analysis*, Reading, MA: Addison-Wesley.

Walker, H. (1940) 'Degrees of freedom', *Journal of Educational Psychology* 31: 253–69.

Index

(Entries in **bold** are SPSS commands and key words)

analysis of covariance 212–14
analysis of variance 82, 199; multivariate, for three or more related measures 117, 145–8; oneway 137–43, 193–4; two-way 193–5
anova 199, 212–14
any 45–6
arithmetic mean *see* mean, arithmetic
arithmetic operators 50

bar chart 77; generation of with SPSS 80
Bartlett–Box *F* test *see F* test, Bartlett–Box
Bartlett's test for sphericity 206–7
batch processing 28
beta weight *see* standardized regression coefficient
between subject design 116, 196–7
binomial distribution 107
binomial test 117, 118–20; generation of with SPSS 118–20
bivariate analysis: and differences 6, 63, 114–48; and relationships 6, 63, 150–87, concept of 6, 63, 150
Blauner, R. 73
Bohrnstedt, G.W. 77
Boneau, C. 118
Bonferroni test 148
box and whisker plot 88, 90–1; generation of with SPSS 92
Box's *M* test 206–7
Brayfield, A. 63, 68, 70–1
breakdown 268
Bridgman, P.W. 4
Bruning, J.L. 144
Bryman, A. 1, 2, 5, 7, 68, 73

Cammann, C. 73
Campbell, D. T. 73

case, notion of in SPSS 19
categorical variable *see* nominal variable
Cattell, R.B. 254, 259
causality, concept of 7–15, 169–70, 217, 246, 250–1
central tendency, concept of 82
Child, J. 62, 67
chi-square test (χ^2): and contingency table analysis 157–62, 175–6, 187, 229, generation of with SPSS 159–61; one sample 117, 120–2, generation of with SPSS 120–2; two or more unrelated samples 117, 123–4, generation with SPSS 123–4; Yates's correction 124
Cochran's *C see F* test, Cochran's *C*
Cochran's *Q* test 117, 126–7
coefficient of determination (r^2) 168–70, 238
Cohen, L. 162, 168
combined design 197, 210–12
command file: running 28–30, 38; writing 22–8, 34–5, 37–8
comment 57
common variance, in factor analysis 257–8
communality, concept of in factor analysis 258
comparing related means: repeated measures 117, 145–8; *t* test 117, 143–4; within-subject design 116
comparing unrelated means: Scheffé test 141–2, 201; *t* test 117, 135–7, 201
comparison group: related, 115–16; unrelated, 115–16
comparison group variable 114
compute 44, 48, 49–53, 200
computers, using 17–18
concepts, measurement of 4, 7, 61–2, 67
concepts, nature of 4, 61
condescriptive 27, 29–30, 268
Conover, W.J. 118
contingency table analysis: and bivariate

analysis 103, 151–62, 187, generation of with SPSS 155–7; and multivariate analysis 218–29, generation of with SPSS 229

contrasts, in analysis of variance 140; a priori 140, 201; planned 140, 201–3; post hoc 141

copy 48

correlated groups see dependent groups

correlation: concept of 5, 65, 162–3; linear 163–71; rank 163, 173–5, 177, 234–5; see also Pearson's product moment correlation coefficient; Kendall's tau; phi; Spearman's rho

correlations 172–3, 233

count 26, 44, 50–2

covariance, analysis of see analysis of covariance

covariate, in multivariate analysis of variance and covariance 195–6, 203–6

Cramer, D. 15

Cramer's V 176, 187, 229; generation of with SPSS 176

criterion variable 114, 195

Cronbach, L.J. 72

Cronbach's alpha 71, 204; generation of with SPSS 71

crosstabs 123–4, 155–7, 174, 176, 229

crosstabulation 103, 151–62, 175

data files, 18–22, 37, 52–5

data list 22, 23–5, 28–9, 33–4

Davis, J.A. 251

decile range 87; generation of with SPSS 88

default, notion of 29

degrees of freedom, concept of 121

dependent groups 116

dependent variable 7–8, 13, 114, 193, 195, 227

Depression Project: data 198; description 197

descriptives 27, 29–32

design see combined design; experimental design; factorial design; mixed between-within design; multiple measures design; panel design; survey/correlational design

dichotomous variable 65, 175, 187

differences, examination of 6

dimensions of concepts 66–9

disks, use of with SPSS/PC+ 23, 37–8

dispersion, concept of 85

distribution-free tests see non-parametric tests

distributions see binomial distribution; normal distribution; t distribution

dummy variables 238, 240–1, 246

Durkheim, E. 4

edit 32

eigenvalue, concept of in factor analysis 258

else 47, 48

error messages 32–7, 44

error term 179–235

error variance, in factor analysis 257

eta 176–7, 187, 229; generation of with SPSS 176

expected frequencies, concept of 120–1, 158, 160

experimental design 3, 5, 6, 10, 13, 15, 195; types of 10–13, 115–16

Eysenck, H.J. 254

Eysenck, S.B.G. 254

factor 264

factor analysis, exploratory 254; compared with confirmatory factor analysis 254; generation of with SPSS 264–5; orthogonality in 258, 261–3; rotation of factors in 260–4; selecting number of factors in 259–60; uses of 68, 253–4

factor, concept of in multivariate analysis of variance 193

factorial design 12, 189–95, 198–203, 216–17

file handle 267

file names 22–3, 35–6

files see command files; data files, system files; tabular files

finish 27, 38

Fiske, D.W. 73

formats 53–5

Freeman, L.C. 175

frequencies 58–9, 80–1, 88, 96

frequency distributions, tables 75–8, 96; generation of with SPSS 58–9, 80

frequency, relative 76

Friedman test 117, 132–3; generation of with SPSS 132–3

F test 177, 239–40, 244; Bartlett–Box 117, 142–3; Cochran's C 117, 142–3; for two unrelated variances 117, 137; for three or more unrelated variances 117, 142–3; Hartley's F_{max} 117, 142–3

Games, P. 118

get file 56

Glock, C.Y. 62

Gorsuch, R.L. 255

Goyder, J. 104

Hall, R.H. 67–9

Hartley's F_{max} see F test, Hartley's F_{max}

heteroscedasticity 184–5

Hirschi, T. 2–6

histogram 78–80, 89–90, 96; generation of with SPSS 80

Holliday, M. 162, 168

Huff, D. 2
Huitema, B. 204
hypothesis: concept of 3–4, 61; directional
    110; nondirectional 110; null 110

if 44, 246
independence, concept of 104
independent groups 116
independent variable 7–8, 13, 193, 227
indicator, nature of an 62, 67–9
inferential statistics 5, 95
interaction effect *see* interaction, statistical
interaction, statistical: concept of 190–2,
    227; in multivariate analysis of variance
    and covariance 190, 200
interactive processing 28
internal validity 10–12; *see also* causality
inter-quartile range 86–7; generation of
    with SPSS 88
interval variable 64–6, 115, 175, 182, 187
intervening variable 218, 222–5, 230, 232

Jackson, P.R. 72
Jenkins, G.D. 73
Job Survey: general description of 19;
    questionnaires 40–2; raw data 20–1;
    variables 24, 66
Jöreskog, K.G. 255

Kaiser's criterion 259
Kendall's rank partial correlation
    coefficient 234–5
Kendall's tau (τ) 173–5, 187, 234;
    compared with Spearman's rho 173;
    generation of with SPSS 173–5
Kintz, B.L. 144
Knoke, D. 77
Kolmogorov–Smirnov test: for one sample
    117, 126–8, generation of with SPSS
    126–8; for two unrelated samples 117,
    127–8, generation of with SPSS 127–8
Kruskal–Wallis *H* test 117, 130–1,
    generation of with SPSS, 130–1

Labovitz, S. 66
Land, K.C. 251
Lawler, E.E. 73
Lazarsfeld, P.F. 67–9
Likert scaling 63
line of best fit 179
list 48–9
listwise deletion *see* missing data
Locke, E.A. 5
logarithmic transformation 167, 200, 203
logical operators 45–6
Long, J.S. 254
Lord, F.M. 116
Lucas, P. 118

McNemar test 117, 124–6; generation of
    with SPSS 124–6
manipulation of variables 5, 13, 193, 216
Mann–Whitney *U* test 117, 129–30,
    137–8; generation of with SPSS
    129–30, 137–8
manova 92, 145–8, 199–212, 269
marginals: column 151–2; row 151–2
Maxwell, S.E. 148
mean 52
mean, arithmetic 82, 93; generation of with
    SPSS 88
means 176–7, 187
median 82–3, 93; generation of with SPSS
    88
median test 128–9; generation of with SPSS
    128–9
Meehl, P.E. 72
Merton, R.K. 2
missing data, values 19, 21, 26–7, 30–2,
    50–2, 103, 161, 172–3, 233–4, 245–6;
    listwise deletion 31–2, 173, 233–4, 246;
    pairwise deletion 30–1, 173, 233–4
missing values 22, 26–7, 44, 52
Mitchell, T.R. 104
mixed between–within design 196–7,
    208–10
mode 83, 88
moderated relationships 216, 218, 225–7,
    230
multicollinearity 236–7, 244–5
multiple causation 218, 227–9, 230, 232
multiple coefficient of determination (R^2)
    238–9, 244
multiple correlation (R) 239, 244–5; and
    statistical significance 240
multiple-item measures 46, 49, 50, 62–3,
    65, 70–1
multiple measures design 196, 206–8
multiple regression *see* regression multiple
multivariate analysis, concept of 6, 7, 15,
    63, 189, 216–17, 220
multivariate analysis of variance and
    covariance (MANOVA) and
    (MANCOVA) 145, 189; and statistical
    significance, classical experimental
    approach 199, 212–14; generation of
    with SPSS 199; hierarchical 199;
    regression approach 199; test of
    homogeneity of slope of regression line
    within cells 203–5

Nadler, D.A. 73
new file, creating a 52–6
new variable, creating a 49–53
nominal variable 19, 64, 75, 115, 175, 187
non-parametric tests: criteria for selecting
    115, 116–18

nonpar corr 174, 234
normal distribution 92–6, 105, 107–8
npar tests 118–21, 125–32, 137
null hypothesis *see* hypothesis, null

O'Brien, R.M. 163
oblique rotation, in factor analysis 261–4
oneway 117, 137–43, 209
operationalization 4, 61; *see also* concepts, measurement of
order effect 197
ordinal variable 64–6, 115, 117–18, 173–5, 187
orthogonal rotation, in factor analysis 261–3
outliers, importance of: in regression 185–6; in univariate analysis 82–3, 85–7
Overall, J.E. 198

pairwise deletion *see* missing data
panel design 15, 125, 217
Panel Study: general description of 125; raw data 125
parametric tests 93, 116–18
partial corr 233–4
partial correlation coefficient 230–5; and Pearson's *r* 230–1; generation of with SPSS 16, 233–4
path analysis 245, 246–51; generation of with SPSS 248–50; overall effects of variables in 248–50
pearson corr 268
Pearson's product moment correlation coefficient (Pearson's *r*) 163–71, 175, 182–3, 187; and statistical significance 171; generation of with SPSS 171–3; implications of size of 167–9
Pedhazur, E.J. 249, 250–1
percentages: in contingency tables 152–4; in frequency distributions 76–7
phi coefficient (ϕ) 162, 175, 187, 229; generation of with SPSS 162
plot 171–3, 186, 246
population, concept of 5, 95, 98
power, statistical 112, 137
principal components analysis: compared with factor analysis 255–8; generation of with SPSS 264–5
probability, concept of 104–8
probability sampling *see* sampling, probability
process if 44
psychology 5

qualitative research 1
quantitative research 1–7

random assignment 11–12
range 85–6; generation of with SPSS 88

range 46
ratio variable 64–5, 115
recode 26, 44, 46–9, 80, 157, 175
recoding variables 46–9, 157, 175
record 21, 23
regression 241–6
regression, bivariate 177–87; compared with correlation 177, 182–3; intercept in 179; use of in prediction 179–83; use of **plot** to generate 186
regression, multiple 235–46; and prediction 235–6; and statistical significance 239–40; generation of with SPSS 241–6; stepwise procedure in 237, 240, 245
relational operators 45
relationship: concept of 6, 8–9, 14, 150–1; curvilinear 167; first order 217–18; negative 165, 167; perfect 153–4, 165–6; positive 165, 167; second order 218; strength of 161, 167–8; zero order 217
relationships, compared to examination of differences 6, 150
reliability 71
reliability of measures: external 70; inter-coder 71–2; internal 70; split-half 70–1, generation of with SPSS 71; test-retest 70; *see also* Cronbach's alpha
repeated measures 117, 145–8, 196–7
respondents 19
Rosenberg, M. 217
Rothe, H. 63, 68, 70–1

sample: convenience 104; multistage cluster 102; representative 5, 99, 103–4; simple random 99–100; stratified 100–2; systematic 100
sampling: concept of 4–5, 95, 98–9; error 103, 157; frame 99; probability 99; problems in 102–4
save 55–6
scatter diagram 163–73, 179, 182–3, 186; generation of with SPSS 171–3, 186
scattergram 268
Scheffé test 141–2, 201; generation of with SPSS 141–2
Schweiger, D.M. 5
scree test 259–60
select if 43–4, 45–6, 238
Siegel, S. 118, 137
significance level 105–6
significance, statistical *see* statistical significance
sign test 131–2; generation of with SPSS 131–2
skewed distributions 95–6
Snizek, W.E. 68
sociology 1, 5

Sörbom, D. 255
specific variance, in factor analysis 257
Spearman's rho (ρ) 173–5, 187; compared
   with Kendall's tau 173; generation of
   with SPSS 16, 173–5
Spiegel, D.K. 198
SPSS, versions of 16, 267–9
SPSS/PC+: editing in 37–9; general
   explanation of 16
spurious relationship 9, 14, 217, 218–22,
   223–4, 229, 230, 232
standard deviation 87, 136; generation of
   with SPSS 29–30, 88
standard error of the estimate 239, 244
standard error of the mean 134–5, 136–7
standardized regression coefficient 236–8,
   244, 247–8; generation of with SPSS
   244; in multiple regression 236, 244
Stark, R. 62
statistical power see power, statistical
statistical significance: concept of 95, 98,
   104–12, 157–8; one-sample test of 109;
   one-tailed test of 111, 140; robustness
   of test of 118; two-tailed test of 111
statistics 29–30, 88, 96, 269
stem and leaf display 88–90; generation of
   with SPSS 92
Stevens, J. 148, 205, 260
Stevens, J.P. 147
Stevens, S.S. 64, 137
structural equations 247
subjects 19
Subtitle 56–7
sum 50
survey/correlational design 3, 5, 10, 13–15,
   216–17
survey research 10; non-response in 103–4;
   use of interviews in 3, 102; use of
   questionnaires in 3, 10, 98; see also
   survey/correlational design
system files 55–6

tabular files 18–22, 37, 52–5
temporary 44

test variable, in multivariate analysis 217,
   219, 227
theory, in quantitative research 2–3, 7, 150
thru 47
Title 56–7
t distribution 108
t-test 135–6, 137, 144–5
t test 117; for one sample 117, 133–4; for
   two related means 117, 135, 143–4, for
   two unrelated means 117, 135–7, 140;
   for two related variances 117, 144–5;
   pooled versus separate variance 136;
   unrelated 117
Tukey, J.W. 88
Tukey test 148
Type I error 106, 111–12, 204, 206
Type II error 106, 112, 204

uncorrelated groups see independent
   groups
unique variance, in factor analysis 257
univariate analysis, concept of 6, 63

validity of measures: concurrent validity 72;
   construct validity 72–3; convergent
   validity 73; discriminant validity 73;
   face validity 72; predictive validity 72
value labels 44, 58–9, 268
variable: nature of a 4, 63; types of 63–6
variable labels 44, 57–9, 268
variable names 22–3, 32–3
variance: analysis of see analysis of
   variance; concept of 115, 150; error,
   residual 138, 194–5; explained 136,
   138, 194–5; pooled 136; separate 136
varimax rotation, in factor analysis 262,
   264–5

Walker, H. 121
Wilcoxon matched-pairs signed rank test
   117, 132–3; generation of with SPSS
   132–3
within-subjects design 116, 196–7
write 54–5